THE CHEMICAL BOND

THE CHEMICAL BOND

A Brief Introduction to Modern Structural Chemistry

By LINUS *Carl* PAULING, *1901-*

CORNELL UNIVERSITY PRESS

Ithaca, New York

The Nature of the Chemical Bond

First edition copyright 1939, second edition copyright 1940, third edition © 1960 by Cornell University

The Chemical Bond

Copyright © 1967 by Cornell University

CORNELL UNIVERSITY PRESS

Library of Congress Catalog Card Number: 67–12533

PRINTED IN THE UNITED STATES OF AMERICA
BY GEORGE BANTA COMPANY, INC.

Preface

THIS book is essentially a shortened version of *The Nature of the Chemical Bond* (Third Edition, Cornell University Press, 1960), and is intended especially for the use of students.

   In the first twelve chapters the less important sections and examples have been omitted.   Chapter 13 of *The Nature of the Chemical Bond*, on the sizes of ions and the structure of ionic crystals, has been replaced by a brief discussion of ionic radii at the end of Chapter 7 of the present book. Chapter 14, the brief summary of resonance, has been omitted.   Significant additions include the discussion of the molecular-orbital description of the electronic structure of molecules (Sec. 6-3) and the sets of exercises at the ends of chapters and appendices.

LINUS PAULING

Salmon Creek
Big Sur, California
14 September 1966

Contents

Preface v

CHAPTER 1
Resonance and the Chemical Bond

1-1. The Development of the Theory of Valence 3
1-2. Types of Chemical Bonds 5
    The Chemical Bond Defined 5
    The Ionic Bond and Other Electrostatic Bonds 5
    The Covalent Bond 6
    The Metallic Bond; Fractional Bonds 8
1-3. The Concept of Resonance 8
1-4. The Hydrogen Molecule-Ion and the One-Electron Bond 11
    The Normal Hydrogen Atom 11
    The Hydrogen Molecule-Ion 11
    The Conditions for the Formation of a One-Electron Bond 16
1-5. The Hydrogen Molecule and the Electron-Pair Bond 17
    Condon's Treatment of the Hydrogen Molecule 17
    The Heitler-London Treatment of the Hydrogen Molecule 18
    The Conditions for the Formation of an Electron-Pair Bond 18
    Exercises 20

CHAPTER 2
The Electronic Structure of Atoms and the Formal Rules
for the Formation of Covalent Bonds

2-1. The Interpretation of Line Spectra 21
2-2. Stationary States; The Bohr Frequency Principle 23
2-3. Stationary States of the Hydrogen Atom 24
2-4. The Electronic Structure of Alkali Atoms 29
2-5. The Spinning Electron and the Fine Structure of Spectral Lines 32
2-6. The Electronic Structure of Atoms with Two or More Valence Electrons . . 33
2-7. The Pauli Exclusion Principle and the Periodic System of the Elements . . . 36
2-8. The Magnetic Properties of Atoms and Monatomic Ions 43
2-9. The Formal Rules for the Formation of Covalent Bonds 45
    Exercises 47

Contents

CHAPTER 3

The Partial Ionic Character of Covalent Bonds and the Relative Electronegativity of Atoms

3-1. The Transition from One Extreme Bond Type to Another 49
    Continuous Change in Bond Type 49
    Discontinuous Change in Bond Type 51
3-2. Bond Type and Atomic Arrangement 52
3-3. The Nature of the Bonds in Diatomic Halogenide Molecules 54
3-4. Bond Energies of Halogenide Molecules; The Energies of Normal Covalent Bonds 57
3-5. Empirical Values of Single-Bond Energies 59
3-6. The Electronegativity Scale of the Elements 63
    The Formulation of the Electronegativity Scale 63
3-7. Heats of Formation of Compounds in Their Standard States; The Complete Electronegativity Scale 64
3-8. Relation to Other Properties 68
3-9. The Electronegativity of Atoms and the Partial Ionic Character of Bonds . 69
    Exercises 72

CHAPTER 4

The Directed Covalent Bond; Bond Strengths and Bond Angles

4-1. The Nature and Bond-forming Power of Atomic Orbitals 74
4-2. Hybrid Bond Orbitals; The Tetrahedral Carbon Atom 77
    Derivation of Results about Tetrahedral Orbitals 80
4-3. The Effect of an Unshared Pair on Hybridization 82
4-4. Orbitals for Incomplete s-p Shells 84
4-5. Concentration of Bond Orbitals 85
4-6. Restricted Rotation about Single Bonds 86
4-7. Orbitals and Bond Angles for Multiple Bonds 87
4-8. Partial Ionic Character of Multiple Bonds 90
    Exercises 90

CHAPTER 5

Complex Bond Orbitals; The Magnetic Criterion for Bond Type

5-1. Bonds Involving d Orbitals 92
5-2. Octahedral Bond Orbitals 94
5-3. Square Bond Orbitals 98
5-4. The Magnetic Criterion for Bond Type 99
5-5. The Magnetic Moments of Octahedral Complexes 101
5-6. The Magnetic Moments of Tetrahedral and Square Coordinated Complexes . 105
5-7. The Electroneutrality Principle and the Stability of Octahedral Complexes . 107

5-8. Ligand Field Theory . ✓ 108
5-9. Configurations for Atoms with Unshared Electron Pairs 110
    Exercises 111

CHAPTER 6

The Resonance of Molecules among Several Valence-Bond Structures

6-1. Resonance in Nitrous Oxide and Benzene 113
6-2. Resonance Energy 118
    Values of Bond Energies for Multiple Bonds 119
    Empirical Values of Resonance Energies 119
6-3. The Structure of Aromatic Molecules 124
    The Quantitative Treatment of Resonance in Aromatic Molecules . . . 128
    More about the Molecular-orbital Method 130
    Exercises 133

CHAPTER 7

Interatomic Distances and Their Relation to the Structure of Molecules and Crystals

7-1. Interatomic Distances in Normal Covalent Molecules: Covalent Radii . . . 135
7-2. The Correction for Electronegativity Difference 138
7-3. Double-Bond and Triple-Bond Radii 139
7-4. Interatomic Distances and Resonance 140
7-5. The Conditions for Equivalence or Nonequivalence of Bonds 143
7-6. Tetrahedral and Octahedral Covalent Radii 145
    Tetrahedral Radii 145
    Octahedral Radii 147
7-7. Interatomic Distances for Fractional Bonds 149
7-8. Values of Single-Bond Metallic Radii 150
7-9. Ionic Radii and van der Waals Radii 150
    Van der Waals Radii 151
    Exercises 153

CHAPTER 8

Types of Resonance in Molecules

8-1. The Structure of Simple Resonating Molecules 156
    Carbon Monoxide 156
    Carbon Dioxide and Related Molecules 157
8-2. The Adjacent-Charge Rule and the Electroneutrality Rule 158
8-3. The Nitro and Carboxyl Groups; Acid Strengths 160
8-4. The Structure of Amides and Peptides 162
8-5. The Carbonate, Nitrate, and Borate Ions and Related Molecules 164

8-6. Resonance in Conjugated Systems 165
8-7. Resonance in Heterocyclic Molecules 166
8-8. Hyperconjugation. 167
 Exercises 168

CHAPTER 9

The Structure of Molecules and Complex Ions Involving Bonds with Partial Double-Bond Character

9-1. The Structure of Silicon Tetrachloride and Related Molecules 171
9-2. The Oxides and Oxygen Acids of the Heavier Elements 173
 Oxides of the Heavier Elements 175
9-3. The Structure and Stability of Carbonyls and Other Covalent Complexes of the Transition Metals 177
 The Cyano and Nitro Complexes of the Transition Elements 180
 Exercises 183

CHAPTER 10

The One-Electron Bond and the Three-Electron Bond; Electron-deficient Substances

10-1. The One-Electron Bond 186
10-2. The Three-Electron Bond 187
 The Conditions for Formation of a Stable Three-Electron Bond 187
 The Helium Molecule-Ion. 189
10-3. The Oxides of Nitrogen and Their Derivatives 189
 Nitric Oxide . . . . ' 189
 Dinitrogen Dioxide 190
 The Nitrosyl Halogenides 190
 Nitrogen Dioxide 191
10-4. The Superoxide Ion and the Oxygen Molecule 192
10-5. Other Molecules Containing the Three-Electron Bond 193
10-6. Electron-deficient Substances 194
10-7. The Structure of the Boranes 197
10-8. Substances Containing Bridging Methyl Groups 199
10-9. Ferrocene and Related Substances 200
 Exercises 201

CHAPTER 11

The Metallic Bond

11-1. The Properties of Metals 203
11-2. Metallic Valence 204
11-3. The Metallic Orbital 206

11-4. Interatomic Distances and Bond Numbers in Metals 207
11-5. The Closest Packing of Spheres 211
11-6. The Atomic Arrangements in Crystals of Metallic Elements 214
    The Cubic Body-centered Arrangement 214
11-7. Icosahedral Structures 215
11-8. Molecules and Crystals Containing Metal-Metal Bonds 217
    Exercises 219

CHAPTER 12
The Hydrogen Bond

12-1. The Nature of the Hydrogen Bond 221
12-2. The Effect of the Hydrogen Bond on the Physical Properties of Substances . . 224
12-3. Ice and Water 227
12-4. Hydrogen Bonds in Proteins 229
    Exercises 231

Appendices and Index

  I. Values of Physical Constants 235
  II. The Bohr Atom 236
 III. Hydrogenlike Orbitals 238
 IV. Russell-Saunders States of Atoms Allowed by the Pauli Exclusion Principle . 241
    The Landé *g*-Factor 242
    Exercises 244
  V. Resonance Energy 245
 VI. Wave Functions for Valence-Bond Structures 248
VII. Electric Polarizabilities and Electric Dipole Moments of Atoms, Ions, and
    Molecules 249
    Electric Polarization and Dielectric Constant 249
    Electronic Polarizability 251
    The Debye Equation for Dielectric Constant 252
    Exercises 254
VIII. The Magnetic Properties of Substances 255
    Diamagnetism 255
    Paramagnetism 256
    Exercises 259
 IX. Bond Energy and Bond-Dissociation Energy 260
    Index 263

THE CHEMICAL BOND

CHAPTER 1

Resonance and the Chemical Bond

MOST of the general principles of molecular structure and the nature of the chemical bond were formulated long ago by chemists by induction from the great body of chemical facts. During recent decades these principles have been made more precise and more useful through the application of the powerful experimental methods and theories of modern physics, and some new principles of structural chemistry have also been discovered. As a result structural chemistry has now become significant not only to the various branches of chemistry but also to biology and medicine.

1-1. THE DEVELOPMENT OF THE THEORY OF VALENCE

The study of the structure of molecules was originally carried on by chemists using methods of investigation that were essentially chemical in nature, relating to the chemical composition of substances, the existence of isomers, the nature of the chemical reactions in which a substance takes part, and so on. From the consideration of facts of this kind Frankland, Kekulé, Couper, and Butlerov* were led a century ago to formulate the

* E. Frankland, *Phil. Trans. Roy. Soc. London* **142,** 417 (1852), proposed the concept of valence in 1852, stating that each element forms compounds by uniting with a definite number of what we now call equivalents of other elements. F. A. Kekulé, *Ann. Chem.* **104,** 129 (1857), and A. W. H. Kolbe, *ibid.* **101,** 257 (1857), then extended the concept of valence to carbon and said that carbon usually has the valence 4. In the following year Kekulé, *ibid.* **106,** 129 (1858), suggested that carbon atoms can unite with an indefinite number of other carbon atoms into long chains. A. S. Couper, a Scottish chemist, independently discussed the quadrivalence of carbon and the ability of carbon atoms to form chains (*Compt. rend.* **46,** 1157 [1858]; *Ann. chim. phys.* **53,** 469 [1858]). Couper's chemical formulas were much like the modern ones; he was the first chemist to use a line between symbols to represent the valence bond.

In 1861 the Russian chemist A. M. Butlerov, *Z. Chem. Pharm.* **4,** 549 (1861), used the term "chemical structure" for the first time and stated that it is essential to express the structure by a single formula, which should show how each atom is linked to other atoms in the molecule of the substance. He stated clearly that all properties of a compound are determined theory of valence and to write the first structural formulas for molecules, van't Hoff and le Bel* were led to bring classical organic stereochemistry into its final form by their brilliant postulate of the tetrahedral orientation of the four valence bonds of the carbon atom, and Werner† was led to his development of the theory of the stereochemistry of complex inorganic substances.

Modern structural chemistry differs from classical structural chemistry with respect to the detailed picture of molecules and crystals that it presents. By various physical methods, including the study of the structure of crystals by the diffraction of x-rays and of gas molecules by the diffraction of electron waves, the measurement of electric and magnetic dipole moments, the interpretation of band spectra, Raman spectra, microwave spectra, and nuclear magnetic resonance spectra, and the determination of entropy values, a great amount of information has been obtained about the atomic configurations of molecules and crystals and even their electronic structures; a discussion of valence and the chemical bond now must take into account this information as well as the facts of chemistry.

In the nineteenth century the valence bond was represented by a line drawn between the symbols of two chemical elements, which expressed in a concise way many chemical facts, but which had only qualitative significance with regard to molecular structure. The nature of the bond was completely unknown. After the discovery of the electron numerous attempts were made to develop an electronic theory of the chemical bond. These culminated in the work of the American chemist Gilbert Newton Lewis, who in his 1916 paper,‡ which forms the basis of the modern electronic theory of valence, discussed not only the formation of ions by the completion of stable shells of electrons but also the formation of a chemical

---

by the molecular structure of the substance and suggested that it should be possible to find the correct structural formula of a substance by studying the ways in which it can be synthesized.

None of these chemists stated that the chemical formulas were to be interpreted as showing the way in which the atoms are bonded together in space; the formulas were used to indicate something about the ways in which the substances take part in chemical reactions. The next step, that of assigning structures in three-dimensional space to the molecules, was then taken by van't Hoff and le Bel. Excerpts from some of the papers mentioned above are to be found in H. M. Leicester and H. S. Klickstein, *A Source Book in Chemistry*, McGraw-Hill Book Co., New York, 1952.

    * J. H. van't Hoff, *Arch. neerland. sci.* **9**, 445 (1874); J. A. le Bel, *Bull. soc. chim. France* **22**, 337 (1874).

    † A. Werner, *Z. anorg. Chem.* **3**, 267 (1893).

    ‡ G. N. Lewis, "The Atom and the Molecule," *J.A.C.S.* **38**, 762 (1916).

bond, now called the covalent bond, by the sharing of two electrons between two atoms.

In the following sections of this chapter there are given, after an introductory survey of the types of chemical bonds, discussions of the concept of resonance and of the nature of the one-electron bond and the electron-pair bond.

1-2. TYPES OF CHEMICAL BONDS

It is convenient to consider three general extreme types of chemical bonds: *electrostatic bonds*, *covalent bonds*, and *metallic bonds*. This classification is not a rigorous one; for, although the bonds of each extreme type have well-defined properties, the transition from one extreme type to another may be gradual, permitting the existence of bonds of intermediate type (see Chap. 3 and later chapters).

The Chemical Bond Defined.—We shall say that *there is a chemical bond between two atoms or groups of atoms in case that the forces acting between them are such as to lead to the formation of an aggregate with sufficient stability to make it convenient for the chemist to consider it as an independent molecular species.*

With this definition we accept in the category of chemical bonds not only the directed valence bond of the organic chemist but also, for example, the bonds between sodium cations and chloride anions in the sodium chloride crystal, those between the aluminum ion and the six surrounding water molecules in the hydrated aluminum ion in solution or in crystals, and even the weak bond that holds together the two O_2 molecules in O_4.   In general we do not consider the weak van der Waals forces between molecules as leading to chemical-bond formation; but in exceptional cases, such as that of the O_4 molecule mentioned above, it may happen that these forces are strong enough to make it convenient to describe the corresponding intermolecular interaction as bond formation.

The Ionic Bond and Other Electrostatic Bonds.—In case that there can be assigned to each of two atoms or groups of atoms a definite electronic structure essentially independent of the presence of the other atom or group and such that electrostatic interactions are set up that lead to strong attraction and the formation of a chemical bond, we say that the bond is an *electrostatic bond*.

The most important electrostatic bond is the *ionic bond*, resulting from the Coulomb attraction of the excess electric charges of oppositely charged ions.   The atoms of metallic elements lose their outer electrons easily, whereas those of nonmetallic elements tend to add additional electrons; in this way stable cations and anions may be formed, which may essentially retain their electronic structures as they approach one another to form a stable molecule or crystal. In the sodium chloride crystal, with the atomic arrangement shown in Figure 1-1, there exist no discrete NaCl molecules. The crystal is instead composed of sodium cations, Na^+, and chloride anions, Cl^-, each of which is strongly attracted to and held by the six oppositely charged ions that surround it octahedrally. We describe the interactions in this crystal by saying that each ion forms ionic

FIG. 1-1.—The atomic arrangement in the sodium chloride crystal.

bonds with its six neighbors, these bonds combining all of the ions in the crystal into one giant molecule.

The Covalent Bond.—Following Lewis, we interpret the ordinary valence bond, as in the formulas H—H, Cl—Cl, H—Cl, $H-\underset{\underset{H}{|}}{\overset{\overset{H}{|}}{C}}-H$,

etc., as involving the sharing of a pair of electrons by the two bonded atoms, and we write corresponding electronic structures, such as

$$H:H, \quad :\overset{..}{\underset{..}{Cl}}:\overset{..}{\underset{..}{Cl}}:, \quad H:\overset{..}{\underset{..}{Cl}}:, \quad H:\overset{H}{\underset{H}{C}}:H, \quad \text{etc. In these Lewis electronic for-}$$

mulas the symbol of the element represents the *kernel* of the atom, consisting of the nucleus and the inner electrons, but not those in the valence shell, which are shown by dots. A pair of electrons held jointly by two atoms is considered for some purposes to do double duty, and to be effective in completing a stable electronic configuration for each atom. It is seen that in methane the carbon atom, with its two inner electrons and its outer shell of eight shared electrons, has assumed the stable ten-electron configuration of neon, and that each of the other atoms in the structures shown has achieved a noble-gas configuration.

A double bond and a triple bond between two atoms can be represented respectively by four and six shared electrons, as in the following examples:

$$\overset{H}{\underset{H}{\diagdown}}C{=}C\overset{H}{\underset{H}{\diagup}} \qquad\qquad \overset{H}{\underset{H}{\cdot}}\overset{\cdot\cdot}{C}::\overset{\cdot\cdot}{C}\overset{H}{\underset{H}{\cdot}}$$

$$H{-}C{\equiv}C{-}H \qquad\qquad H:C:::C:H$$

$$N{\equiv}N \qquad\qquad\qquad :N:::N:$$

In order that the nitrogen atom in trimethylamine oxide, $(CH_3)_3NO$, might be assigned the neon structure with a completed octet of valence

electrons, Lewis wrote for it the electronic structure $\;\overset{R}{\underset{R}{R:\overset{..}{N}:\overset{..}{\underset{..}{O}}:}}\;$ (with

$R = CH_3$), in which the nitrogen atom forms four single covalent bonds and the oxygen atom one. If it is assumed that the electrons of a shared pair are divided between the two atoms which they connect, it is found on counting electrons for this formula that the nitrogen atom has the electric charge $+1$ (in units equal in magnitude to the electronic charge, with changed sign) and the oxygen atom the charge -1. We shall call these charges, calculated with use of an electronic structure by dividing shared electrons equally between the bonded atoms, the *formal charges* of the atoms for the corresponding structure, and we shall often represent them by signs near the symbols of the atoms, as in the following examples:

Trimethylamine oxide,

$$R-\overset{\displaystyle R}{\underset{\displaystyle R}{\overset{|}{\underset{|}{N}}}}\overset{+}{}\,\overset{..}{\underset{..}{O}}{:}^{-}$$

Sulfate ion,

$$\left[\begin{array}{c} \overset{..}{\underset{..}{O}}{:}^{-} \\ :\overset{..}{O}{}^{-}-\overset{|}{\underset{|}{S}}{}^{++}-\overset{..}{O}{:}^{-} \\ :\overset{..}{\underset{..}{O}}{:}^{-} \end{array}\right]^{--}$$

Ammonium ion,

$$\left[\begin{array}{c} H \\ | \\ H-\overset{+}{\underset{|}{N}}-H \\ | \\ H \end{array}\right]^{+}$$

These formal charges are, as indicated by their name, to be considered as conventional in significance; they do not show in general the actual distribution of electric charges among the atoms in a molecule or complex ion.   Thus in the ammonium ion the unit positive charge of the complex is not to be considered as residing exclusively on the nitrogen atom; as a consequence of the partial ionic character of the N—H bonds, discussed in Chapter 3, part of the excess positive charge can be considered to be transferred to each of the hydrogen atoms.

In a few molecules there occur covalent bonds involving one electron or three electrons, instead of a shared pair.   These *one-electron* and *three-electron bonds* are discussed in Section 1-4 and Chapter 10.

The Metallic Bond; Fractional Bonds.—The most striking characteristic of the bond that holds atoms together in a metallic aggregate is the mobility of the bonding electrons, which gives rise to the high electric and thermal conductivity of metals.   A discussion of the metallic bond and its relation to the covalent bond is given in Chapter 11.   The bonds in metals may be described as fractional bonds.   A discussion of other substances involving fractional bonds, called electron-deficient compounds, is given in Chapter 10.

1-3. THE CONCEPT OF RESONANCE

There is one fundamental principle of quantum mechanics that finds expression in most of the chemical applications of the theory to problems dealing with the normal states of molecules.   This is the principle that underlies the concept of *resonance*.   A structure for a system is represented in quantum mechanics by a wave function, usually called ψ, a function of the coordinates that in classical theory would be used (with their conjugate momenta) in describing the system. The methods for finding the wave function for a system in a particular state are described in treatises on quantum mechanics. In our discussion of the nature of the chemical bond we shall restrict our interest in the main to the normal states of molecules. The stationary quantum states of a molecule or other system are states that are characterized by definite values of the total energy of the system. These states are designated by a quantum number, represented by the letter n, say, or by a set of two or more quantum numbers, each of which can assume any one of certain integral values. The system in the nth stationary quantum state has the definite energy value W_n and is represented by the wave function ψ_n. Predictions can be made about the behavior of the system known to be in the nth quantum state by use of the wave function. These predictions, which relate to the expected results of experiments to be carried out on the system, are in general not unique, but instead statistical in nature. For example, it is not possible to make a definite prediction of the position of the electron relative to the nucleus in a normal hydrogen atom; instead, a corresponding probability distribution function can be found.

The stationary quantum state that has the lowest value of the total energy of the system, corresponding to maximum stability, is called the normal state. The quantum numbers are usually assigned values 1 or 0 for this state.

Let ψ_0 be the correct wave function for the normal state of the system under discussion. The fundamental principle of quantum mechanics in which we are interested states that *the energy value W_0 calculated by the equations of quantum mechanics with use of the correct wave function ψ_0 for the normal state of the system is less than that calculated with any other wave function ψ that might be proposed;* in consequence, *the actual structure of the normal state of a system is that one, of all conceivable structures, that gives the system the maximum stability.*

Now let us consider two structures, I and II, that might reasonably or conceivably represent the normal state of the system under consideration. The methods of the theory are such that the more general function

$$\psi = a\psi_{\mathrm{I}} + b\psi_{\mathrm{II}} \tag{1-1}$$

formed by multiplying ψ_{I} and ψ_{II} by arbitrary numerical coefficients and adding is also a possible wave function for the system. Only the ratio b/a is significant, the nature of the function not being changed by multiplication by a constant. By calculating the energy corresponding to ψ as a function of the ratio b/a, the value of b/a that gives the energy its minimum value can be found.   The corresponding wave function is then the best approximation to the correct wave function for the normal state of the system that can be constructed in this way.   If the best value of b/a turns out to be very small, then the best wave function ψ will be essentially equal to ψ_I and the normal state will be represented more closely by structure I than by any other structure of those considered.   It may well happen, however, that the best value of b/a is neither very small nor very large (in the latter case the best ψ would differ little from ψ_{II}), but is of the order of magnitude of unity.   In this case the best wave function ψ would be formed in part from ψ_I and in part from ψ_{II} and the normal state of the system would be described correspondingly as involving both structure I and structure II.   It has become conventional to speak of such a system as *resonating* between structures I and II, or as being a *resonance hybrid* of structures I and II.

The structure of such a system is not, however, exactly intermediate in character between structures I and II, because as a consequence of the resonance it is stabilized by a certain amount of energy, the *resonance energy*.   The best value of b/a is that which gives the total energy of the system its minimum value, this value lying below that for either ψ_I or ψ_{II} by an amount that depends on the magnitude of the interaction between structures I and II and on their energy difference (see Sec. 1-4).   It is this extra stability of the system, relative to structure I or structure II (whichever is the more stable), that is called the resonance energy.

The concept of resonance was introduced into quantum mechanics in 1926 by the German physicist Werner Heisenberg in connection with the discussion of the quantum states of the helium atom.   He pointed out that a quantum-mechanical treatment somewhat analogous to the classical treatment of a system of resonating coupled harmonic oscillators can be applied to many systems.   The resonance phenomenon of classical mechanics is observed, for example, for a system of two tuning forks with the same characteristic frequency of oscillation and attached to a common base, which provides an interaction between them.   When one fork is struck, it gradually ceases to oscillate, transferring its energy to the other, which begins its oscillation; the process is then reversed, and the energy resonates back and forth between the two forks until it is dissipated by frictional and other losses.   The same phenomenon is shown by two similar pendulums connected by a weak spring.   The qualitative analogy between this classical resonance phenomenon and the quantum-mechanical resonance phenomenon described in the first part of this section is obvious; the analogy does not, however, provide a simple nonmathematical explanation of a most important feature of quantum-mechanical resonance in its chemical applications, that of stabilization of the system by the resonance energy, and we shall accordingly not pursue it further. The student of chemistry will, I believe, be able to develop a reliable and useful intuitive understanding of the concept of resonance by the study of its applications to various problems as described throughout this book.

1-4. THE HYDROGEN MOLECULE-ION AND THE
ONE-ELECTRON BOND

In this section we make the first chemical application of the idea of resonance, in connection with the structure of the simplest of all molecules, the hydrogen molecule-ion, H_2^+, and the simplest of all chemical bonds, the one-electron bond, which involves one electron shared by two atoms.

The Normal Hydrogen Atom.—According to the Bohr theory, the electron in the normal hydrogen atom moved about the nucleus in a circular orbit with radius $a_0 = 0.530$ Å and the constant speed $v_0 = 2.182 \times 10^8$ cm/sec. The quantum-mechanical picture is similar but less definite. The wave function ψ_{1s} that represents the orbital motion of the electron in this atom, shown in Figure 1-2, is large in magnitude only within a region close to the nucleus; beyond 1 or 2 Å it falls off rapidly toward zero. The square of ψ represents the *probability distribution function* for the position of the electron, such that $\psi^2 dV$ is the probability that the electron be in the volume element dV, and $4\pi r^2 \psi^2 dr$ is the probability that it be between the distances r and $r + dr$ from the nucleus. It is seen from the figure that this last function has its maximum value at $r = a_0$. The most probable distance of the electron from the nucleus is thus just the Bohr radius a_0; the electron is, however, not restricted to this one distance. The speed of the electron also is not constant, but can be represented by a distribution function, such that the root-mean-square speed has just the Bohr value v_0. We can accordingly describe the normal hydrogen atom by saying that the electron moves in and out about the nucleus, remaining usually within a distance of about 0.5 Å, with a speed that is variable but is of the order of magnitude of v_0. Over a period of time long enough to permit many cycles of motion of the electron the atom can be described as consisting of the nucleus surrounded by a spherically symmetrical ball of negative electricity (the electron blurred by a time-exposure of its rapid motion), as indicated in Figure 1-3.

The Hydrogen Molecule-Ion.—The structure of the hydrogen molecule-ion, H_2^+, as of any molecule, is discussed theoretically by first considering the motion of the electron (or of all the electrons in case that there are several) in the field of the atomic nuclei considered to be fixed in a definite configuration.   The electronic energy of the molecule is thus obtained as a function of the nuclear configuration.   The configuration for the normal state of the molecule is that corresponding to the minimum value of this energy function, and thus giving the molecule the maximum stability.

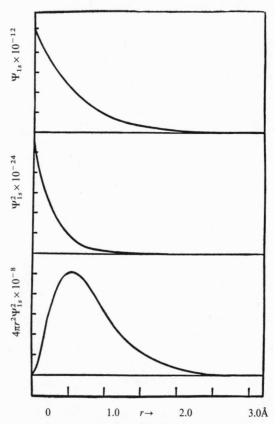

FIG. 1-2.—The wave function ψ_{1s}, its square, and the radial probability distribution function $4\pi r^2\psi_{1s}^2$ for the normal hydrogen atom.

For the hydrogen molecule-ion our problem is to evaluate the energy as a function of the distance r_{AB} between the two nuclei A and B.   For large values of r_{AB} the system in its normal state consists of a normal hydrogen atom (the electron and nucleus A, say) and a hydrogen ion (nucleus B), which interact with one another only weakly.   If we assume the same structure $H\cdot + H^+$ to hold as the nuclei approach one another, we find on calculation that the interaction energy has the form shown by the dashed curve in Figure 1-4, with no minimum.   From this calculation we would say that a hydrogen atom and a hydrogen ion repel one another, rather than attract one another to form a stable molecule-ion.

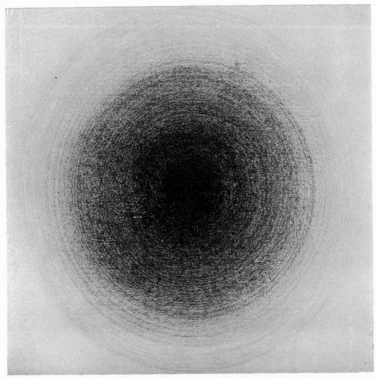

Fig. 1-3.—A drawing illustrating the decrease in electron density with increasing distance from the nucleus in the normal hydrogen atom.

However, the structure assumed is too simple to represent the system satisfactorily.   We have assumed that the electron forms a normal hydrogen atom with nucleus A:

$$\text{Structure I} \qquad H_A{\cdot} \qquad H_B^+$$

The structure in which the electron forms a normal hydrogen atom with nucleus B, which then interacts with nucleus A, is just as stable a structure as the first:

$$\text{Structure II} \qquad H_A^+ \qquad {\cdot}H_B$$

and we must consider the possibility of resonance between these two structures. These structures are equivalent, and correspond separately to exactly the same energy; the principles of quantum mechanics require that in such a case *the two structures make equal contributions to the normal state of the system.* On repetition of the calculation of the energy curve with use of the corresponding wave function, formed by adding the wave functions for structures I and II, the lower full curve shown in Figure 1-4 is obtained. This curve has a pronounced minimum at about

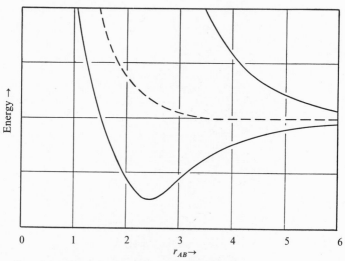

Fig. 1-4.—Curves showing the energy of interaction of a hydrogen atom and a proton. The lower curve corresponds to the formation of a hydrogen molecule-ion in its stable normal state. The scale for the internuclear distance r_{AB} is based on the unit $a_0 = 0.530$ Å.

$r_{AB} = 1.06$ Å, showing that *as a result of the resonance of the electron between the two nuclei a stable one-electron bond is formed*, the energy of the bond being about 50 kcal/mole. The way in which this extra stability and the consequent formation of a bond result from the combination of structures I and II cannot be simply explained; it is the result of the quantum-mechanical resonance phenomenon. The bond can be described as owing its stability to the resonance of the electron back and forth between the two nuclei, with a resonance frequency equal to the resonance energy, 50 kcal/mole, divided by Planck's constant h. This frequency for the normal molecule-ion is 7×10^{14} sec^{-1}, which is about one-fifth as great as the frequency of orbital motion of the electron about the nucleus in the normal hydrogen atom.

(The upper full curve in Figure 1-4 represents another way in which a normal hydrogen atom and a hydrogen ion can interact. The structures I and II contribute equally to this curve also, the resonance energy in this case making the system less stable rather than more stable. The chances are equal that a hydrogen atom and a hydrogen ion on approach repel one another as indicated by this curve or that they attract one another to form the normal molecule-ion.)

Very accurate calculations have led to the value

$$D_0(H_2^+) = 60.95 \pm 0.10 \text{ kcal/mole}$$

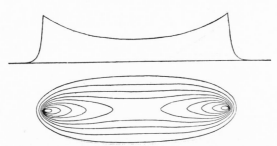

FIG. 1-5.—The electron distribution function for the hydrogen molecule-ion. The upper curve shows the value of the function along the line through the two nuclei, and the lower figure shows contour lines, increasing from 0.1 for the outermost to 1 at the nuclei.

for the energy of formation of the normal hydrogen molecule-ion from a hydrogen atom and a hydrogen ion. This is in agreement with the experimental value, which is less accurately known. The calculated values of the equilibrium internuclear distance, 1.06 Å, and the vibrational frequency, 2250 cm^{-1}, also agree with the experimental values to within the accuracy of their calculation and experimental determination.

The electron distribution function for the molecule-ion is shown in Figure 1-5. It is seen that the electron remains for most of the time in the small region just between the nuclei, only rarely getting on the far side of one of them; and we may feel that the presence of the electron between the two nuclei, where it can draw them together, provides some explanation of the stability of the bond. The electron distribution function is concentrated relative to that for the hydrogen atom, the volume within the outermost contour surface shown (with one-tenth the maximum value) being only 63 percent as great as for the atom.

For convenience we may represent the one-electron bond by a dot midway between the symbols of the bonded atoms, the hydrogen molecule-ion then having the structural formula $(H \cdot H)^+$.

The Conditions for the Formation of a One-Electron Bond.—The magnitude of the resonance energy of the one-electron bond in the hydrogen molecule-ion is determined by the amount of interaction of the two structures I and II ($H \cdot H^+$ and $H^+ \cdot H$), as calculated by the methods of quantum mechanics. Because the two structures correspond to the same energy, the interaction energy is completely manifested as resonance energy;

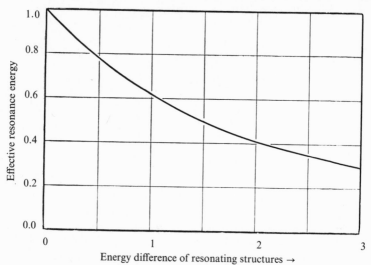

Fig. 1-6.—Curve showing the amount of energy stabilizing the normal state of a system with two resonating structures, relative to the more stable of the two resonating structures, as a function of the energy difference of the two structures. The unit of energy used in the graph is the interaction energy of the two structures (the resonance integral).

there is complete resonance. If, however, the two nuclei A and B were unlike, so that the two structures

$$\text{I} \quad A\cdot \qquad B^+$$
$$\text{and} \qquad \text{II} \quad A^+ \qquad \cdot B$$

corresponded to different energy values, the conditions for complete resonance would not be satisfied. The more stable of the two structures (structure I, say) would contribute more to the normal state of the system than the other, and the system would be stabilized (relative to structure I) by an amount of resonance energy less than the interaction energy. A curve showing the effect of difference in energy of two resonating structures in inhibiting resonance is shown in Figure 1-6. The way in which this curve is calculated is described in Appendix V.   As structure I becomes more and more stable relative to structure II it makes up a larger and larger part of the normal state of the system, and resonance with structure II stabilizes the system by a smaller and smaller amount.   For this reason we expect the one-electron bond to be formed only between like atoms or occasionally between unlike atoms which happen to be of such a nature (similarity in electronegativity) as to make structures I and II approximately equal in energy.

1-5. THE HYDROGEN MOLECULE AND THE ELECTRON-PAIR BOND

Before 1927 there was no satisfactory theory of the covalent bond.   The chemist had postulated the existence of the valence bond between atoms and had built up a body of empirical information about it, but his inquiries into its structure had been futile.   The step taken by G. N. Lewis of associating two electrons with a bond can hardly be called the development of a theory, since it left unanswered the fundamental questions as to the nature of the interactions involved and the source of the energy of the bond.   Only in 1927 was the development of the theory of the covalent bond initiated by the work of Condon and of Heitler and London on the hydrogen molecule, described in the following paragraphs.

Condon's Treatment of the Hydrogen Molecule.—The American physicist E. U. Condon gave a discussion of the hydrogen molecule based on the treatment of the hydrogen molecule-ion.   He introduced two electrons into the normal-state orbital for the one electron of H_2^+.   The total energy of the H_2 molecule for this structure consists of four parts: the energy of repulsion of the two nuclei, the energy of the first electron moving in the field of the two nuclei, the equal energy of the second electron, and the energy of mutual electrostatic repulsion of the two electrons.   Condon made an approximate calculation of these terms, and obtained an energy curve for H_2 with its minimum at $r_{AB} = 0.73$ Å and with bond energy 100 kcal/mole, in excellent agreement with experiment.

Condon's treatment is the prototype of the molecular-orbital method of discussing the electronic structure of molecules.   In this method a wave function is formulated that involves the introduction of a pair of electrons in an electron orbital that extends about two or more atomic nuclei.

The second method of discussing the electronic structure of molecules, usually called the valence-bond method, involves the use of a wave function of such a nature that the two electrons of the electron-pair bond between two atoms tend to remain on the two different atoms.   The prototype of this method is the treatment of the hydrogen molecule carried out in 1927 by the German physicists W. Heitler and F. London, which we shall now discuss.

The Heitler-London Treatment of the Hydrogen Molecule.—The hydrogen molecule consists of two nuclei, which may be designated A and B, and two electrons, 1 and 2. As in the treatment of the hydrogen molecule-ion, we calculate the interaction energy for various values of the internuclear distance r_{AB}. When the nuclei are far apart the normal state of the system involves two normal hydrogen atoms. Let us assume that one of the electrons, electron 1, say, is associated with nucleus A, and the other, electron 2, with nucleus B. When the interaction energy is calculated as a function of the internuclear distance, it is found that at large distances there is a weak attraction, which soon turns into strong repulsion as r_{AB} is further diminished (dashed curve of Figure 1-7). According to this calculation the two atoms would not combine to form a stable molecule.

Here again, however, we have neglected the resonance phenomenon; for the structure with electron 2 attached to nucleus A and electron 1 to nucleus B is just as stable as the equivalent structure assumed above, and in accordance with quantum-mechanical principles we must consider as a representation of the normal state of the system neither one structure nor the other, but rather a combination to which the two contribute equally; that is, we must make the calculation in such a way as to take into consideration the possibility of the exchange of places of the two electrons:

Structure I	$H_A \cdot 1$	$2 \cdot H_B$
Structure II	$H_A \cdot 2$	$1 \cdot H_B$

In this way there is obtained an interaction-energy curve (the lower full curve in Figure 1-7) that shows a pronounced minimum, corresponding to the formation of a stable molecule. The energy of formation of the molecule from separated atoms as calculated in this simple way is about 67 percent of the experimental value of 102.6 kcal/mole, and the calculated equilibrium distance between the nuclei is 0.05 Å larger than the observed value 0.74 Å. A more refined quantum mechanical calculation gives complete agreement with experiment.

Hence we see that a very simple treatment of the system of two hydrogen atoms leads to an explanation of the formation of a stable molecule, *the energy of the electron-pair bond being in the main the resonance energy corresponding to the interchange of the two electrons between the two atomic orbitals.*

The Conditions for the Formation of an Electron-Pair Bond.—In Section 1-4 it was pointed out that the resonance that leads to the formation of a stable one-electron bond between two atoms is in general largely inhibited in case that the two atoms are unlike, and that in consequence such a bond occurs only rarely. We see that for the electron-pair bond no such restriction exists; the two structures I and II that differ only in interchange of the two electrons 1 and 2 by two atoms A and B are equivalent even though the two atoms involved are unlike, and accordingly complete

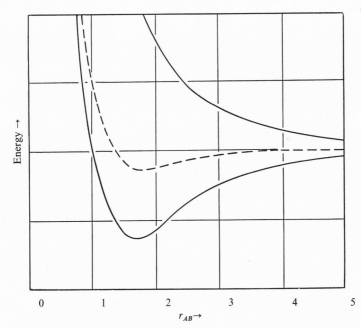

F$_{IG}$. 1-7.—Curves showing the energy of interaction of two normal hydrogen atoms. The scale for the internuclear distance r_{AB} is based on the unit $a_0 = 0.530$ Å.

resonance occurs for unlike atoms as well as for like atoms, the resonance energy of the bond being equal to the interaction energy of the two structures. Thus there is no special condition as to the nature of the atoms that must be satisfied in order for an electron-pair bond to be formed, and we need not be surprised by the widespread occurrence and great importance of this bond.

A detailed discussion of the electronic structure of atoms is given in the following chapter, preliminary to the statement of the formal rules for covalent-bond formation at the end of the chapter.

EXERCISES

1-1.—By measuring the middle curve of Figure 1-2 (or, better, the top curve), calculate the electron density at 0.53 Å from the nucleus of the normal hydrogen atom, relative to the value at the center. (Ans. About 15%.   The correct answer, given by the wave function, is 13.5%.)

1-2.—What is the value of the electron density at the point midway between the two protons in H_2^+ (0.53 Å from each proton), relative to that at either nucleus?   (Ans. About 47%.)

1-3—According to the molecular-orbital (Condon) treatment of the hydrogen molecule, what is the probability that both electrons are on the proton-*A* side of the symmetry plane perpendicular to the internuclear axis?   What amount of $H_A^- : H_B^+$ ionic character does this treatment assign to the molecule?   What amount does the Heitler-London treatment assign to it?

The Electronic Structure of Atoms and the Formal Rules for the Formation of Covalent Bonds

AN understanding of the electronic structure of atoms is necessary for the study of the electronic structure of molecules and the nature of the chemical bond. Our knowledge of the electronic structure of atoms has been obtained almost entirely from the analysis of the spectra of gases. In this chapter we shall discuss the nature of spectra and the information about the electronic structure of atoms that has been derived from this information, in preparation for the later chapters of the book. The chapter ends with the statement of the formal rules for the formation of covalent bonds.

2-1. THE INTERPRETATION OF LINE SPECTRA

When the radiation emitted from a source of light is resolved into a spectrum by use of a prism or a grating it is found that the distribution of intensity with wavelength depends on the nature of the source. The intensity of light from a glowing solid body varies gradually from place to place in the spectrum and is a function principally of the temperature of the body. A hot gas or a gas excited to the emission of light by an electric discharge or in some other way may emit an *emission spectrum* that consists of sharp lines, each line having a well-defined wavelength. Such a spectrum is called a *line spectrum*. Sometimes many lines occur close together and separated by approximately equal intervals; they are then said to compose a band, and the spectrum is called a *band spectrum*. Lines and bands are also observed to be absorbed when continuous radiation is passed through a gas. Such a spectrum of dark lines or bands on a light background is called an *absorption spectrum*.

Band spectra are produced in emission or absorption by molecules containing two or more atoms, and line spectra by single atoms or monatomic ions. The structure of bands is related to the vibration of the nuclei of the atoms within the molecule and to the rotation of the molecule.

The intensities and wavelengths of spectral lines are characteristic of the emitting atoms or molecules. The position of a line in the spectrum is indicated by giving either its wavelength λ, usually measured in Ångström units, its frequency $v = c/\lambda$ (with c the velocity of light), measured in $\sec^{-1}$, or its wave number or reciprocal wavelength $\tilde{v} = 1/\lambda$, measured in cm^{-1}.

The concept of the atom as a system of one nucleus and one or more electrons was developed to explain the experiments of Lenard and of Rutherford on the passage of anode rays (rapidly moving positive ions) and of alpha particles (helium nuclei emitted by radioactive materials) through matter. The electrons and the nuclei are very small in comparison with atoms—their diameters are between 10^{-13} and 10^{-12} cm, that is, between 10^{-5} and 10^{-4} Å, whereas atoms have diameters of the order of 2 to 5 Å. The magnitude of the charge of a nucleus is always an integral multiple of that of the electron, with positive sign; it is expressed as Ze, Z being the atomic number of the element. An electrically neutral atom has Z electrons about the nucleus.

According to the laws of classical mechanics the system of electrons and nucleus comprising an atom would reach final equilibrium only when the electrons had fallen into the nucleus. The electrons would be expected, according to classical mechanics, to describe orbits about the nucleus, and the acceleration of the charged particles, the electrons, in the orbits would give rise to the emission of energy as radiation. The frequencies involved in the motion of the electrons would then gradually change during the emission of light. This sort of structure for the atom is incompatible with the observed sharply defined frequencies of spectral lines. The existence of nonradiating normal states of atoms in which the electrons have certainly not fallen into the nucleus is a further point of disagreement with classical theory, indicating the necessity for the development of a new atomic mechanics, differing from the classical mechanics of macroscopic systems. This new atomic mechanics is called quantum mechanics.

Two postulates that are fundamental to the interpretation of spectra are the *existence of stationary states* and the *Bohr frequency rule*. They were enunciated by Bohr in 1913 in the famous paper that led in a few years to the complete elucidation of spectral phenomena. Planck had previously announced (in 1900) that the amount of energy dW in unit volume (1 cm^3) and contained between the frequencies v and $v + dv$ in empty space in equilibrium with matter at temperature T, as measured experimentally, could be represented by the equation

$$dW = \frac{8\pi h v^3}{c^3(e^{hv/kT} - 1)} \, dv \tag{2-1}$$

in which v is the frequency of the light, k is Boltzmann's constant, T is the absolute temperature, and h is a constant of nature that has been given the name Planck's constant. This equation is not the one that would be obtained from classical statistical mechanics; Planck showed that it could be derived if the assumption were made that radiant energy (light) is not emitted continuously by atoms or molecules, but only in discrete portions, each portion carrying the quantity of energy hv. Einstein suggested that one of these energy quantities is not emitted uniformly in all directions by a radiating atom, but instead in one direction, like a particle. These portions of radiant energy are called *photons* or *light quanta*.

The next phenomenon explained in terms of quanta was the photoelectric effect, which was interpreted by Einstein in 1908. When light falls on a metal plate electrons are emitted from the surface of the plate, but not with velocities related to the intensity of the light, as would be expected from classical theory. Instead, the maximum velocity of the ejected electrons (the photoelectrons) depends on the frequency of the light: it corresponds to the conversion of just the energy hv of one light quantum into the energy of removal of the electron from the metal plate plus the kinetic energy of the liberated electron. Einstein also announced at the same time his law of photochemical equivalence, according to which the absorption of one light quantum of energy hv may activate one molecule to chemical reaction. In all of these cases the system (atom, molecule, or crystal) emitting or absorbing radiation in quanta changes discontinuously from a state with a given amount of energy to one with energy hv less or greater.

2-2. STATIONARY STATES; THE BOHR FREQUENCY PRINCIPLE

These facts and some observations about the frequencies of spectral lines were the inspiration for Bohr's two postulates, which may be expressed in the following way:

I. The existence of stationary states. *An atomic system can exist in certain stationary states, each one corresponding to a definite value of the energy W of the system, and transition from one state to another is accompanied by the emission or absorption as radiation, or the transfer to or from another system of atoms or molecules, of an amount of energy equal to the energy difference of the two states.*

II. The Bohr frequency rule. *The frequency of the radiation absorbed by a system and associated with the transition from an initial state with energy W_1 to a final state with energy W_2 is*

$$v = \frac{W_2 - W_1}{h} \tag{2-2}$$

(negative values of v correspond to emission).

The two postulates are compatible with the observation that the frequencies of the spectral lines emitted by an atom can be represented as the

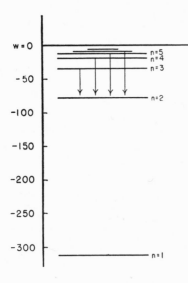

Fig. 2-1.—Energy levels for the hydrogen atom. The arrows indicate the transitions that give the first four lines of the Balmer series in emission.

differences between pairs of a set of frequency values, called the *term values* or *spectral terms* of the atom. These term values are now seen to be the values of the energy of the stationary states divided by h (to give frequency, in $\sec^{-1}$), or by hc (to give wave number, in cm^{-1}, as is customarily given in tables of term values).

2-3. STATIONARY STATES OF THE HYDROGEN ATOM

An *energy-level diagram* for the hydrogen atom is given in Figure 2-1. The reference state, with zero energy, is that of a proton and an electron infinitely separated from one another, that is, the ionized hydrogen atom. The stationary states of the hydrogen atom have negative energy values with reference to the ionized state. The values of the energy for the various stationary states are given by the Bohr equation

$$W_n = -\frac{R_H hc}{n^2} \tag{2-3}$$

In this equation R_H is called the Rydberg constant for hydrogen; the value for the Rydberg constant for hydrogen is $109,677.76 \text{ cm}^{-1}$. The letter h is Planck's constant, and c the velocity of light. The letter n is the *total quantum number;* it may have integral values $1, 2, 3, 4, \cdots$.

The frequencies of the spectral lines emitted by a hydrogen atom when it undergoes transition from one stationary state to a lower stationary state can be calculated by the Bohr frequency rule, with use of this expression for the energy values of the stationary state. It is seen, for example, that the frequencies for the lines corresponding to the transitions indicated by arrows in Figure 2-1, corresponding to transitions from states with $n = 3, 4, 5, \cdots$ to the state with $n = 2$, are given by the equation

$$\nu = R_H c \left(\frac{1}{2^2} - \frac{1}{n^2} \right) \tag{2-4}$$

This equation was discovered by Balmer in 1885. These spectral lines constitute the Balmer series. Other series of lines for hydrogen correspond to transitions from upper states to the state with $n = 1$ (the Lyman series), to the state with $n = 3$ (the Paschen series), and so on.

The value of the Rydberg constant R_H, as determined from the measured wavelength of the lines of the Lyman series and the other series for atomic hydrogen, is such that the energy of the normal state of the hydrogen atom, with $n = 1$, is -313.6 kcal/mole (-13.60 ev). The amount of energy required to ionize the normal hydrogen atom is accordingly 313.6 kcal /mole; this is called the *ionization energy* of hydrogen. Spectroscopic studies have provided values for the ionization energy of atoms of most of the elements.

In his 1913 papers Bohr developed a theory of the stationary states of the hydrogen atom. According to his theory the electron was to be considered as moving in a circular orbit about the proton. The amount of angular momentum for a stationary state was assumed by Bohr to be equal to $nh/2\pi$, with $n = 1, 2, 3, \cdots$. In Appendix II there is given the derivation of the energy values for the Bohr circular orbits. For an electron moving about a nucleus with charge Ze (a hydrogen atom for $Z = 1$, helium ion He^+ for $Z = 2$, etc.), the Bohr theory leads to the following expression for the energy of the stationary states:

$$W = -\frac{2\pi^2 m_0 Z^2 e^4}{n^2 h^2} \tag{2-5}$$

Bohr showed that the known values of the mass of the electron, m_0, the electronic charge, e, and Planck's constant, h, led to a value of $2\pi^2 m_0 e^4/ch^3$ equal to the experimental value for the Rydberg constant for hydrogen, and his theory was immediately accepted by other physicists.

According to the Bohr theory the electron in a circular orbit in a normal hydrogen atom moves with the speed $v_0 = 2\pi e^2/h$, which is 2.18×10^8 cm/sec. The speed changes in proportion to $1/n$ for the excited states, and in the hydrogenlike ions, He^+ and so forth, it is proportional to Z. The radius of the normal Bohr orbit is $a_0 = h^2/4\pi^2 m_0 e^2$, which is equal to 0.530 Å. The Bohr radius for excited states is proportional to n^2; that is, it is four times as great for $n = 2$, nine times as great for $n = 3$, and so on. For hydrogenlike ions the radius is proportional to $1/Z$.

Some changes in this picture of the atom have been made as a result of the discovery of quantum mechanics. The motion of the electron in the hydrogen atom according to quantum mechanics is described by means of a wave function ψ, as mentioned in Chapter 1. Expressions for the wave function ψ for the normal state of the hydrogen atom and various excited states are given in Appendix III. These wave functions are designated by three quantum numbers: the total quantum number n, with values $1, 2, \cdots$; the azimuthal quantum number l, with values $0, 1, 2, \cdots,$ $n - 1$; and the magnetic quantum number m_l, with values $-l,$ $-l + 1, \cdots, 0, \cdots, +l$. For the hydrogen atom and hydrogenlike ions the energy depends only on the total quantum number n (except for very small changes in energy determined by the other quantum numbers). The normal state of the hydrogen atom, with $n = 1$, is represented by a single set of quantum numbers: $n = 1$, $l = 0$, and $m_l = 0$.

The azimuthal quantum number l is a measure of the angular momentum of the electron in its orbit. The orbital angular momentum is equal to $\sqrt{l(l + 1)} h/2\pi$. The electron in the hydrogen atom in its normal state (with $l = 0$) does not have any angular momentum, and the picture that we must form of the normal hydrogen atom is accordingly somewhat different from that assumed by Bohr. On the left in Figure 2-2 there is shown the Bohr circular orbit for hydrogen, with the electron moving in a circular orbit with radius a_0. This picture is unsatisfactory because it gives orbital angular momentum to the atom, and it has been found by experiment that the normal hydrogen atom does not have any orbital angular momentum. On the right of Figure 2-2 there is shown the extreme case of an elliptical orbit with zero minor axis, that is, the orbit corresponding to zero angular momentum. This picture represents a type of classical motion of a particle about an attracting center. It corresponds to describing the electron as moving out from the nucleus to the distance $2a_0$ and then returning to the nucleus. Comparison with Figure 1-3, representing the electron distribution in the normal hydrogen atom, shows that the electron is to be considered as moving in and out from the nucleus in all directions in space, so as to give spherical symmetry to the atom; moreover, the distance of the electron from the nucleus is not limited rigorously to values less than $2a_0$. The Heisenberg uncertainty principle of quantum mechanics, according to which the position and the momentum of a particle cannot be exactly measured simultaneously, shows that we cannot hope to describe the motion of the electron in the

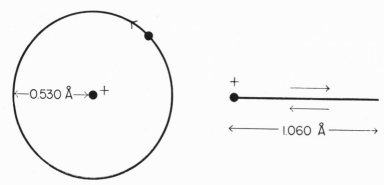

FIG. 2-2.—At the left is represented the circular orbit of the Bohr atom. At the right is shown the very eccentric orbit (line orbit), with no angular momentum, that corresponds somewhat more closely to the description of the hydrogen atom in its normal state given by quantum mechanics.

normal hydrogen atom in terms of a definite orbit, such as that shown in Figure 2-2; nevertheless, there is some value in discussing the type of classical motion that corresponds reasonably closely to the quantum-mechanical description of the normal hydrogen atom.

In Figure 2-3 there are shown drawings of the Bohr orbits for hydrogen in the excited states with $n = 2$, $n = 3$, and $n = 4$, with the angular momentum taken equal to $\sqrt{l(l + 1)}h/2\pi$, as required by quantum mechanics. An electron with $l = 0$ is said to be an s electron, one with $l = 1$ a p electron, and so on through the sequence $d, f, g, h, \cdots$. An s electron does not have any angular momentum, whereas $p, d, f, \cdots$ electrons have angular momentum, with increasing magnitude in this sequence.

The electrons with a given value of the total quantum number n constitute an *electron shell*. The shells have been given the designations $K, L, M, N, O, \cdots$, corresponding to $n = 1, 2, 3, 4, 5, \cdots$. Another classification of electron shells that is especially useful in chemistry (the helium shell, neon shell, argon shell, etc.) is described in Section 2-7.

There is only one *s* orbital in each shell (see App. III); it corresponds to the values $l = 0$, $m_l = 0$ for these quantum numbers. There are three *p* orbitals (with $l = 1$) in each shell (beginning with the *L* shell) corresponding to the values -1, 0, and $+1$ for the magnetic quantum number m_l. Similarly, there are five *d* orbitals per shell from the *M* shell on ($m_l = -2$, -1, 0, $+1$, $+2$), and seven *f* orbitals from the *N* shell on ($m_l = -3$, -2,

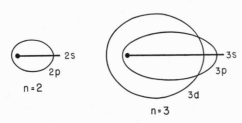

n = 2

n = 3

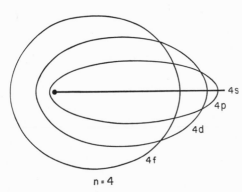

n = 4

FIG. 2-3.—Bohr orbits for the hydrogen atom, total quantum number 2, 3, and 4. These orbits are represented as having the values of angular momentum given by quantum mechanics.

-1, 0, $+1$, $+2$, $+3$). The orbitals with given values of both *n* and *l* are called *subshells*.

The different values of the magnetic quantum number m_l correspond to different orientations in space of the angular momentum vector for the electron. It is customary to represent the angular momentum of a system by a vector; for example, the angular momentum vector for a circular Bohr orbit would extend in a direction perpendicular to the plane of the orbit and would have magnitude proportional to the magnitude of the angular momentum. The magnetic quantum number m_l represents the component of angular momentum along a designated direction in space, in particular the direction of a magnetic field. The diagrams in Figure 2-4 show the angles between the angular momentum vector and the field direction for the *p* orbitals, the *d* orbitals, and the *f* orbitals. The value

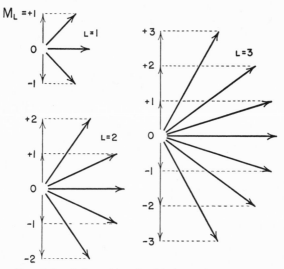

Fig. 2-4.—Orientation of orbital angular momentum vectors for values 1, 2, and 3 of the angular momentum quantum number L.

$m_l = 0$, in each case, corresponds to zero component of angular momentum in the field direction, the value $m_l = +1$ to the component $h/2\pi$, $m_l = +2$ to $2h/2\pi$, and so on.

2-4. THE ELECTRONIC STRUCTURE OF ALKALI ATOMS

The normal lithium atom has two electrons in the K shell, with $n = 1$, and one electron in the $2s$ orbital of the L shell. The electronic configurations of all of the alkali atoms are given in Table 2-1; in each case there is a single electron in the outermost shell.

Some of the energy levels for the lithium atom, as found by the analysis of the line spectrum of lithium, are shown in Figure 2-5. It is seen that

TABLE 2.1—Electron Configurations of Alkali Atoms

Atom	Z	Configuration
Li	3	$1s^2 2s$
Na	11	$1s^2 2s^2 2p^6 3s$
K	19	$1s^2 2s^2 2p^6 3s^2 3p^6 4s$
Rb	37	$1s^2 2s^2 2p^6 3s^2 3p^6 3d^{10} 4s^2 4p^6 5s$
Cs	55	$1s^2 2s^2 2p^6 3s^2 3p^6 3d^{10} 4s^2 4p^6 4d^{10} 5s^2 5p^6 6s$
Fr	87	$1s^2 2s^2 2p^6 3s^2 3p^6 3d^{10} 4s^2 4p^6 4d^{10} 4f^{14} 5s^2 5p^6 5d^{10} 6s^2 6p^6 7s$

there is a significant difference from the energy-level diagram for hydrogen: for hydrogen the levels 2s and 2p have the same energy value, as have also 3s, 3p, and 3d, and so on, whereas for lithium the levels are split—the energy depends on the azimuthal quantum number *l* as well as on the total quantum number.

The energy values 4f, 5f, and 6f lie very close to those for hydrogen,

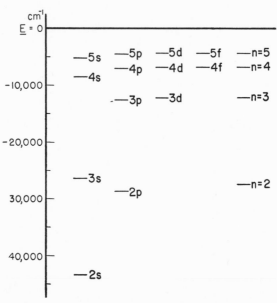

FIG. 2-5.—Energy levels for the lithium atom. The symbols 2s and so forth give the quantum number for one electron; the other two electrons are in the 1s orbital. The levels at the right are those for hydrogen.

which are represented at the right side of the diagram. Those for 3d, 4d, ⋯ lie somewhat below the hydrogen values, those for the *p* states still lower, and those for the *s* states much lower. An explanation of this behavior was suggested by Schrödinger in 1921, before the development of quantum mechanics. This explanation is indicated by the drawings in Figures 2-6 and 2-7. Schrödinger suggested that the inner electron shell of lithium might be replaced by an equivalent charge of electricity distributed uniformly over the surface of a sphere of suitable radius, which for lithium would be about 0.28 Å. The valence electron, outside this shell, would be moving in an electric field due to the nucleus, with charge $+3e$, plus the two K electrons, with charge $-2e$, that is, in a field

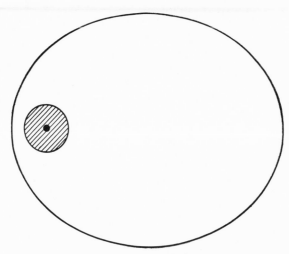

Fɪɢ. 2-6.—A nonpenetrating orbit in an alkali-like atom.
The inner electrons are represented by the shaded region
about the nucleus.

due to a charge $+e$, the same as the charge of the proton. So long as the
electron stayed outside the K shell, it could be expected to behave in a way
corresponding to a hydrogenlike electron. An orbit of this sort, shown in
Figure 2-6, is called a *nonpenetrating orbit*. Reference to Figure 2-3 indicates that an f electron or a d electron in an excited lithium atom would
be essentially nonpenetrating, but that surely an s electron, in an orbit
that extends to the nucleus, would penetrate the K shell, and probably a p
electron would also penetrate the K shell to some extent. An electron
in a *penetrating orbit* (Fig. 2-7) would move into the field of attraction of
the nucleus with charge $+3e$ only partially shielded by the K electrons and
would accordingly be stabilized by a large amount.

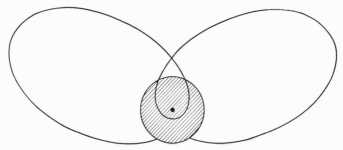

Fɪɢ. 2-7.—Penetrating orbit in an alkali-like atom.

2-5. THE SPINNING ELECTRON AND THE FINE STRUCTURE
OF SPECTRAL LINES

The atomic model that has been discussed in the preceding paragraphs gives a good representation of simple spectra, but not a complete one. For example, the transition from the state $2p$ to the state $2s$ for lithium, indicated in Figure 2-5 to be a single line (wavelength 6707.8 Å), is in fact a doublet, consisting of two components with wavelengths differing by 0.15 Å. Similarly, the transition from $3p$ to $3s$ for sodium is also a doublet, consisting of two components with wavelengths 5889.95 Å and 5895.92 Å; these are the well-known yellow doublet lines of sodium, seen in sodium vapor lamps.

The explanation of this complexity of the energy levels is that the individual electrons have rotatory motion, a spin. Each electron has the angular momentum $\sqrt{s(s + 1)}h/2\pi$ with s, the spin quantum number, always $\frac{1}{2}$. The electron has a magnetic moment associated with this rotation. The experiments that have been carried out on the properties of the electron show that the magnetic moment of the electron is

$$2 \cdot \frac{e}{2m_0c} \cdot \frac{\sqrt{3}}{2} \cdot \frac{h}{2\pi}$$

The electron accordingly has the following properties:

charge $-e = -4.803 \times 10^{-10}$ statcoulombs

mass $m_0 \ = 0.911 \times 10^{-22}$ g

angular momentum $\dfrac{\sqrt{3}}{2} \cdot \dfrac{h}{2\pi} = 0.913 \times 10^{-27}$ erg seconds

magnetic moment $\dfrac{\sqrt{3}}{2} \cdot \dfrac{h}{2\pi} \cdot \dfrac{e}{m_0c} = 1.608 \times 10^{-20}$ erg gauss^{-1}

It is especially interesting that the factor $2e/2m_0c$ relating the magnetic moment of the spinning electron and its angular momentum is twice as great as the factor $e/2m_0c$ that relates the orbital magnetic moment (the magnetic moment of an electron moving in an orbit) to the corresponding angular momentum.

The energy levels are represented by certain symbols, called *Russell-Saunders symbols*. For example, the normal state of the lithium atom is represented by the symbol $2s\,^2S_{\frac{1}{2}}$. The symbol $2s$ means that the valence electron is occupying a $2s$ orbital. The remaining symbol, $^2S_{\frac{1}{2}}$, describes the various angular momenta in the atom. A Russell-Saunders symbol, such as $^2S_{\frac{1}{2}}$, gives the values of three quantum numbers for the atom: the quantum number S, which is the quantum number that represents the resultant spin of all of the electrons in the atom*; the quantum number L, which is the quantum number that represents the resultant orbital angular momentum of all of the electrons in the atom; and the quantum number J, which is the quantum number that represents the total angular momentum of the atom, due to both spin and orbital motion of the electrons, and is the resultant of S and L. S, the spin quantum number for the atom, has the value $\frac{1}{2}$ when there is only one valence electron in the atom. The superscript on the left side of the term symbol is equal to $2S + 1$ (which is equal to 2, for $S = \frac{1}{2}$); it represents the *multiplicity* of the energy level and corresponds to the number of ways in which the quantum number S can be oriented in space. The capital letter in the symbol gives the value of the quantum number for the orbital angular momentum; the letters $S, P, D, F, G, \cdots$ correspond respectively to $L = 0, 1, 2, 3, 4, \cdots$. For an atom with a single valence electron the capital letter is identical with the small letter representing the orbital of the valence electron. The subscript gives the value of the resultant quantum number J, corresponding to the resultant of the spin angular momentum and the orbital angular momentum.

For a single valence electron S is equal to $\frac{1}{2}$, and there are only two possible values for J, namely, $L + \frac{1}{2}$ and $L - \frac{1}{2}$. Vector diagrams showing the composition of the spin angular momentum and the orbital angular momentum for the two states $^2D_{\frac{3}{2}}$ and $^2D_{\frac{5}{2}}$ are shown in Figure 2-8.

It is seen from the term diagram that the energy of interaction of the spin of the electron and its orbital motion is not very great. This energy of interaction increases rapidly with increase in the atomic number of the element and becomes large for the heavy atoms.

2-6. THE ELECTRONIC STRUCTURE OF ATOMS WITH TWO OR MORE VALENCE ELECTRONS

The energy of an atom containing two or more electrons depends upon many kinds of interaction of the electrons and the nucleus. First of all, there are the interactions of each electron with the nucleus, which in a simple theory give rise to energy terms similar to those described for a single electron in Section 2-4; in general all of the electrons may be described as occupying penetrating orbitals. Other interactions can be correlated with the spin of the electrons and with their orbital angular momenta. The spectroscopists have developed a *vector model* of the atom that provides a simple way of describing the stationary states of the

---

* Note that the capital letter S is used in two different ways.

atom.   In the following paragraphs we shall discuss the Russell-Saunders vector model, in which, as mentioned in the preceding section, the vectors representing the spin of the individual electrons combine to form a resultant spin vector, represented by the quantum number S, the vectors representing the orbital angular momenta combine to form an orbital angular momentum vector, represented by the quantum number L, and these two resultant vectors combine to form a total angular momentum vector for the atom, represented by the quantum number J.   This description of the atom has been found to be a good one for light atoms, with small atomic number; the electronic structure of the heavier atoms is usually more

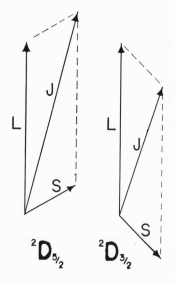

FIG. 2-8.—The interaction of spin angular momentum and orbital angular momentum to form the total angular momentum for the states $^2D_{\frac{5}{2}}$ and $^2D_{\frac{3}{2}}$.

complicated, and, although the Russell-Saunders symbols are commonly used in the description of the stationary states of the heavier atoms, the rules corresponding to the symbols do not in general apply well to the heavier elements.

Let us consider an atom with two s electrons, with different total quantum numbers; for example, a beryllium atom with one valence electron in a $2s$ orbital and the other in a $3s$ orbital, in addition to the two electrons in the K shell.   The orbital angular momenta of the two valence electrons are zero ($l_1 = 0$, $l_2 = 0$), and accordingly the resultant angular momentum is zero ($L=0$).   Each of the two electrons has spin quantum number $\frac{1}{2}$ ($s_1 = \frac{1}{2}$, $s_2 = \frac{1}{2}$), and each spin angular momentum vector accordingly has the magnitude $\sqrt{\dfrac{1}{2}\cdot\dfrac{3}{2}}\,\dfrac{h}{2\pi}$.   These two vectors can combine to form a resultant vector corresponding to the values 0 and 1 for the total spin quantum number S, as shown in Figure 2-9. The state $S = 1$ is usually described by saying that the two vectors are parallel (the figure shows that they are not exactly parallel, but are as close to parallel as is allowed by nature) and the state $S = 0$ by saying that they are antiparallel. Inasmuch as L is equal to 0, the total angular momentum quantum number J for the atoms is equal to 0 when S equals 0 and is equal to 1 when S equals 1.

Experience shows that these two states differ greatly in energy. The interaction energy of the magnetic moment of the two electron spins is very small, and the observed energy difference is not due to a direct spin-spin magnetic interaction. It was shown by Heisenberg that the differ-

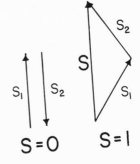

FIG. 2-9.—The interaction of the spin angular momentum vectors of two electrons to form a resultant total spin angular momentum vector, corresponding to the value of the total spin quantum number $S = 0$ or $S = 1$.

ence between the state with $S = 0$ (which is called a singlet state) and the state with $S = 1$ (which is called a triplet state) is due to the resonance phenomenon, which has been discussed briefly in Chapter 1.

The way in which the resonance energy contributes to the energy of an atom is correlated with the relative orientation of the electron spins. The resonance energy is in fact a result of the electrostatic repulsion of the electrons and not of a direct spin-spin interaction, but it is correlated with the relative orientation of the spins in such a way that it can be discussed as though it were a spin-spin interaction.

Now let us consider the states of the atom of beryllium in which one of the valence electrons occupies a $2p$ orbital and the other occupies a $3p$ orbital. The two electron spins can combine, as shown in Figure 2-9, to form the resultant $S = 0$ or $S = 1$. The two orbital moments, corresponding to $l_1 = 1$ and $l_2 = 1$, can combine in three ways, as shown in Figure 2-10, to give the resultant $L = 0$ (an S state), $L = 1$ (a P state), or $L = 2$ (a D state). The vectors S and L can then combine in various ways, one of which is represented in Figure 2-11, to give the states $^3D_1$, $^3D_2$, $^3D_3$, $^3P_0$, $^3P_1$, $^3P_2$, $^3S_1$, $^1D_2$, $^1P_1$, and $^1S_0$.

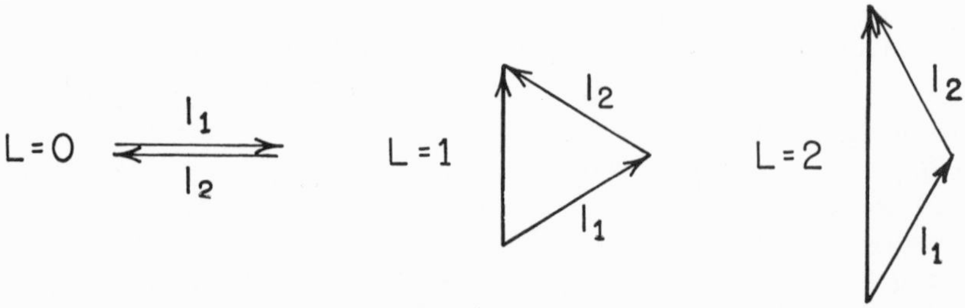

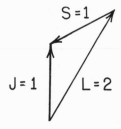

FIG. 2-10.—The interaction of the orbital angular momentum vectors for two p electrons ($l_1 = 1$, $l_2 = 1$) to form the resultant total angular momentum vector, with values corresponding to 0, 1, and 2 for the total angular momentum quantum number L.

2-7. THE PAULI EXCLUSION PRINCIPLE AND THE PERIODIC SYSTEM OF THE ELEMENTS

A principle of extreme importance to spectroscopy as well as to other phases of physics and chemistry is the *exclusion principle* discovered by Pauli in 1925.

Let us consider an atom in an external magnetic field so strong that the couplings among the various electrons are broken and the electrons orient themselves independently with respect to the field. The state of each electron is then given by fixing the values of a set of quantum numbers: for each electron we may give the values of the total quantum number n of the orbit, the azimuthal quantum number l, the orbital magnetic quantum number m_l (stating the component of orbital angular momentum in the field direction), the spin quantum number s (which has the value $\frac{1}{2}$ for every electron), and the spin magnetic quantum number m_s (which can be equal to either $+\frac{1}{2}$, corresponding to the spin oriented roughly in the direction of the field, or $-\frac{1}{2}$, corresponding to the spin oriented roughly in the opposite direction). The Pauli exclusion principle can be expressed in the following way: *there cannot exist an atom in such a quantum state that two electrons within it have the same set of quantum numbers.*

FIG. 2-11.—The arrangement of angular momentum vectors for the state $^3D_1$.

The Pauli exclusion principle provides an immediate explanation of the principal features of the periodic system of the elements.

Let us first discuss the helium atom. The most stable orbital in the helium atom is the $1s$ orbital, with $n = 1, l = 0, m_l = 0$. There are two electrons in the neutral helium atom, which we place in the $1s$ orbital. In the discussion above of the beryllium atom, it was pointed out that two s electrons give rise to the Russell-Saunders states $^3S_1$ and $^1S_0$. The discussion concerned, however, a $2s$ electron and a $3s$ electron; the two electrons differ in the value of the total quantum number n. For the helium atom with two electrons in the $1s$ orbital, the Pauli exclusion principle requires that the two electrons differ in the value of one quantum number. Their values of n, l, and m_l are the same; moreover, they have the same spin quantum number, $s = \frac{1}{2}$. Accordingly they must differ in the value of m_s, which can have the value $+\frac{1}{2}$ for one electron and $-\frac{1}{2}$ for the other. The resultant spin for the two electrons must accordingly be 0: only the singlet state $^1S_0$ can exist for two electrons in the $1s$ orbital. The normal state of the helium atom is accordingly $1s^2\,^1S_0$, and there is no other state based upon the electron configuration $1s^2$.

An atom of lithium, with three electrons, can have only two electrons in the $1s$ orbital, and these two electrons must have their spins opposed. Two electrons constitute a *completed K shell* in any atom. A third electron must occupy an outer orbital. The next most stable orbital is the $2s$ orbital, which penetrates deeply into the inner electron shell and is hence more stable than $2p$, so that lithium in the normal state has the configuration $1s^2 2s\,^2S_{\frac{1}{2}}$.

In general two electrons, with opposed spins, may occupy each atomic orbital. There is one s orbital in each electron shell, with a given value of the total quantum number n; three p orbitals, corresponding to $m_l = -1, 0$, and $+1$, in each shell beginning with the L shell; five d orbitals in each shell beginning with the M shell, and so on. The numbers of electrons in completed subshells and shells of an atom are shown in Table 2-2. Note that there are alternative ways of naming the shells.

The nature of the normal states of all atoms can be discussed in terms of the principles that have been mentioned in the preceding paragraphs and sections. The normal state of an atom is the state with lowest energy. The terms that make the principal contribution to the energy of the atom are the energy values of the individual electrons, which depend upon the orbitals assigned to them. The $1s$ orbital, of the K shell, is the most stable orbital in all atoms. Next come the $2s$ orbital and then the three $2p$ orbitals, of the L shell. The following shells overlap one another, in a way determined by the atomic number of the atom and its degree of ioniza-

TABLE 2-2.—NAMES OF ELECTRON SHELLS

Spectroscopists' names	Chemists' names
$K\ 1s^2$	Helium $1s^2$
$L\ 2s^22p^6$	Neon $2s^22p^6$
$M\ 3s^23p^63d^{10}$	Argon $3s^23p^6$
$N\ 4s^24p^64d^{10}4f^{14}$	Krypton $3d^{10}4s^24p^6$
	Xenon $4d^{10}5s^25p^6$
	Radon $4f^{14}5d^{10}6s^26p^6$
	Eka-radon $5f^{14}6d^{10}7s^27p^6$

tion. The $3s$ orbital is the next most stable, followed by the three $3p$ orbitals; but for the lighter elements, such as potassium, the $4s$ orbital, of the N shell, is more stable than the five $3d$ orbitals of the M shell. The sequence of stabilities of the orbitals is represented to good approximation in Figure 2-12. This representation is only approximate; for ex-

FIG. 2-12.—The approximate sequence of energy values for atomic orbitals, the lowest circle representing the most stable orbital ($1s$). Each circle represents one atomic orbital, which can be occupied either by one electron or by two electrons with opposed spins.

ample, for copper, with atomic number 29, the configuration of the normal state is $1s^2 2s^2 2p^6 3s^2 3p^6 3d^{10} 4s$; there are ten $3d$ electrons and one $4s$ electron, rather than nine $3d$ electrons and two $4s$ electrons as indicated in Figure 2-12.

The electronic configuration and the Russell-Saunders term symbols for the elements as determined spectroscopically or as predicted are given in Table 2-3. It must be emphasized that these electronic configurations do not have great chemical significance, because for many of the atoms there are excited states differing only by a small amount of energy from the normal state of the atom, and the electronic structure of the atom in a molecule may be more closely represented by one of the excited states than by the normal state, or, as is in fact usually the case, the electronic structure in a molecule or crystal is in general to be described as corresponding to a resonance hybrid of many of the low-lying states of the isolated atom. For copper, for example, the state $1s^2 2s^2 2p^6 3s^2 3p^6 3d^9 4s^2$ $^2D_{\frac{5}{2}}$ lies only 11,202 cm^{-1} (31.9 kcal/mole) above the normal state.

It has been pointed out above that two electrons in the $1s$ orbital must have their spins opposed, and hence give rise to the singlet state $^1S_0$, with no spin or orbital angular momentum, and hence with no magnetic moment. Similarly it is found that a completed subshell of electrons, such as six electrons occupying the three $2p$ orbitals, must have $S = 0$ and $L = 0$, corresponding to the Russell-Saunders term symbol $^1S_0$; such a completed subshell has spherical symmetry and zero magnetic moment. The application of the Pauli exclusion principle to electron configurations in which there are several electrons in the same subshell is discussed in Appendix IV.

The stability of the various Russell-Saunders states resulting from the same electron configuration (the same distribution of electrons among orbitals) can be described by means of a set of rules usually called Hund's rules. These rules are the following:

1. *Of the Russell-Saunders states arising from a given electron configuration those with the largest value of S lie lowest, those with the next largest next, and so on; in other words, the states with the largest multiplicity are the most stable.*

2. *Of the group of terms with a given value of S, that with the largest value of L lies lowest.*

3. *Of the states with given values of S and L in a configuration consisting of less than half the electrons in a completed subgroup, the state with the smallest value of J is usually the most stable, and for a configuration consisting of more than half the electrons in a subgroup the state with largest J is the most stable.* The multiplets of the first sort, smallest *J* most stable,

TABLE 2-3.—ELECTRON CONFIGURATION OF ATOMS IN THEIR NORMAL STATES

		He $1s$	Neon $2s$ $2p$	Argon $3s$ $3p$	Krypton $3d$ $4s$ $4p$	Xenon $4d$ $5s$ $5p$	Radon $4f$ $5d$ $6s$ $6p$	Eka-radon $5f$ $6d$ $7s$ $7p$	Term symbol
H	1	1							$^2S_{1/2}$
He	2	2							$^1S_0$
Li	3	2	1						$^2S_{1/2}$
Be	4	2	2						$^1S_0$
B	5	2	2 1						$^2P_{1/2}$
C	6	2	2 2						$^3P_0$
N	7	2	2 3						$^4S_{3/2}$
O	8	2	2 4						$^3P_2$
F	9	2	2 5						$^2P_{3/2}$
Ne	10	2	2 6						$^1S_0$
Na	11			1					$^2S_{1/2}$
Mg	12			2					$^1S_0$
Al	13			2 1					$^2P_{1/2}$
Si	14	10	Neon core	2 2					$^3P_0$
P	15			2 3					$^4S_{3/2}$
S	16			2 4					$^3P_2$
Cl	17			2 5					$^2P_{3/2}$
Ar	18	2	2 6	2 6					$^1S_0$
K	19				1				$^2S_{1/2}$
Ca	20				2				$^1S_0$
Sc	21				1 2				$^2D_{3/2}$
Ti	22				2 2				$^3F_2$
V	23				3 2				$^4F_{3/2}$
Cr	24				5 1				$^7S_3$
Mn	25				5 2				$^6S_{5/2}$
Fe	26				6 2				$^5D_4$
Co	27	18	Argon core		7 2				$^4F_{9/2}$
Ni	28				8 2				$^3F_4$
Cu	29				10 1				$^2S_{1/2}$
Zn	30				10 2				$^1S_0$
Ga	31				10 2 1				$^2P_{1/2}$
Ge	32				10 2 2				$^3P_0$
As	33				10 2 3				$^4S_{3/2}$
Se	34				10 2 4				$^3P_2$
Br	35				10 2 5				$^2P_{3/2}$
Kr	36	2	2 6	2 6	10 2 6				$^1S_0$
Rb	37					1			$^2S_{1/2}$
Sr	38					2			$^1S_0$
Y	39					1 2			$^2D_{3/2}$
Zr	40					2 2			$^3F_2$
Nb	41					4 1			$^6D_{1/2}$
Mo	42					5 1			$^7S_3$
Tc	43					5 2			$^6S_{5/2}$
Ru	44					7 1			$^5F_5$
Rh	45		36	Krypton core		8 1			$^4F_{9/2}$
Pd	46					10			$^1S_0$
Ag	47					10 1			$^2S_{1/2}$
Cd	48					10 2			$^1S_0$
In	49					10 2 1			$^2P_{1/2}$
Sn	50					10 2 2			$^3P_0$
Sb	51					10 2 3			$^4S_{3/2}$
Te	52					10 2 4			$^3P_2$
I	53					10 2 5			$^2P_{3/2}$

TABLE 2-3.—(continued)

		He	Neon		Argon		Krypton			Xenon			Radon				Eka-radon				Term symbol
		1s	2s	2p	3s	3p	3d	4s	4p	4d	5s	5p	4f	5d	6s	6p	5f	6d	7s	7p	
Xe	54	2	2	6	2	6	10	2	6	10	2	6									$^1S_0$
Cs	55														1						$^2S_{1/2}$
Ba	56														2						$^1S_0$
La	57													1	2						$^2D_{3/2}$
Ce	58												1	1	2						$^3H_4$
Pr	59												2	1	2						$^4K_{11/2}$
Nd	60												3	1	2						$^5L_6$
Pm	61												4	1	2						$^6L_{9/2}$
Sm	62												5	1	2						$^7K_4$
Eu	63												6	1	2						$^8H_{3/2}$
Gd	64												7	1	2						$^9D_2$
Tb	65												8	1	2						$^8H_{17/2}$
Dy	66												9	1	2						$^7K_{10}$
Ho	67												10	1	2						$^6K_{19/2}$
Er	68												11	1	2						$^5L_{10}$
Tm	69							54					12	1	2						$^4K_{17/2}$
Yb	70						Xenon core						13	1	2						$^3H_6$
Lu	71												14	1	2						$^2D_{3/2}$
Hf	72												14	2	2						$^3F_2$
Ta	73												14	3	2						$^4F_{3/2}$
W	74												14	4	2						$^5D_0$
Re	75												14	5	2						$^6S_{5/2}$
Os	76												14	6	2						$^5D_4$
Ir	77												14	7	2						$^4F_{9/2}$
Pt	78												14	9	1						$^3D_3$
Au	79												14	10	1						$^2S_{1/2}$
Hg	80												14	10	2						$^1S_0$
Tl	81												14	10	2	1					$^2P_{1/2}$
Pb	82												14	10	2	2					$^3P_0$
Bi	83												14	10	2	3					$^4S_{3/2}$
Po	84												14	10	2	4					$^3P_2$
At	85												14	10	2	5					$^2P_{3/2}$
Rn	86	2	2	6	2	6	10	2	6	10	2	6	14	10	2	6					$^1S_0$
Fr	87																		1		$^2S_{1/2}$
Ra	88																		2		$^1S_0$
Ac	89							86										1	2		$^2D_{3/2}$
Th	90						Radon core											2	2		$^3F_2$
Pa	91																	3	2		$^4F_{3/2}$
U	92																	4	2		$^5D_0$
Eka-Rn	118	2	2	6	2	6	10	2	6	10	2	6	14	10	2	6	14	10	2	6	$^1S_0$

are called normal multiplets, and those of the second sort are called inverted multiplets.

The application of these rules may be illustrated by the example of the carbon atom and the oxygen atom, for which the most stable spectroscopic states are indicated in the diagrams of Figures 2-13 and 2-14. The stable electron configuration for carbon is $1s^2 2s^2 2p^2$, which gives rise to the Russell-Saunders states ^1S, ^1D, and ^3P. For oxygen the stable configuration is $1s^2 2s^2 2p^4$, which gives rise to the same set of Russell-Saunders states. (Note that the same set of Russell-Saunders states results from x electrons missing from a completed subshell as from x electrons present in the subshell.) As seen from the figures, the states ^3P are the most stable for each atom, with ^1D next, and ^1S least stable, in accordance with the first two Hund rules. Carbon, with two electrons in the $2p$ subshell (which can hold six electrons) is predicted by the third

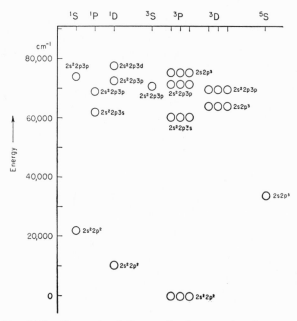

FIG. 2-13.—Energy-level diagram for the neutral carbon atom.

rule to give a normal multiplet, with the smallest value of J lowest, whereas oxygen, with four $2p$ electrons, should give rise to inverted multiplets. The rule corresponds to the spectroscopic observations.

The correlation between the discussion of the electronic structure of atoms and the periodic system of the elements can be seen by comparing the energy-level diagram of Figure 2-12 with the periodic table, shown as Figure 2-15. It is seen that each of the noble gases has eight electrons in its outer shell, two s electrons and six p electrons. This electron configuration corresponds to a special stability. The first long period and the second long period result from the introduction of ten electrons into the five $3d$ orbitals and the five $4d$ orbitals, respectively, as well as the addition of the eight electrons that constitute the outer shell of the corresponding noble-gas atoms. The first very long period involves the introduction of 14 electrons into the seven 4*f* orbitals, in addition to the 18 in the 5*d*, 6*s*, and 6*p* orbitals. The heaviest elements that have been

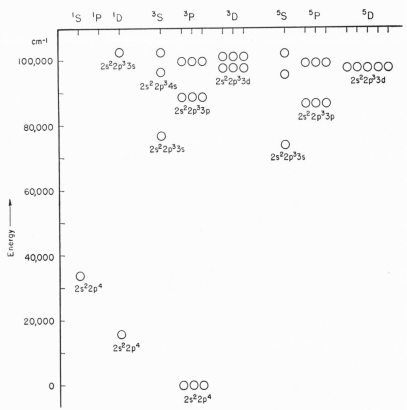

FIG. 2-14.—Energy-level diagram for the neutral oxygen atom.

discovered or made are in the second very long period, which involves occupancy of the 5*f* orbitals as well as the 6*d*, 7*s*, and 7*p* orbitals.

2-8. THE MAGNETIC PROPERTIES OF ATOMS AND MONATOMIC IONS

An electron moving in a circular orbit around an atomic nucleus can be thought of as equivalent to an electric current in a loop of wire, and according to electromagnetic theory there should be a magnetic moment associated with it. The ratio of magnetic moment to angular momentum for an electron moving in an orbit is $e/2m_0c$.

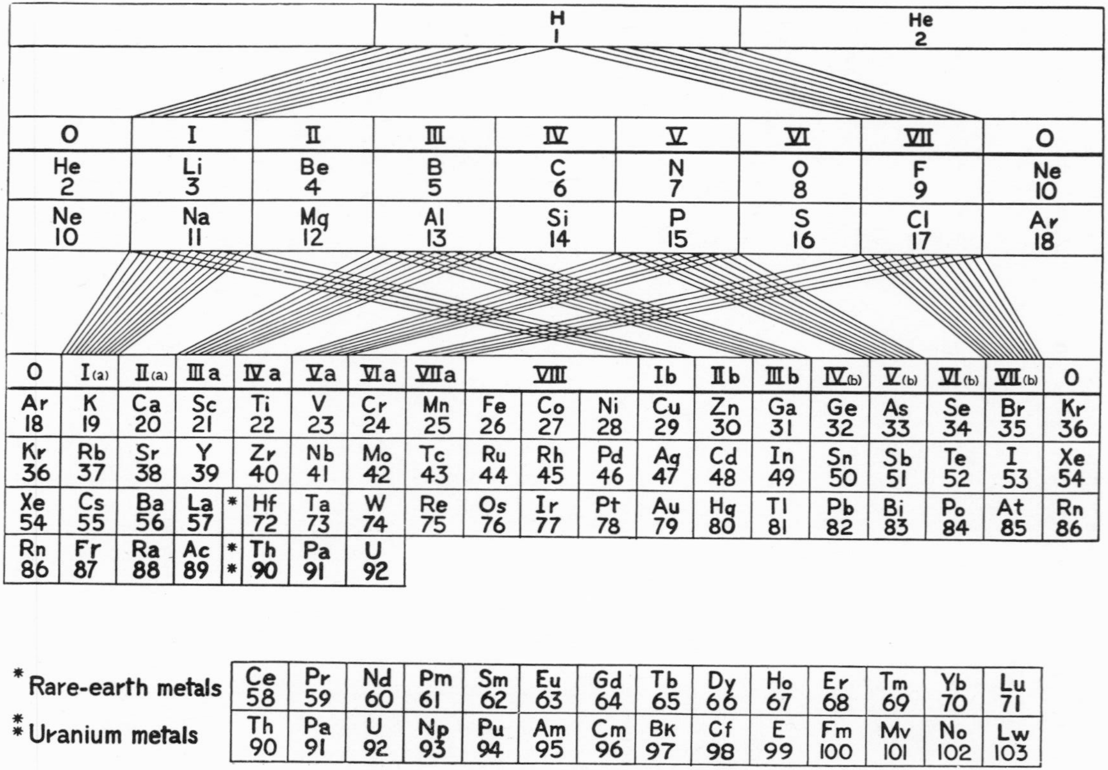

											H 1						He 2	

O	I	II	III	IV	V	VI	VII	O
He 2	Li 3	Be 4	B 5	C 6	N 7	O 8	F 9	Ne 10
Ne 10	Na 11	Mg 12	Al 13	Si 14	P 15	S 16	Cl 17	Ar 18

O	I(a)	II(a)	IIIa	IVa	Va	VIa	VIIa	VIII			Ib	IIb	IIIb	IV(b)	V(b)	VI(b)	VII(b)	O
Ar 18	K 19	Ca 20	Sc 21	Ti 22	V 23	Cr 24	Mn 25	Fe 26	Co 27	Ni 28	Cu 29	Zn 30	Ga 31	Ge 32	As 33	Se 34	Br 35	Kr 36
Kr 36	Rb 37	Sr 38	Y 39	Zr 40	Nb 41	Mo 42	Tc 43	Ru 44	Rh 45	Pd 46	Ag 47	Cd 48	In 49	Sn 50	Sb 51	Te 52	I 53	Xe 54
Xe 54	Cs 55	Ba 56	La 57 *	Hf 72	Ta 73	W 74	Re 75	Os 76	Ir 77	Pt 78	Au 79	Hg 80	Tl 81	Pb 82	Bi 83	Po 84	At 85	Rn 86
Rn 86	Fr 87	Ra 88	Ac 89 **	Th 90	Pa 91	U 92												

* Rare-earth metals

Ce 58	Pr 59	Nd 60	Pm 61	Sm 62	Eu 63	Gd 64	Tb 65	Dy 66	Ho 67	Er 68	Tm 69	Yb 70	Lu 71

** Uranium metals

Th 90	Pa 91	U 92	Np 93	Pu 94	Am 95	Cm 96	Bk 97	Cf 98	E 99	Fm 100	Mv 101	No 102	Lw 103

FIG. 2-15.—The periodic system of the elements.

Spectroscopic measurements of the magnetic moment of atoms, involving the splitting of spectral lines into a number of components by the application of an external magnetic field to the emitting atoms, led to the discovery that often the magnetic moment is not related to the angular momentum in this simple way. The ratio is written $ge/2m_0c$, in which the g-factor has the value 1 if the angular momentum of the atom is due entirely to orbital motion of electrons. When it is due entirely to the spin of the electrons the value of the g-factor is 2. This value of the g-factor for spin cannot be explained in any simple way; it has to be accepted as part of the nature of the electron.

In case that the electronic state of the atom is such as to approximate closely to Russell-Saunders coupling the value of the g-factor can be calculated by consideration of the angles between the vectors representing the spin angular momentum, the orbital angular momentum, and the total angular momentum. It is found that the value of g is given by the equation

$$g = 1 + \frac{J(J + 1) + S(S + 1) - L(L + 1)}{2J(J + 1)}$$

Values of g are given in Appendix IV, Table 3.

The modern unit of magnetic moment is $he/4\pi m_0c$. This unit is called the Bohr magneton. Its value is 0.9273×10^{-20} erg gauss^{-1}. The magnetic moment of an atom with total angular momentum quantum number J is equal, in Bohr magnetons, to $g\sqrt{J(J + 1)}$.

Values of the magnetic moments of molecules and ions can be determined experimentally by measuring the magnetic susceptibility of substances. These values may provide information about electronic structure. The magnetic moments of complexes are discussed in Chapter 5.

2-9. THE FORMAL RULES FOR THE FORMATION OF COVALENT BONDS

The formal results of the quantum-mechanical treatment of valence can be given the following simple statement: *an atom can form an electron-pair bond for each stable orbital*, the bond being of the type described for the hydrogen molecule and owing its stability to the same resonance phenomenon. In other words, for the formation of an electron-pair bond two electrons with opposed spins and a stable orbital of each of the two bonded atoms are needed.

The carbon atom, nitrogen atom, and other first-row atoms are limited to four covalent bonds using the four orbitals of the L shell. This restriction forms much of the justification of the importance of the octet postulated by Lewis.

For second-row atoms too the octet retains some significance, since the $3s$ and $3p$ orbitals are more stable than the $3d$ orbitals. In a molecule such as phosphine, with the structure

$$\overset{\overset{\displaystyle H}{\cdot\cdot}}{\underset{\overset{\cdot\cdot}{\displaystyle H}}{:P:H}}$$

three of the M orbitals of phosphorus are used for bond formation and one for an unshared pair, and in the phosphonium ion

$$\left[\,\overset{\overset{\displaystyle H}{\cdot\cdot}}{\underset{\overset{\cdot\cdot}{\displaystyle H}}{H:P:H}}\,\right]^{+}$$

four M orbitals are used for bond formation, the five $3d$ orbitals in the M shell not being called on for bond formation. In phosphorus penta-chloride, on the other hand, for which the structure

$$\mathrm{Cl\!-\!\overset{\displaystyle \overset{Cl}{\diagup}\overset{\displaystyle Cl}{}}{\underset{\underset{Cl}{\diagdown}\underset{\displaystyle Cl}{}}{P}}}$$

can be written, one of the $3d$ orbitals as well as the $3s$ and three $3p$ orbitals must be called on.

The octet rule similarly retains some significance for third-row atoms and still heavier atoms, aside from those of the transition elements. Thus we can, for example, assign to arsine and stibine structures analogous to those for phosphine, using the four s and p orbitals of the valence shell of the central atom.

For the transition elements use is often made in covalent bond formation of some of the d orbitals of the shell just inside the valence shell, as well as of the s and p orbitals of the valence shell. We write for the hexachloro-palladate ion, for example, the structure

$$\left[\,\begin{matrix} Cl & & Cl \\ & \diagdown\ \diagup & \\ Cl\!-\!\!&Pd&\!\!-\!Cl \\ & \diagup\ \diagdown & \\ Cl & & Cl \end{matrix}\,\right]^{--}$$

with six covalent bonds from the palladium atom to the six surrounding chlorine atoms. There are in the palladium atom, in addition to the six bonding electron pairs, 42 electrons. These, in pairs, occupy the 1s, 2s, three 2p, 3s, three 3p, five 3d, 4s, three 4p, and three of the 4d orbitals. The six bonds are formed by use of the remaining two 4d orbitals, the 5s orbital, and the three 5p orbitals. A detailed discussion of the selection and use of atomic orbitals in bond formation is given in later chapters.

EXERCISES

2-1.—Assign electron configurations to the normal states of the following ions: N^+, O^-, Cr^{+++}, Tl^+. Also assign Russell-Saunders symbols. How many unpaired electrons does each ion have?

2-2.—Write the structural formula for the ammonium ion, NH_4^+. To what covalence of nitrogen does it correspond? If shared electron pairs are split between the bonded atoms, what is the formal charge of the nitrogen atom? The electron configuration?

2-3.—Why do the 2s and 2p energy levels have the same energy value for the hydrogen atom but different values for the lithium atom?

2-4.—It is found by experiment that bombardment of lithium atoms with electrons produces lithium ions only if the bombarding electrons have been accelerated by an electric potential difference of 5.39 volts; for sodium, potassium, rubidium, and cesium atoms the values are 5.14, 4.34, 4.18, and 3.89 volts, respectively. What are the first ionization energies of these atoms in kcal/mole? (See App. I.)

2-5.—In Section 2-5 it is said that the sodium D lines (transition from 3p to 3s) have wavelengths about 5890 Å. To what 3p—3s energy difference in kcal/mole does this wavelength correspond? (See App. I.)

2-6.—What is the structural formula for the chlorostannate ion, $SnCl_6^{--}$? What orbitals of tin are used in bond formation?

2-7.—An electronic structure is assigned to the phosphine molecule in Section 2-9. How many inner electrons does the phosphorus atom have? What orbitals do they occupy? To what orbital would you assign the unshared pair of the outer shell of the phosphorus atom?

2-8.—Although nitrogen and phosphorus are congeners, and phosphorus pentachloride can be synthesized, nitrogen pentachloride has never been made. Can you suggest an explanation of the instability of the NCl_5 molecule?

2-9.—What is the electronic structure of H_2S? Of H_2S_2? Of the S_8 molecules present in rhombic sulfur and in sulfur vapor? What orbitals are used by the sulfur atom for bonds, for unshared electron pairs, and for inner electrons?

2-10.—In Section 2-3 it is stated that the radius of the circular Bohr orbit for the normal state of hydrogen is $a_0 = 0.530$ Å, and that for hydrogenlike ions the radius is proportional to $1/Z$. What is the radius for a K electron in the uranium atom? For an L electron? (Ans. About 0.0058 Å, 0.023 Å.)

The Partial Ionic Character of Covalent Bonds and the Relative Electro-negativity of Atoms

IN the present and the following chapter we shall concentrate our attention on the single bond and on substances for which one valence-bond structure involving only single bonds provides a satisfactory representation of the molecule.

3-1. THE TRANSITION FROM ONE EXTREME BOND TYPE TO ANOTHER

After the development some decades ago of the modern ideas of the ionic bond and the covalent bond the following question was formulated and vigorously discussed: If it were possible to vary continuously one or more of the parameters determining the nature of a molecule or a crystal, such as the effective nuclear charges of the atoms, then would the transition from one extreme bond type to another take place continuously, or would it show discontinuities? With the extension of our understanding of the nature of the chemical bond we may now answer this question; the pertinent argument, given in the following paragraph, leads to the conclusion that in some cases the transition would take place continuously, whereas in others an effective discontinuity would appear.

Continuous Change in Bond Type.—Let us first consider the case of a molecule involving a single bond between two atoms, A and B, which for certain values of the structural parameters for the molecule is a normal covalent bond of the type formed by like atoms and discussed in Sections 1-5 and 3-4 and for other values is an ionic bond A^+B^-, the more electronegative of the two atoms holding both of the electrons as an unshared pair occupying one of the orbitals of its outer shell. For intermediate values of the structural parameters of the molecule the wave function

49

$a\psi_{A:B} + b\psi_{A^+B^-}$, formed by the linear combination of the wave functions corresponding to the normal covalent structure A:B and the ionic structure A^+B^-, with numerical coefficients a and b, can be used to represent the structure of the molecule, the value of the ratio of the coefficients, b/a, for each set of values of the structural parameters being such as to make the bond energy a maximum. As the parameters of the molecule (in particular, the relative electronegativity of A and B) were changed, the ratio b/a would change from zero to infinity, the bond changing in type without discontinuity from the covalent extreme to the ionic extreme by passing through all intermediate stages. In the case under discussion the two extreme structures are of such a nature (each involving only paired electrons and essentially the same configuration of the atomic nuclei) as to permit resonance, and hence the transition from one extreme type of bond to the other would be continuous.

For an intermediate value of the relative electronegativity of A and B such that the coefficients a and b in the wave function $a\psi_{A:B} + b\psi_{A^+B^-}$ are about equal in magnitude, the bond might be described as *resonating between the covalent extreme and the ionic extreme*, the contributions of the two being given by the values of a^2 and b^2. If the extreme covalent structure A:B and the extreme ionic structure A^+B^- correspond separately to the same bond-energy value, then the two structures will contribute equally to the actual state of the molecule, and the actual bond energy will be greater than the bond energy for either structure alone by an amount equal to the interaction energy of the two structures; that is, resonance between the two structures will stabilize the molecule. If one of the two extreme structures corresponds to a greater bond energy than the other, the more stable structure will contribute more to the actual state of the molecule than the less stable one, and the actual bond energy will be increased somewhat by resonance over that for the more stable structure.

For a molecule such as hydrogen chloride we write the two reasonable electronic structures $H : \overset{..}{\underset{..}{Cl}} :$ and $H^+ : \overset{..}{\underset{..}{Cl}} :^-$. (The third structure that suggests itself, $H :^- \overset{..}{\underset{..}{Cl}} :^+$, is not given much importance because hydrogen is recognized as less electronegative than chlorine; a discussion of the extent to which such a structure contributes to the normal state of a molecule is given in Sec. 3-3.) In accordance with the foregoing argument the actual state of the molecule can be described as corresponding to resonance between these two structures. The extent to which each structure contributes its character to the bond is discussed in detail for hydrogen chloride and other molecules in the following sections of this chapter.

Instead of using this description of the bond as involving resonance between an extreme covalent bond H:C̈l: and an extreme ionic bond H^+Cl^-, we may describe the bond as a *covalent bond with partial ionic character*, and make use of the *valence line*, writing H—Cl (or H—C̈l:) in place of {H:C̈l:, H^+Cl^-} or some similar complex symbol showing resonance between the two extremes.   This alternative description is to be recognized as equivalent to the first; whenever a question arises as to the properties expected for a covalent bond with partial ionic character, it is to be answered by consideration of the corresponding resonating structures.

The amount of ionic character of a bond in a molecule must not be confused with the tendency of the molecule to ionize in a suitable solvent. The ionic character of the bond is determined by the importance of the ionic structure (A^+B^-) *when the nuclei are at their equilibrium distance* (1.275 Å for HCl, for example), whereas the tendency to ionize in solution is determined by the relative stability of the actual molecules in the solution and the separated ions in the solution.   It is reasonable, however, for the tendency toward ionization in solution to accompany large ionic character of bonds in general, since both result from great difference in electronegativity of the bonded atoms.

Transitions between other extreme types of bonds (covalent to metallic, covalent to ion-dipole, etc.) can also occur without discontinuity, and the bonds of intermediate character can be discussed in terms of resonance between structures of extreme type in the same way as for covalent-ionic bonds.

Discontinuous Change in Bond Type.—In molecules and complex ions of certain types continuous transition from one extreme bond type to another is not possible.   In order for continuous transition to be possible between two extreme bond types the conditions for resonance between the corresponding structures must be satisfied.   The most important of these conditions is that the two structures must involve the same numbers of unpaired electrons.   *If the two structures under consideration involve different numbers of unpaired electrons, then the transition between the two must be discontinuous, the discontinuity being associated with the pairing or unpairing of electrons.*

The most important molecules and complex ions for which this phenomenon occurs are those containing a transition-group atom.   Let us discuss as an example the octahedral complexes FeX_6 of ferric iron.   In some of these complexes ($[FeF_6]^{---}$, $[Fe(H_2O)_6]^{+++}$) the bonds are of such a nature that the electronic structure about the iron nucleus is the same as for the Fe^{+++} ion; of the 23 electrons of this ion, 18 occupy the $1s$, $2s$, three $2p$, $3s$, and three $3p$ orbitals in pairs and the remaining five occupy the five $3d$ orbitals without pairing, as described in Section 2-7.   If, however, covalent Fe—X bonds are formed with use of two of the $3d$ orbitals (as well as some of the other orbitals—see Chap. 5), as in the ferricyanide ion, $[(Fe(CN)_6]^{\equiv}$, then the five unshared $3d$ electrons of the iron atom must crowd into the remaining three $3d$ orbitals, with formation of two pairs.   This complex contains only one unpaired electron, whereas the complexes of the first kind contain five unpaired electrons. Transition between these structures cannot be continuous.

3-2. BOND TYPE AND ATOMIC ARRANGEMENT

The properties of a substance depend in part upon the type of bonds between the atoms of the substance and in part upon the atomic arrangement and the distribution of the bonds.   The atomic arrangement is itself determined to a great extent by the nature of the bonds: the directed character of covalent bonds (as in the tetrahedral carbon atom) plays an especially important part in determining the configurations of molecules and crystals; an important part is also played by the interatomic repulsive forces that give "size" to atoms and ions (Chap. 7).

Since 1913 a great amount of information about the atomic arrangement in molecules and crystals has been collected.   This information can often be interpreted in terms of the nature and distribution of bonds; a detailed discussion of the dependence of interatomic distances and bond angles on bond type will be given in later chapters.

An abrupt change in properties in a series of compounds, such as in the melting points or boiling points of metal halogenides, has sometimes been considered to indicate an abrupt change in bond type.   Thus of the fluorides of the second-row elements,

	NaF	MgF$_2$	AlF$_3$	SiF$_4$	PF$_5$	SF$_6$
Melting point	995°	1263°	1257°	−90°	−94°	−51°C

those of high melting points have been described as salts, and the others as covalent compounds; and the great change in melting points from aluminum fluoride to silicon fluoride has been interpreted as showing that the bonds change sharply from the extreme ionic type to the extreme covalent type.   I consider the bonds in aluminum fluoride to be only slightly different in character from those in silicon fluoride, and I attribute the abrupt change in properties to a change in the nature of the atomic arrangement.   In NaF, MgF$_2$, and AlF$_3$ the relative sizes of the metal and nonmetal atoms are such as to make the stable ligancy (coordination number) of the metal six; each of the metal atoms is surrounded by an octahedron of fluorine atoms, and the stoichiometric relations then require that each fluorine atom be held jointly by six sodium atoms in NaF (which has the sodium chloride structure, Fig. 1-1), by three magnesium atoms in MgF_2 (with the rutile structure, Fig. 3-1), or by two aluminum atoms in AlF_3.   In each of these crystals the molecules are thus combined into giant polymers, and the processes of fusion and vaporization can take place only by breaking the strong chemical bonds between metal and nonmetal atoms; in consequence the substances have high melting

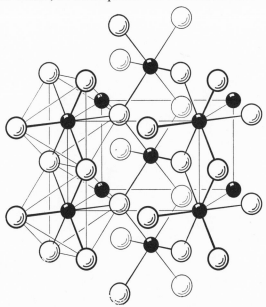

FIG. 3-1.—The atomic arrangement of the tetragonal crystal rutile, TiO_2.   Large circles represent oxygen atoms, small circles titanium atoms.   Each titanium atom is surrounded by oxygen atoms at the corners of an octahedron.   Each octahedron shares two opposite edges with adjacent octahedra, to form long strings of octahedra that extend along the c axis of the crystal (vertically, in the drawing).

points and boiling points.   The stable ligancy of silicon relative to fluorine is, on the other hand, four, so that the SiF_4 molecule has little tendency to form polymers.   The crystal of silicon fluoride consists of SiF_4 molecules piled together as shown in Figure 3-2, and held together only by weak van der Waals forces.   Fusion and vaporization of this substance involve no great change in the molecule; the strong Si—F bonds are not broken, but only the weak intermolecular bonds, and hence the melting point and boiling point are low.   Volatility and many other properties such as hardness and cleavability depend mainly not so much on bond type as on the atomic arrangement and the distribution of bonds.

3-3. THE NATURE OF THE BONDS IN DIATOMIC
HALOGENIDE MOLECULES

In the hydrogen molecule a quantum-mechanical treatment has shown that the two ionic structures H^+H^- and H^-H^+ enter into resonance with the extreme covalent structure $H:H$ to only a small extent, each ionic structure contributing only about 2 percent to the normal state of the molecule (Sec. 1-5). The reason for this small contribution by the ionic

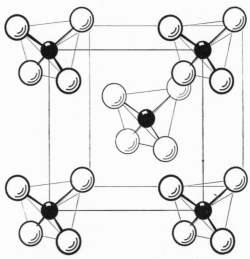

FIG. 3-2.—The atomic arrangement in the cubic crystal SiF_4. The atoms form tetrahedral molecules, with four fluorine atoms surrounding a silicon atom. The molecules are arranged at the points of a body-centered cubic lattice.

structures is that these structures are unstable relative to the covalent structure, the large amount of energy (295 kcal/mole) required to transfer an electron from one nucleus to the other and form a positive and a negative ion not being completely counterbalanced by the mutual Coulomb energy of the ions.

In hydrogen chloride the energy of formation of the ions H^+ and Cl^- from atoms is 226 kcal/mole, and that of the ions H^- and Cl^+ is 283 kcal/mole. The ionic structure H^-Cl^+ is accordingly very much less important than the structure H^+Cl^-. A qualitative estimate of the extent to which the ionic structures H^+X^- and the extreme covalent structures $H:\overset{..}{\underset{..}{X}}:$ contribute to the normal states of the hydrogen halogenides

can be made by the consideration of energy curves. In Figure
3-3 calculated energy curves are
shown for the structures H^+X^-
and $H:\ddot{X}:$ for each of the molecules HF, HCl, HBr, and HI.
It is seen that in the neighborhood of the equilibrium internuclear distances (at the minima
of the curves) the covalent curves
for HCl, HBr, and HI lie below
the ionic curves, the separation
increasing from HCl to HI.
This shows that the bonds in
these molecules are essentially
covalent, with, however, a small
amount of H^+X^- ionic character, which is presumably
greatest in HCl (of the three) and
least in HI. The effect of resonance on the energy is shown by
the full lines in the figure, representing actual states (normal
and excited) of the molecules.

In hydrogen fluoride the situation is different. For this molecule the ionic curve and the covalent curve are nearly coinci-
dent in the neighborhood of the

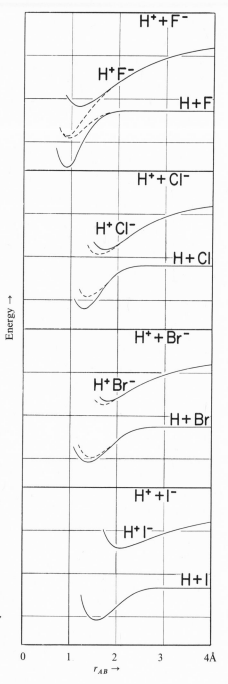

FIG. 3-3.—Calculated energy curves
for the hydrogen halogenide molecules.
The two dashed curves for each molecule represent extreme ionic and extreme covalent structures, and the two
full curves represent the actual structures resulting from resonance between these extreme structures. The
dashed curves for HI lie very close to
the full curves. The unit of energy is
100 kcal/mole.

TABLE 3-1.—ELECTRONIC DIPOLE MOMENTS AND IONIC CHARACTER OF
HYDROGEN HALOGENIDE MOLECULES

	r_0	er_0	μ	μ/er_0
HF	0.92 Å	4.42 D[a]	1.98 D	0.45
HCl	1.28	6.07	1.03	.17
HBr	1.43	6.82	0.79	.12
HI	1.62	7.74	.38	.05

[a] The unit 1 D (one debye) is equal to 1×10^{-18} statcoulomb centimeters.

equilibrium internuclear distance. In consequence of this *the ionic structure* H^+F^- *and the covalent structure* $H\!:\!\ddot{F}\!:$ *make nearly equal contributions to the normal state of the molecule;* the hydrogen-fluorine bond has about 50 percent ionic character. Because the two energy curves lie close together, resonance is nearly complete, and almost the entire interaction energy between the two structures is effective as resonance energy.

We may attempt to make a rough quantitative statement about the bond type in these molecules by the use of the values of their electric dipole moments. For the hydrogen halogenides only very small electric dipole moments would be expected in case that the bonds were purely covalent. For the ionic structure H^+X^-, on the other hand, moments approximating the product of the electronic charge and the internuclear separations would be expected. (Some reduction would result from polarization of the anion by the cation; this we neglect.) In Table 3-1 are given values of the equilibrium internuclear distances r_0, the electric moments er_0 calculated for the ionic structure H^+X^-, the observed values of the electric moments μ, and the ratios of these to the values of er_0.* These ratios may be interpreted in a simple way as representing approximately the magnitudes of the contributions of the ionic structure to the normal states of the molecules; that is, the amounts of ionic character of the bonds. It is seen that on this basis the bond in hydrogen fluoride is 45 percent ionic, that in hydrogen chloride 17 percent ionic, that in hydrogen bromide 12 percent ionic, and that in hydrogen iodide 5 percent ionic.

The values of the electric dipole moments of the alkali halogenide gas molecules are found to be about 80 percent of er_0; for example, for KCl the value of r_0 is 2.671 Å and that of μ is 10.48 D, which is 82 percent of er_0. The deviation of μ from er_0 is about the magnitude expected to result

* For a discussion of electric dipole moments of molecules see App. VII.

from the polarization of each ion in the electric field of the other, and because of the uncertainty in the theoretical calculation of the polarization correction it is not possible to say more than that the observed moments agree roughly with those expected for completely ionic structures.

The discussion of the amount of partial ionic character of single bonds will be continued in Section 3-9.

3-4. BOND ENERGIES OF HALOGENIDE MOLECULES; THE ENERGIES OF NORMAL COVALENT BONDS

The wave function representing the single bond in a symmetric molecule A—A can be written in the form

$$a\psi_{A:A} + b\psi_{A^+A^-} + b\psi_{A^-A^+} \tag{3-1}$$

and a similar expression can be written for another molecule B—B. The ratio b/a, determining the contributions of the ionic structures, is small, and probably about the same for all bonds between like atoms.

Now let us consider a molecule A—B, involving a single bond between two unlike atoms. If the atoms were closely similar in character, the bond in this molecule could be represented by a wave function such as 3-1, an average of those for the symmetric molecules A—A and B—B. Let us describe such a bond as a *normal covalent bond*.

If, now, we consider a molecule A—B in which the atoms A and B are dissimilar, one being more electronegative than the other, we must use a more general wave function,

$$a\psi_{A:B} + c\psi_{A^+B^-} + d\psi_{A^-B^+} \tag{3-2}$$

to represent the bond, the best values of c/a and d/a being those that make the bond energy a maximum (minimize the total energy of the molecule). These values will in general be different from b/a of Equation 3-1, one being smaller and one larger. Since they make the bond energy a maximum, we see that *the energy of an actual bond between unlike atoms is greater than (or equal to) the energy of a normal covalent bond between these atoms.* This additional bond energy is due to the *additional ionic character of the bond;* that is, it is the *additional ionic resonance energy* that the bond has as compared with a bond between like atoms. In referring to these quantities later we shall omit the word "additional" and say "ionic character of the bond" and "ionic resonance energy."

To test this conclusion we need values of the energies of normal covalent bonds between unlike atoms. These values might be calculated by quantum-mechanical methods; it is simpler, however, to make a postulate and test it empirically. Since a normal covalent bond A—B is similar

TABLE 3-2.—BOND ENERGIES FOR HYDROGEN HALOGENIDE AND HALOGEN
HALOGENIDE MOLECULES (KCAL/MOLE)

	H—H	F—F	Cl—Cl	Br—Br	I—I
Bond energy	104.2	36.6	58.0	46.1	36.1

	H—F	H—Cl	H—Br	H—I
Bond energy	134.6	103.2	87.5	71.4
$\frac{1}{2}\{D(H—H) + D(X—X)\}$	70.4	81.1	75.2	70.2
Δ	64.2	22.1	12.3	1.2

	Cl—F	Br—Cl	I—Cl	I—Br
Bond energy	60.6	52.3	50.3	42.5
$\frac{1}{2}\{D(X—X) + D(X'—X')\}$	47.3	52.1	47.1	41.1
Δ	13.3	0.2	3.2	1.4

in character to the bonds A—A and B—B, we expect the value of the bond energy to be intermediate between the values for A—A and B—B. This result follows from the *postulate of the additivity of normal covalent bonds*. That is, we assume that the arithmetic mean of the two bond-energy values $D(A—A)$ and $D(B—B)$ is the energy of the normal covalent bond between the unlike atoms A and B.

If this postulate were true, actual bond energies $D(A—B)$ between unlike atoms would always be greater than or equal to the arithmetic means of the corresponding symmetrical bond energies; the difference Δ defined as

$$\Delta = D(A—B) - \tfrac{1}{2}\{D(A—A) + D(B—B)\} \tag{3-3}$$

would never be negative. In Table 3-2 values of bond energies and of Δ for the hydrogen halogenides and halogen halogenides are given.* It is seen that *for each of the eight molecules Δ is positive*. Moreover, the magnitudes of the Δ values, which measure the resonance energy due to ionic character of the unsymmetrical bonds, are in agreement with our previously formed conceptions as to the nature of the bonds in these molecules. In the series HI, HBr, HCl, HF we have estimated the

---

* In Tables 3-2 and 3-3 the enthalpies at 25°C are used as the basis for the calculation of bond energies, which accordingly include not only the energies of dissociation D_0 of the molecules but also small terms corresponding to the rotational, oscillational, and translational energy of the molecules and a pressure-volume term. These small terms are not significant for our arguments. Enthalpies rather than energy values are used to give uniformity with Sec. 3-5.

amounts of ionic character of the bonds to be 5, 12, 17, and 45 percent, respectively. The corresponding values of Δ, 1.2, 12.3, 22.1, and 64.2 kcal/mole, increase in the same general way and show the expected large change from HCl to HF. (The only unexpected feature is the very small value of Δ for HI.) The molecule BrCl approaches the normal covalent type still more closely, with Δ equal to only 0.2 kcal/mole. This is the expected result for a bond between two atoms that resemble one another as closely as chlorine and bromine. The values of Δ for IBr and ICl are also small, but that for ClF is about as large as that for HBr, showing that chlorine fluoride is about as ionic in character as hydrogen bromide. Chlorine, bromine, and iodine do not differ greatly in electronegativity, chlorine and bromine being more nearly alike in this respect, as in other respects, than bromine and iodine. But fluorine is very much more electronegative than the other halogens; it deserves to be classed by itself as a superhalogen.

It is seen that the quantity Δ is just the heat liberated in the reaction

$$\tfrac{1}{2}A_2(g) + \tfrac{1}{2}B_2(g) \rightarrow AB(g) \tag{3-4}$$

and our requirement that Δ be greater than or equal to zero is equivalent to the requirement that a reaction of this type not be endothermic.

It will be shown in the following section that the postulate of additivity is valid for a large number of single bonds and that the values of Δ can be used as the basis for the formulation of an extensive scale of electronegativities of the elements.

3-5. EMPIRICAL VALUES OF SINGLE-BOND ENERGIES

Empirical values of bond energies in diatomic molecules are given directly by the energies of dissociation into atoms, which may be determined by thermochemical or spectroscopic methods. In the case of a polyatomic molecule thermochemical data provide a value for the total energy of dissociation into atoms, that is, for the sum of the bond energies in the molecule, but not for the individual bond energies. Thus from the enthalpy of formation of gaseous water from the elements (57.80 kcal/mole) and the enthalpies of dissociation of hydrogen and oxygen (104.18 and 118.32 kcal/mole, respectively), we find that the enthalpy of the reaction

$$2H + O \rightarrow H_2O(g) \tag{3-5}$$

is 221.14 kcal/mole. This is the sum of the amounts of energy required to remove first one hydrogen atom from the water molecule, breaking one O—H bond, and then the second hydrogen atom, breaking the other

O—H bond. These two energy quantities are not equal, although they are not much different in value. It is convenient for us to define their average, 110.6 kcal/mole, as the energy of the O—H bond in the water molecule. In a similar way values can be obtained for bond energies in polyatomic molecules in which all the bonds are alike. It is to be emphasized that each of these bond-energy values represents not the amount of

TABLE 3-3.—ENERGY VALUES FOR SINGLE BONDS (KCAL/MOLE)

Bond	Bond energy	Bond	Bond energy	Bond	Bond energy
H—H	104.2	P—H	76.4	Si—Cl	85.7
C—C	83.1	As—H	58.6	Si—Br	69.1
Si—Si	42.2	O—H	110.6	Si—I	50.9
Ge—Ge	37.6	S—H	81.1	Ge—Cl	97.5
Sn—Sn	34.2	Se—H	66.1	N—F	64.5
N—N	38.4	Te—H	57.5	N—Cl	47.7
P—P	51.3	H—F	134.6	P—Cl	79.1
As—As	32.1	H—Cl	103.2	P—Br	65.4
Sb—Sb	30.2	H—Br	87.5	P—I	51.4
Bi—Bi	25	H—I	71.4	As—F	111.3
O—O	33.2	C—Si	69.3	As—Cl	68.9
S—S	50.9	C—N	69.7	As—Br	56.5
Se—Se	44.0	C—O	84.0	As—I	41.6
Te—Te	33	C—S	62.0	O—F	44.2
F—F	36.6	C—F	105.4	O—Cl	49.5
Cl—Cl	58.0	C—Cl	78.5	S—Cl	59.7
Br—Br	46.1	C—Br	65.9	S—Br	50.7
I—I	36.1	C—I	57.4	Cl—F	60.6
C—H	98.8	Si—O	88.2	Br—Cl	52.3
Si—H	70.4	Si—S	54.2	I—Cl	50.3
N—H	93.4	Si—F	129.3	I—Br	42.5

energy required to break one bond in the molecule, but instead the average amount required to break all the bonds.[*]

Values for single-bond energies, defined in this way, for many bonds can be found by this process—for the S—S bond from the S_8 molecule (an eight-membered ring containing eight S—S bonds), for N—H, P—H, S—H, and so forth from NH_3, PH_3, H_2S, and so forth. These values are given in Table 3-3.

There is no allotropic form of oxygen in which the atoms are connected by single O—O bonds. The value of the O—O bond energy given in the

---

[*] A discussion of *bond dissociation energy*, the energy required to break one bond in a molecule, is given in App. IX.

table has been obtained from the heat of formation of hydrogen peroxide, with use of the assumption that the H—O bond energy in H_2O_2 is the same as in H_2O. The calculation, typical of those used in evaluating bond energies from thermochemical information, is made in the following way: The enthalpy of formation of $H_2O_2(g)$ from the elements in the standard state is 31.83 kcal/mole. By adding 104.2 and 118.3, for H_2 and O_2, we obtain 254.3 kcal/mole as the enthalpy of formation of $H_2O_2(g)$ from the atoms 2H and 2O. Subtraction of 221.1 for two O—H bonds leaves 33.2 kcal/mole as the energy of the O—O bond; this is the value given in the table.

The methods used in obtaining the remaining values in the table are described in the following paragraphs.

TABLE 3-4.—ENTHALPY (IN KCAL/MOLE) OF MONATOMIC GASES OF
ELEMENTS RELATIVE TO THEIR STANDARD STATES

H	52.09								
Li	37.07	C	171.70	N	113.0	O	59.16	F	18.3
Na	25.98	Si	88.04	P	75.18	S	53.25	Cl	29.01
K	21.51	Ge	78.44	As	60.64	Se	48.37	Br	26.71
Rb	20.51	Sn	72	Sb	60.8	Te	47.6	I	25.48
Cs	18.83	Pb	46.34	Bi	49.7				

The thermochemical values used in this work have been taken for the most part from the compilation *Selected Values of Chemical Thermodynamic Properties*, by F. D. Rossini, D. D. Wagman, W. H. Evans, S. Levine, and I. Jaffe (Circular of the National Bureau of Standards 500, Government Printing Office, Washington, D. C., 1952). The bond-energy values are so chosen that their sums represent the enthalpy changes $(-\Delta H)$ at 25°C accompanying the formation of molecules from atoms, all in the gas phase.

The values given in Table 3-4 were used for the enthalpies of the gases of atoms in their normal states (the reference states for the bond energies) relative to the standard states of the elements, to which the enthalpies of formation given in the Bureau of Standards compilation refer.

In the discussion of heats of combustion the following values of the enthalpy of reaction at 25°C are useful:

$$H_2(g) + \tfrac{1}{2}O_2(g) \rightarrow H_2O(g) - \Delta H° = 57.7979 \text{ kcal/mole} \qquad (3\text{-}6)$$
$$H_2(g) + \tfrac{1}{2}O_2(g) \rightarrow H_2O(l) - \Delta H° = 68.3174 \text{ kcal/mole} \qquad (3\text{-}7)$$
$$C \text{ (graphite)} + O_2(g) \rightarrow CO_2(g) - \Delta H° = 94.0518 \text{ kcal/mole} \qquad (3\text{-}8)$$
$$C \text{ (graphite)} + \tfrac{1}{2}O_2(g) \rightarrow CO(g) - \Delta H° = 26.4157 \text{ kcal/mole} \qquad (3\text{-}9)$$

The bond-energy value given for each of the bonds H—H, F—F, Cl—Cl, Br—Br, I—I, H—F, H—Cl, H—Br, H—I, Cl—F, Br—Cl, I—Cl, and I—Br is the thermochemically or spectroscopically determined value of the enthalpy of dissociation of the corresponding diatomic molecule. The values for the bonds Si—Si and Ge—Ge are half the enthalpies of sublimation of the crystals, which have the diamond structure.

A fundamental assumption adopted in the formulation and use of the bond-energy values of Table 3-3 is that the energy of a molecule to which a single valence-bond structure can be confidently assigned can be approximated closely by the sum of constant terms corresponding to the bonds. This assumption is found to be justified empirically to a considerable extent, the enthalpies of formation calculated by summing the bond energies agreeing with the experimental values to within a few kcal/mole for nearly all molecules.   As an example selected at random, the enthalpy of formation of $CH_2FCH_2OH(g)$ from elements in their standard states is 95.7 kcal/mole; this leads to 777.0 kcal/mole on addition of the suitable terms from Table 3-4 for the enthalpy of formation from monatomic gases. The sum of the bond energies for four C—H bonds, one C—F bond, one C—C bond, one C—O bond, and one O—H bond from Table 3-3 is 778.3 kcal/mole, the agreement in this case thus being excellent.

The bond-energy values are devised for use only with molecules containing atoms that show their normal covalences (four for carbon, three for nitrogen, etc.).   An ammonium salt or a substance such as trimethylamine oxide cannot be treated in this way.   The bond energies are also not expected to be valid for a molecule such as phosphorus pentachloride.   It is interesting to point out that the enthalpy of the reaction $PCl_3(g) + 2Cl(g) \rightarrow PCl_5(g)$, 80.2 kcal/mole, corresponds to the formation of two new P—Cl bonds with apparent bond energy 40.1 kcal/mole, which is much less than the normal P—Cl bond energy, 79.1 kcal/mole.

Bond energies can be used in the discussion of the structure of molecules.   For example, the enthalpy of formation expected for ozone from molecular oxygen would be -77.9 kcal/mole (or less if a correction were made for strain in the three-membered ring), if the molecule had the

structure   ; the observed value, -34.0 kcal/mole, differs

from this by so great an amount as to permit this structure for ozone to be eliminated.   A similar discrepancy between the value -103.8 calculated

for the structure
$$:\overset{\cdot\cdot}{O}\!\!-\!\!\overset{\cdot\cdot}{O}:$$
$$\mid\quad\mid$$
$$:\overset{\cdot\cdot}{O}\!\!-\!\!\overset{\cdot\cdot}{O}:$$
and the observed enthalpy of formation

0.16 kcal/mole of the molecule O_4 eliminates this structure. Evidence is now available from spectroscopic, electron diffraction, and x-ray diffraction studies also showing that these single-bonded structures are not correct for O_3 and O_4.

The use of bond energies in the discussion of molecules containing multiple bonds and of molecules that cannot be represented satisfactorily by one valence-bond structure will be presented in Chapters 6 and 8.

3-6. THE ELECTRONEGATIVITY SCALE OF THE ELEMENTS

The Formulation of the Electronegativity Scale.—In Section 3-4 it was pointed out that the values of the difference Δ between the energy $D(A\!-\!B)$ of the bond between two atoms A and B and the energy expected for a normal covalent bond, assumed to be the arithmetic mean of the bond energies $D(A\!-\!A)$ and $D(B\!-\!B)$, increase as the two atoms A and B become more and more unlike with respect to the qualitative property that the chemist calls electronegativity, the power of an atom in a molecule to attract electrons to itself. Thus Δ increases rapidly in the sequence HI, HBr, HCl, HF (Table 3-2), in which the halogen changes from iodine, which is recognized by its general chemical properties to be only a little more electronegative than hydrogen, to fluorine, the most electronegative of all the elements.

The property of the electronegativity of an atom in a molecule is different from the electrode potential of the element, which depends on the difference in free energy of the element in its standard state and in ionic solution, and it is different from the ionization potential of the atom and from its electron affinity, although it is related to these properties in a general way.

It has been found possible to formulate an electronegativity scale of the elements by the analysis of the values of Δ given by the single-bond energies. It is found that the bond energy, in kcal/mole, for a bond A—B is given approximately by the equation

$$\Delta = D(A\!-\!B) - \tfrac{1}{2}\{D(A\!-\!A) + D(B\!-\!B)\} = 23(x_A - x_B)^2 \quad (3\text{-}10)$$

In this equation x_A and x_B are values of the electronegativity assigned to atoms A and B. In the original formulation of the electronegativity scale the electron volt, 23 kcal/mole, was used as the unit of energy; this use accounts for the factor 23 in Equation 3-10, and for the range of the electronegativity scale.

Partial Ionic Character of Covalent Bonds

Values of the electronegativity found in this way and the way described in the following section are given in Table 3-5 and shown graphically in

TABLE 3-5.—THE COMPLETE ELECTRONEGATIVITY SCALE

Li	Be	B											C	N	O	F
1.0	1.5	2.0											2.5	3.0	3.5	4.0
Na	Mg	Al											Si	P	S	Cl
0.9	1.2	1.5											1.8	2.1	2.5	3.0
K	Ca	Sc	Ti	V	Cr	Mn	Fe	Co	Ni	Cu	Zn	Ga	Ge	As	Se	Br
0.8	1.0	1.3	1.4	1.6	1.6	1.5	1.8	1.8	1.8	1.9	1.6	1.6	1.8	2.0	2.4	2.8
Rb	Sr	Y	Zr	Nb	Mo	Tc	Ru	Rh	Pd	Ag	Cd	In	Sn	Sb	Te	I
0.8	1.0	1.2	1.4	1.6	1.8	1.9	2.2	2.2	2.2	1.9	1.7	1.7	1.8	1.9	2.1	2.5
Cs	Ba	La-Lu	Hf	Ta	W	Re	Os	Ir	Pt	Au	Hg	Tl	Pb	Bl	Po	At
0.7	0.9	1.1–1.2	1.3	1.5	1.7	1.9	2.2	2.2	2.2	2.4	1.9	1.8	1.8	1.9	2.0	2.2
Fr	Ra	Ra	Th	Pa	U	Np-No										
0.7	0.9	1.1	1.3	1.5	1.7	1.3										

Figure 3-4. The derivation of the values may be illustrated by the example of the H—Br bond. The value of Δ for this bond is given in Table 3-2 as 12.3 kcal/mole. From Equation 3-10 we conclude that x_H and x_{Br} differ by approximately $\sqrt{12.3/23} = \sqrt{0.535} = 0.73$. In fact, the values $x_H = 2.1$ and $x_{Br} = 2.8$ given in Table 3-5 differ by 0.7.

In constructing Table 3-5 all of the available data were considered and the x value that led to the best general agreement for each atom was selected. These values are given only to one decimal place on the scale; this is probably the limit of their reliability.

The relation of the electronegativity values of Table 3-5 to the periodic system is the expected one. Fluorine and oxygen are by far the most electronegative of the atoms, with fluorine much more electronegative than oxygen. It is interesting that nitrogen and chlorine have the same electronegativity, as have also carbon, sulfur, and iodine. The contours of equal electronegativity cut diagonally across the periodic table, from the upper left- to the lower right-hand region.

3-7. HEATS OF FORMATION OF COMPOUNDS IN THEIR STANDARD STATES; THE COMPLETE ELECTRONEGATIVITY SCALE

The method just described for formulating the electronegativity scale cannot be used for the remaining elements in general because of lack of knowledge of enthalpies of formation of their compounds as gases and of the values of single-bond energies for the elements themselves. The following extension of the method can, however, be used.

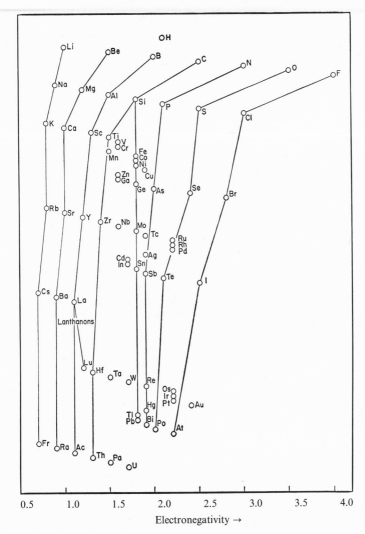

FIG. 3-4.—Electronegativity values of the elements.

Except for nitrogen and oxygen, which are discussed below, the elements in their standard states do not differ very much in energy from states involving normal single covalent bonds between the atoms. It is known that the standard states of bromine, iodine, sulfur, carbon (diamond), and many other nonmetallic elements are those in which the atoms are attached to adjacent atoms by single bonds. Moreover, the standard states of the metals too are probably not much different from states involving single bonds; there is a close resemblance in properties of the metallic bond and the covalent bond (Chap. 11).

Many elements in their standard states are, however, liquids or crystals, rather than gases, and many compounds in which we are interested are liquids or crystals.   The energy of a liquid or a crystal may be described as involving not only the bond energies but also the energy of the van der Waals interaction of adjacent nonbonded atoms.   As an approximation we may assume that the energy of the van der Waals stabilization of a substance in its standard state is approximately equal to the van der Waals stabilization of the elements from which the substance is formed, in their standard states, and that accordingly the enthalpy of formation referred to standard states is approximately equal to the enthalpy of formation of the gaseous compound from gaseous elements.   Moreover, except with first-row atoms, the formation of stable double bonds and triple bonds is unusual, and we may assume with reasonable confidence that a substance of unknown bond type does not contain multiple bonds of sufficiently different energy from the corresponding number of single bonds to introduce very great error in the electronegativity calculations.

The contribution of each bond to the heat of formation of a substance is, according to Equation 3-10, equal to $23(x_A - x_B)^2$; and, except for the corrections for nitrogen and oxygen that we shall now discuss, the heat of formation would be obtained by summing this expression over all the bonds in the molecule.

The standard state $N_2(g)$ for nitrogen is far more stable than it would be if the molecule involved single N—N bonds.From the bond-energy value 38.4 kcal/mole for N—N and the value $2N \rightarrow N_2 + 226.0$ kcal/mole, we see that this extra stability of the standard state amounts to 110.8 kcal/mole for N_2, or 55.4 kcal/mole per nitrogen atom.   Similarly, the values 33.2 kcal/mole for O—O and $2O \rightarrow O_2 + 118.3$ kcal/mole lead to an extra stability of 52.0 kcal/mole for O_2 in its standard state, or 26.0 per oxygen atom.   These correction terms for nitrogen and oxygen are due to the fact that N_2 contains a triple bond that is much more stable than three single bonds, and O_2 a bond of special character (Chap. 10) that is more stable than two single bonds.   Accordingly the enthalpy of formation of a substance in its standard state can be calculated approximately by use of the expression

$$Q = 23 \sum (x_A - x_B)^2 - 55.4n_N - 26.0n_O \qquad (3\text{-}11)$$

in which n_N is the number of nitrogen atoms in the molecule and n_O the number of oxygen atoms, and the indicated summation is to be carried over all the bonds in the molecule; the value of Q is given in kcal/mole. The equation does not apply to substances containing double or triple bonds.

It is the unusual stability of multiple bonds for oxygen and nitrogen, stabilizing their normal states, that often leads to negative values of the enthalpy of formation of substances. The enthalpy of formation of a molecule containing an atom of nitrogen held by single bonds to other atoms with the same electronegativity should be about -55.4 kcal/mole; the compound would accordingly be very unstable relative to the elements. Nitrogen trichloride is such a compound; in the molecule of this substance the bonds are normal covalent bonds, similar to N—N and Cl—Cl single bonds; it is not the weakness of the N—Cl bonds, but rather the extraordinary strength of the triple bond in N_2 that makes nitrogen trichloride unstable. Its measured enthalpy of formation, in solution in carbon tetrachloride, is -54.7 kcal/mole, in close agreement with the expected value. In nitrogen trifluoride the ionic resonance energy of the N—F bonds is great enough to overcome this handicap and to give the molecule NF_3 a positive enthalpy of formation (27.2 kcal/mole). For OF_2 and Cl_2O (with $x_A - x_B = 0.5$) the ionic character is not enough to counteract the term -26.0 kcal/mole for the oxygen atom; these substances have negative enthalpies of formation, whereas the enthalpies of formation of other normal oxides are positive.

By the use of Equation 3-11 the difference in electronegativity of two elements can be calculated from the enthalpy of formation of the compounds formed by them, and in this way, through study of the compounds of the element with elements with electronegativity values given in Table 3-5, the electronegativity of the element can be evaluated. For example, the enthalpies of formation of $BeCl_2$, $BeBr_2$, BeI_2, and BeS from the elements in their standard states are 122.3, 88.4, 50.6, and 55.9 kcal/mole, respectively. These values lead to 1.56, 1.33, 1.03, and 1.06 for the electronegativity differences, and hence to 1.44, 1.47, 1.47, and 1.44 for the electronegativity of beryllium. The value 1.5 has been accepted for the element. Many of the values given in Table 3-5 have been obtained in this way.

The electronegativity scale brings a certain amount of systematization into the field of inorganic thermochemistry, in which on first survey little order can be detected. It is possible to calculate rough values expected for enthalpies of formation of compounds by the use of the electronegativity values of Table 3-5, which vary in a regular way from element to element in the periodic system, the enthalpies of reaction of the elements to form compounds being attributed in the main to the extra resonance energy that results from the partial ionic character of the bonds between unlike atoms and that increases as the atoms become more and more unlike. This order is brought out of apparent lack of order in the thermochemical values largely through the corrections for the two elements nitrogen and oxygen, which are alone among the elements in having their standard states much different in stability from single-bonded states.

3-8. RELATION TO OTHER PROPERTIES

The property of electronegativity that we have been discussing represents the attraction of a neutral atom in a stable molecule for electrons. The first ionization energy of an atom, the energy of the reaction $X^+ + e^- \rightarrow X$, may be considered as the average of the electron attraction of the atom and the positive ion, and the electron affinity, the energy of the reaction $X + e^- \rightarrow X^-$, may be thought of similarly as the average of the electron attraction of the atom and the negative ion. It was pointed out by Mulliken that the average of the first ionization energy and the electron affinity of an atom should be a measure of the electron attraction of the neutral atom and hence of its electronegativity. For multivalent atoms the significance of these energy quantities is complicated by the nature of the states of the atoms and ions, and corrections must be made that need not be discussed here. For univalent atoms (hydrogen, the halogens, the alkali metals) the treatment is straightforward. The values of the energy quantities concerned are given in Table 3-6, it being assumed that the electron affinity of the alkali metals is zero. It is seen

TABLE 3-6.—COMPARISON OF ELECTRONEGATIVITY WITH AVERAGE OF IONIZATION ENERGY AND ELECTRON AFFINITY[a]

	Ionization energy	Electron affinity	Sum/125	x
F	403.3	83.5	3.90	4.0
Cl	300.3	87.3	3.10	3.0
Br	274.6	82.0	2.86	2.8
I	242.2	75.7	2.54	2.5
H	315.0	17.8	2.66	2.1
Li	125.8	0	1.01	1.0
Na	120.0	0	.96	0.9
K	101.6	0	.81	.8
Rb	97.8	0	.78	.8
Cs	91.3	0	.73	.7

[a] All values are for $-\Delta H°$ at 25°C.

that the values of x are closely proportional to those of the sum of the two energy quantities except for hydrogen, which, with its unique electronic structure, might be expected to misbehave. This comparison and others were used in fixing the origin for the electronegativity scale.

Many other properties of substances have been correlated with the electronegativity values. Some of these properties are mentioned in later sections of this book.

3-9. THE ELECTRONEGATIVITY OF ATOMS AND THE PARTIAL IONIC CHARACTER OF BONDS

It would be convenient in discussing bonds to be able to make quantitative statements about their nature—to say that certain bonds are essentially covalent, with only 5 percent or 10 percent of ionic character, that others are about equally ionic and covalent, and that others are essentially ionic. It is difficult to formulate a reliable relation between the partial ionic character of a bond and the difference in electronegativity of the two atoms between which the bond is formed, because the description of a bond as a hybrid between a normal covalent bond and an extreme ionic bond is only a rough approximation. An approximate equation for the amount of ionic character of the single bond between atoms A and B, with electronegativities x_A and x_B, can, however, be used:

$$\text{Amount of ionic character} = 1 - e^{-1/4(x_A - x_B)} \qquad (3\text{-}12)$$

This equation corresponds to the amounts 4, 11, 19, and 60 percent of ionic character for HI, HBr, HCl, and HF, respectively. The values for the first three of these hydrogen halides are closely equal to those indicated by the electric dipole moments of the molecules, as given in Table 3-1. At the time when the equation was formulated the value of the dipole moment of HF was not known, and an estimate of 60 percent was made for the partial ionic character in this molecule. As shown in Table 3-1, the dipole moment of HF corresponds to only 45 percent partial ionic character.

Equation 3-12 leads to the amounts of ionic character for various values of the electronegativity difference given in Table 3-7. The function is shown as the curve in Figure 3-5, together with the experimental values of the ratio of the observed electric dipole moment to the product of the electronic charge and internuclear distance for a number of diatomic molecules composed of univalent elements. Points are shown for the hydrogen halogenides, halogen halogenides, and alkali halogenides. The experimental values for the electric dipole moments for the alkali halogenides are those determined by methods of microwave spectroscopy or molecular-beam spectroscopy. It is seen that the curve agrees only roughly with the experimental points.

According to Equation 3-12 bonds between atoms with electronegativity difference 1.7 have 50 percent ionic character and 50 percent covalent character. Thus bonds between fluorine and any of the metals or of the elements H, B, P, As, Te, with electronegativity near 2, are largely ionic in character, and bonds between oxygen and any of the metals are 50 percent or more ionic.

We may now summarize the conclusions that can be drawn about the partial ionic character of the single bonds formed by the elements.

TABLE 3-7—RELATION BETWEEN ELECTRONEGATIVITY DIFFERENCE AND
AMOUNT OF PARTIAL IONIC CHARACTER OF SINGLE BONDS

$x_A - x_B$	Amount of ionic character	$x_A - x_B$	Amount of ionic character
0.2	1 percent	1.8	55 percent
.4	4	2.0	63
.6	9	2.2	70
.8	15	2.4	76
1.0	22	2.6	82
1.2	30	2.8	86
1.4	39	3.0	89
1.6	47	3.2	92

The Alkali Metals.—Bonds of the alkali metals with all nonmetals are essentially ionic (with more than 50 percent ionic character—electronegativity difference greater than 1.7) except for Li—I, Li—C, and Li—S, with about 43 percent ionic character.

The Alkaline-Earth Metals.—Magnesium, calcium, strontium, and barium form essentially ionic bonds with the more nonmetallic elements. Beryllium bonds have the following amounts of ionic character: Be—F, 79 percent; Be—O, 63 percent; Be—Cl, 44 percent; Be—Br, 35 percent; Be—I, 22 percent.

The Third-Group Elements.—The B—F bond has about 63 percent ionic character, B—O 44 percent, B—Cl 22 percent, and so forth. Boron forms normal covalent bonds with hydrogen. The aluminum bonds are similar to those of beryllium in ionic character.

The Fourth-Group Elements.—The C—F bond, with 44 percent ionic character, is the most ionic of the bonds of carbon with nonmetallic elements. The Si—F bond has 70 percent ionic character, and Si—Cl 30

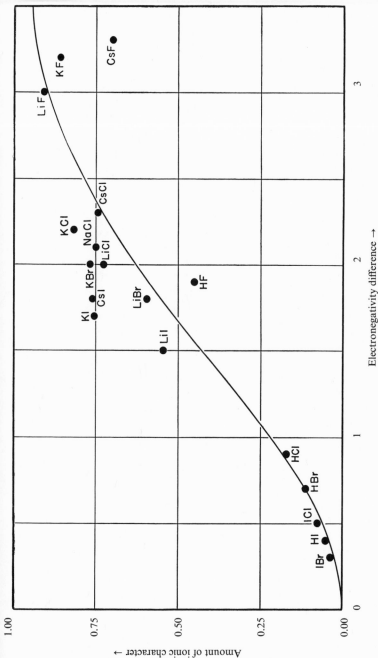

Fig. 3-5.—Curve relating the amount of ionic character of a bond to the electronegativity difference of the two atoms. Experimental points, based upon observed values of the electric dipole moment of diatomic molecules, are shown for 18 bonds.

percent.   The Si—O bond is of especial interest because of its importance in the silicates.   It is seen to have 50 percent ionic character, the value of $x_O - x_{Si}$ being 1.7.

The Remaining Nonmetallic Elements.—The bonds formed by fluorine with all of the metals are essentially ionic in character, and those with the intermediate elements (H, B, P, etc.) have a little more than 50 percent ionic character.   The C—F, S—F, and I—F bonds are expected to have 44 percent ionic character.   In CF_4, SF_6, IF_5, and IF_7 the amounts of ionic character of the bonds are probably somewhat less than this value because of the transfer of positive charge to the central atom, which increases its x value and decreases the ionic character of the bonds.

The bonds of oxygen with all metals are largely ionic.

Since the nonmetallic elements in each row of the periodic table are separated by intervals of 0.5, the bonds formed by a nonmetallic atom with immediate neighbors in the same row have 6 percent ionic character and those with its neighbors once removed 22 percent.

EXERCISES

3-1.—The ionization energy of the hydrogen atom $(H \rightarrow H^+ + e^-)$ is 314 kcal/mole and the electron affinity of the fluorine atom $(F + e^- \rightarrow F^-)$ is 84 kcal/mole.   How much energy is required to convert separated atoms H + F to separated ions $H^+ + F^-$?   (Ans. 230 kcal/mole.)

3-2.—The H—F internuclear distance in the molecule HF in its normal state is 0.92 Å.   What is the difference in Coulomb energy $(-e^2/r)$ of two ions H^+ and F^- this distance apart and very far apart?   Neglecting other interactions, evaluate the energy of H^+F^- at this distance relative to H + F.   (Ans. -363 kcal/mole, -133 kcal/mole.)

3-3.—For an extreme covalent structure for HF the bond energy would be expected to be about 70 kcal/mole (average of bond energies for H—H and F—F).   Using Fig. 3-3 as a model, plot a hypothetical energy curve for this extreme covalent structure, and also plot the Coulomb energy function $-e^2/r$ for the extreme ionic structure (ignoring the repulsion energy of H^+ and F^- that occurs at small internuclear distances, when the proton begins to penetrate the outer electron shell of the fluoride ion).   What is the energy of the extreme ionic structure, at 0.92 Å, relative to that of the extreme covalent structure?   (Ans. -63 kcal/mole.)

3-4.—The values of the electron affinity of Cl, Br, and I are 87, 82, and 76 kcal/mole, respectively, and the values of the internuclear distance in HCl, HBr, and HI are 1.27, 1.41, and 1.61 Å, respectively.   Calculate the energy H^+X^- at these distances relative to the extreme covalent structures

(Ex. 3-3) and use the values to explain qualitatively the decrease in ionic character in the sequence HF to HI.

3-5.—The observed value of the electric dipole moment of the gas molecule LiH is 5.88D. To what changes (statcoulombs) centered at the nuclei does this value correspond? (The internuclear distance is 1.60 Å.) To what amount of ionic character for the bond? (Ans. 3.7×10^{-10}; 77 percent.)

3-6.—Observed values of the enthalpy of $AlCl_3$, $AlBr_3$, AlI_3, Al_2O_3, and Al_2S_3 (all as crystalline solids), relative to the elements in their standard states, are -166, -126, -75, -399, and -122 kcal/mole, respectively. Using Equation 3-11, evaluate the electronegativity of aluminum. (Ans. 1.46, 1.46, 1.46, 1.65, 1.58.)

3-7.—The bond energy of the molecule $Cu_2(g)$ is 45.5 kcal/mole, and that of $CuCl(g)$ is 78.5 kcal/mole. To what value of the electronegativity of copper do these values lead? (Ans. 1.92.)

3-8.—Observed values of bond energies in the gas molecules Cu_2, Ag_2, Au_2, CuAg, CuAu, and AgAu are 45.4, 37.6, 51.5, 40.7, 54.5, and 47.6 kcal/mole, respectively. From these values and the value $x = 1.9$ for Cu obtain values of x for Ag and Au. (Ans. 2.0, 2.4.)

CHAPTER 4

The Directed Covalent Bond;

Bond Strengths and Bond Angles

MUCH progress has been made in the development of a detailed under-standing of the nature of covalent bonds through the consideration of the atomic orbitals (bond orbitals) that can be used as the basis of the quan-tum-mechanical treatment of the bonds.

4-1. THE NATURE AND BOND-FORMING POWER OF ATOMIC ORBITALS

The energy of a covalent bond is largely the energy of resonance of two electrons between two atoms (Sec. 1-5). Examination of the form of the resonance integral shows that the resonance energy increases in magnitude with increase in the *overlapping* of the two atomic orbitals involved in the formation of the bond, the word "overlapping" signifying the extent to which the regions in space in which the two orbital wave functions have large values coincide. (Since the square of an orbital wave function is the probability distribution function for the electron, the overlapping is essentially a measure of the amount of interpenetration of the bond-electron distributions of the two atoms.) Consequently it is expected that *of two orbitals in an atom the one that can overlap more with an orbital of another atom will form the stronger bond with that atom, and, moreover, the bond formed by a given orbital will tend to lie in that direction in which the orbital is concentrated.*

The orbitals of an atom differ from one another in their dependence on the distance r of the electron from the nucleus and on the polar angles θ and ϕ, that is, on their angular distribution. The dependence on r has been discussed for the hydrogen atom in Section 1-4. It is this depend-ence that in the main determines the *stability* of the atomic orbital, and the primary significance of the orbital for bond formation can be dis-cussed in terms of stability. Stable bonds are formed only with use of

74

stable atomic orbitals—the 1s orbital for hydrogen, the 2s and 2p orbitals for the first-row atoms, and so on.

The different stable orbitals of an atom which can be used for bond formation do not differ very much from one another in their dependence on r, but they may show a great difference in their angular distribution. This can be seen from Figure 4-1, representing the angular distribution

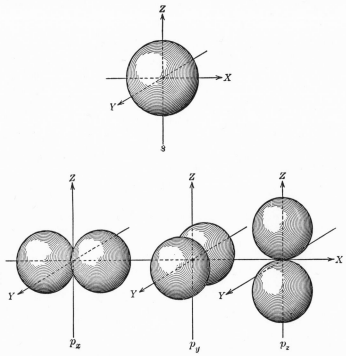

FIG. 4-1.—Representations of the relative magnitudes of sp orbitals in dependence on angle.

of an s orbital and the three p orbitals.* The s orbital is spherically symmetrical, and hence can form a bond in one direction as well as in any other, whereas the three p orbitals are directed along the three Cartesian axes and will tend to form bonds in these directions. Moreover, the p orbitals are concentrated in these directions and have magnitudes $\sqrt{3}$ times as great as that of an s orbital, so far as the angular dependence is concerned. Since the radial part of an s orbital and that of the p orbitals of the same shell do not differ much, the p orbitals can

* This figure gives a general idea of the distribution of an electron occupying these orbitals so far as orientation is concerned, but it does not show the dependence on r.

The Directed Covalent Bond

overlap the orbital of another atom more effectively than can the *s* orbital of the same shell; *p bonds are stronger than s bonds*. It has been found on quantitative study that the energy of a bond is about proportional to the product of the magnitudes of the bond orbitals of the two atoms (in their angular dependence); an *s-p* bond would have bond energy about $\sqrt{3}$ times that of an *s-s* bond, and a *p-p* bond would be stronger than an *s-s* bond by a factor of about 3. It is convenient to call the magnitude of a bond orbital in its angular dependence the *strength* of the bond orbital, with value 1 for an *s* orbital and 1.732 for a *p* orbital.

The conclusion that *p bonds tend to be at right angles to one another* is verified to some extent by experiment (Table 4-1). In water, with the structure $: \overset{\text{H}}{\underset{..}{\text{O}}} : \text{H}$, the bond angle is 104.5°. We expect the bonds to be *p* bonds rather than *s* bonds for the following reason: A 2*s* elec-

TABLE 4-1.—OBSERVED VALUES OF BOND ANGLES IN HYDRIDES

Substance	Method[a]	Bond angle	Experimental value
H_2O	I, M	HOH	104.45° ± 0.10°
H_3N	I	HNH	107.3° ± 0.2°
H_2S	M	HSH	92.2° ± 0.1°
H_3P	M	HPH	93.3° ± 0.2°
H_2Se	M	HSeH	91.0° ± 1°
H_3As	M	HAsH	91.8° ± 0.3°
H_2Te	I	HTeH	89.5° ± 1°
H_3Sb	M	HSbH	91.3° ± 0.3°

[a] I = infrared spectroscopy, M = microwave spectroscopy.

tron of oxygen is more stable than a 2*p* electron by about 200 kcal/mole; and if the *s* orbital were used in bond formation (being then occupied effectively by only one electron) rather than for an unshared pair the molecule would be made unstable to this extent. The difference of 14.5° between the observed value of the bond angle and the expected value of 90° is probably to be attributed in the main to the partial ionic character of the O—H bonds, estimated to be 39 percent. This would give a resultant positive charge to the hydrogen atoms, which would repel one another and thus cause an increase in the bond angle. This effect is discussed in the more detailed treatment of bond angles that is given in Section 4-3. The large value for ammonia, 107°, may be attributed to the same cause.

In hydrogen sulfide, phosphine, and the hydrides of their heavier congeners, in which the bonds are nearly normal covalent bonds, the bond angles are observed to be close to 90° (Table 4-1). The values given in the table apply to the deuterium compounds as well as to the protium compounds.

With larger atoms attached to the central atom the bond angles lie between 94° and 111° (Table 4-2). The increase above 90° may be attributed to steric repulsion of these larger atoms (Sec. 4-3).

TABLE 4-2.—SOME OBSERVED VALUES OF BOND ANGLES

Substance	Method[a]	Bond angle	Experimental value
OF_2	E	FOF	$103.2° \pm 1°$
Cl_2O	E	ClOCl	$110.8° \pm 1°$
$(CH_3)_2O$	E	COC	$111°\ \pm 3°$
S_8	E	SSS	$105°\ \pm 2°$
SCl_2	E	ClSCl	$102°\ \pm 3°$
$(CH_3)_2S$	E	CSC	$105°\ \pm 3°$
P (black)	X	PPP	$99°\ \pm 1°$
			$102°\ \pm 1°$
$P(CH_3)_3$	M	CPC	$99.1° \pm 0.2°$
PF_3	E	FPF	$104°\ \pm 4°$
PCl_3	M	ClPCl	$100.0° \pm 0.3°$
PBr_3	E	BrPBr	$101.5° \pm 1.5°$
PI_3	E	IPI	$102°\ \pm 2°$

[a] The letters E, M, and X designate electron diffraction of gas molecules, microwave spectroscopy of gas molecules, and x-ray diffraction of crystals, respectively.

4-2. HYBRID BOND ORBITALS; THE TETRAHEDRAL CARBON ATOM

From the foregoing discussion it might be inferred that the quadrivalent carbon atom would form three bonds at right angles to one another and a fourth weaker bond (using the *s* orbital) in some arbitrary direction. This is, of course, not so; and, instead, it is found on quantum-mechanical study of the problem that *the four bonds of carbon are equivalent and are directed toward the corners of a regular tetrahedron*, as had been inferred from the facts of organic chemistry.

The simple theory that we use is based on the reasonable postulate given at the beginning of this chapter about the dependence of the bond-forming power (the strength) of a bond orbital on its angular distribution. From it, by the use of general quantum-mechanical principles, there is derived the whole body of results about directed valence, including not only the tetrahedral arrangement of the four single bonds of the carbon atom but also octahedral and square configurations of bonds (as well as other configurations), together with rules for the occurrence of these configurations, the strengths of the bonds, and the relation of configuration to magnetic properties.   In this way a single reasonable postulate is made the basis of a large number of the rules of stereochemistry and is found to lead to several new stereochemical results.

There are four orbitals in the valence shell of the carbon atom.   We have described these as the $2s$ and the three $2p$ orbitals, with bond strengths 1 and 1.732, respectively.   These are, however, not the orbitals used directly in bond formation by the atom.   (They are especially suited to the description of the free carbon atom; if quantum theory had been developed by the chemist rather than the spectroscopist it is probable that the tetrahedral orbitals described below would play the fundamental role in the theory, in place of the s and p orbitals.)   In general a wave function for a system can be constructed by adding together other functions, the wave function for the normal state being the one that minimizes the energy of the system.   The energy of a system of a carbon atom and four attached atoms is minimized by making the bond energies as large as possible.   It is found that a bond orbital formed by linear combination of s and p orbitals, taken with a certain ratio of numerical coefficients, has a bond strength greater than that for an s or p orbital alone, the strength of the best s-p hybrid bond orbital being as great as 2.   The angular dependence of this orbital is shown in Figure 4-2.   It is seen that the orbital is greatly concentrated in the bond direction (its axis of rotational symmetry), and it can be understood that this orbital would overlap greatly with the orbital of another atom and would form a very strong bond.   We expect this hybridization to take place in order that the bond energy may be a maximum.

A surprising result of the calculations, of great chemical significance, is the following: when it is sought to make the energy of a second bond as large as possible, by forming another hybrid orbital of maximum bond-forming power, it is found that this second best bond orbital is equivalent to the first, with strength 2, and that *its bond direction makes the tetrahedral angle 109°28' with that of the first*.   Moreover, a third and a fourth equivalent orbital can be constructed, the four being directed toward the corners of a regular tetrahedron; but then no more orbitals are left in the valence shell.   It is convenient to call these four best s-p bond orbitals *tetrahedral orbitals*.

The postulate of the tetrahedral carbon atom in classical stereochemistry requires that the atom have a configuration that is tetrahedral but is not necessarily that of a regular tetrahedron; so long as the four bonds have a general tetrahedral orientation the phenomenon of optical activity is accounted for. There is no need for the R_1—C—R_2 bond angle in $CR_1R_2R_3R_4$ to be near 109°28′; it might be 150° or more. The result of the bond orbital treatment described above requires, however, that the carbon bond angles be close to the tetrahedral angle, since change from this value is associated with loss in bond strength of the carbon orbitals and hence with decrease in stability of the system. It is of great interest that in hundreds of molecules containing a carbon

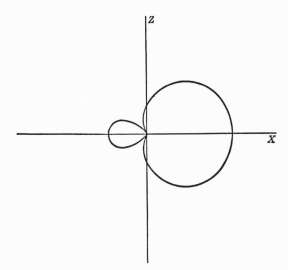

Fig. 4-2.—The angular dependence of a tetrahedral orbital with bond direction along the x axis.

atom attached by four single bonds to atoms of different kinds experimental values of bond angles have been determined that almost without exception lie within 2° of the value 109°28′ corresponding to tetrahedral orbitals. A few of these values are given in Table 4-3.

An interesting feature of these values is the surprisingly large value of the HCH angle. With this exception, the bond angles clearly reflect the differences in the van der Waals radii of the ligands. For example, the XCX values (X = halogen) for the trihalogenomethanes HCF_3, $HCCl_3$, $HCBr_3$, and HCI_3 are 108.8°, 110.4°, 110.8°, and 113.0°, respectively; the angle increases with increase in size of the halogen atom, as would be expected because of the van der Waals repulsion, which is greater for two halogen atoms than for a halogen atom and a hydrogen atom. However, although the hydrogen atom is smaller than any halogen atom, the HCH angle is found in general to be larger than the HCX angles; for the six methyl and methylene halogenides in the table the average value of the HCH angle is 111.5° and that of the HCX angles is 108.4°. This difference can be accounted for as the result of the difference in size of the atoms, when the difference in C—X and C—H bond lengths is also taken into consideration.

A still more surprising result about the significance of the concept of

TABLE 4-3.—OBSERVED VALUES OF BOND ANGLES FOR QUADRICOVALENT ATOMS

Substance	Method[a]	Bond angle	Experimental value
CH_3Cl	M	HCH	110.5° ± 0.5°
CH_2Cl_2	M	HCH	112.0° ± 0.3°
		ClCCl	111.8° ± 0.3°
$CHCl_3$	M	ClCCl	110.4° ± 1°
CH_3Br	M	HCH	111.2° ± 0.5°
$CHBr_3$	M	BrCBr	110.8° ± 0.3°
CH_3I	M	HCH	111.4° ± 0.1°
CHI_3	E	ICI	113.0° ± 1°
CH_2F_2	M	FCF	108.3° ± 0.1°
		HCH	111.9° ± 0.4°
CHF_3	M	FCF	108.8° ± 0.8°
	E	FCF	108.5° ± 0.5°
CH_2ClF	M	ClCF	110.0° ± 0.1°
		HCCl	109.1° ± 0.2°
		HCH	111.9° ± 0.5°

[a] The letters E, M, and X designate electron diffraction, microwave spectroscopy, and x-ray diffraction, respectively.

the carbon atom as a regular tetrahedron is provided by the methylethylenes. The picture of the carbon-carbon double bond as involving the sharing of an edge by two regular tetrahedra leads to the tetrahedral value 125°16′ for the single-bond:double-bond angle. The electron-diffraction value for this angle in both isobutene and tetramethylethylene is 124°20′ ± 1°, and the microwave value for phosgene, $Cl_2C{=}O$, is 124.3°.

Derivation of Results about Tetrahedral Orbitals.—The results about tetrahedral bond orbitals described above are derived in the following way. We assume that the radial parts of the wave functions ψ_s and ψ_{p_x}, ψ_{p_y}, ψ_{p_z} are so closely similar that their differences can be neglected. The angular parts are

$$\left.\begin{array}{l} s = 1 \\ p_x = \sqrt{3}\,\sin\theta\,\cos\phi \\ p_y = \sqrt{3}\,\sin\theta\,\sin\phi \\ p_z = \sqrt{3}\,\cos\theta \end{array}\right\} \qquad (4\text{-}1)$$

θ and ϕ being the angles used in spherical polar coordinates. These functions are *normalized to* 4π, the integral

$$\int_0^{2\pi}\int_0^\pi f^2 \sin\theta\,d\theta\,d\phi$$

of the square of the function taken over the surface of a sphere having the value 4π. The functions are *mutually orthogonal*, the integral of the product of any two of them (sp_z, say) over the surface of a sphere being zero.

Now we ask whether a new function

$$f = as + bp_x + cp_y + dp_z \qquad (4\text{-}2)$$

normalized to 4π (this requiring that $a^2 + b^2 + c^2 + d^2 = 1$) can be formed which has a larger bond strength than 1.732, and, if so, what function of this type has the maximum bond strength. The direction of the bond is immaterial; let us choose the z axis. It is easily shown that p_x and p_y do not increase the strength of a bond in this direction, but decrease it, so they are ignored, the function thus assuming the form

$$f_1 = as + \sqrt{1 - a^2}\,p_z \qquad (4\text{-}3)$$

in which d is replaced by $\sqrt{1 - a^2}$ for normalization. The value of this in the bond direction $\theta = 0$ is, on substituting the expressions for s and p_z,

$$f_1(\theta = 0) = a + \sqrt{3(1 - a^2)}$$

This is made a maximum by differentiating with respect to a, equating to zero, and solving, the value $a = \frac{1}{2}$ being obtained. Hence the best bond orbital in the z direction is

$$f_1 = \frac{1}{2}s + \frac{\sqrt{3}}{2}p_z = \frac{1}{2} + \frac{3}{2}\cos\theta \qquad (4\text{-}4)$$

This orbital has the form shown in Figure 4-2. Its strength is seen to be 2 by placing $\theta = 0$, $\cos\theta = 1$.

We now consider the function

$$f_2 = as + bp_z + dp_z$$

which is orthogonal to f_1, satisfying the requirement

$$\int_0^{2\pi} \int_0^\pi f_1 f_2 \sin\theta d\theta d\phi = 0,$$

and which has the maximum value possible in some direction. (This direction will lie in the xz plane; i.e., $\phi = 0$, since p_y has been left out.) It is found on solving the problem that the function is

$$f_2 = \frac{1}{2}s + \frac{\sqrt{2}}{\sqrt{3}}p_x - \frac{1}{2\sqrt{3}}p_z \tag{4-5}$$

This function is seen on examination to be identical with f_1 except that it is rotated through $109°28'$ from f_1. In the same way two more functions can be constructed, each identical with f_1 except for orientation.

An equivalent set of tetrahedral bond orbitals, differing from these only in orientation, is

$$t_{111} = \tfrac{1}{2}(s + p_x + p_y + p_z)$$
$$t_{1\overline{1}\overline{1}} = \tfrac{1}{2}(s + p_x - p_y - p_z)$$
$$t_{\overline{1}1\overline{1}} = \tfrac{1}{2}(s - p_x + p_y - p_z)$$
$$t_{\overline{1}\overline{1}1} = \tfrac{1}{2}(s - p_x - p_y + p_z)$$

The strength of an s-p hybrid orbital increases with increase in the amount of p involved from 1 (pure s) to a maximum value of 2 (tetrahedral orbital) and then decreases to 1.732 (pure p), in the way shown by the dashed curves in Figure 4-3, in which the square of the bond strength (that is, the product of the strengths of equivalent orbitals of two atoms forming a bond) is shown as a function of the nature of the orbitals. That the strength of the orbital is a measure of its bond-forming power is shown by the approximation of these curves to the full curves, which represent the calculated energy of a one-electron bond as a function of the nature of the bond orbitals.

4-3. THE EFFECT OF AN UNSHARED PAIR ON HYBRIDIZATION

Since tetrahedral orbitals form stronger bonds than other s-p orbitals it might be thought that hybridization to tetrahedral orbitals would always occur in bond formation. The tendency to use the best bond orbitals is, however, resisted in the case of atoms with an unshared pair (or more than one) by the tendency to keep the unshared pair in the *s* orbital, which is more stable than the *p* orbitals. In OF_2, for example, the use of tetrahedral orbitals in bond formation would require that half of the *s* orbital (which is divided equally among the four tetrahedral

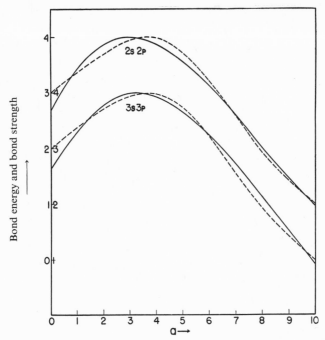

FIG. 4-3.—Square of bond strength (dashed curves) and calculated bond-energy values (full curves) for hybrid *sp* orbitals varying from pure *p* orbitals ($a = 0$, left) to pure *s* orbitals ($a = 10$, right). The upper pair of curves are for *L* orbitals (2*s* and 2*p*), and the lower, with shifted vertical scale, for *M* orbitals (3*s* and 3*p*).

orbitals) be used for shared pairs and only half for unshared pairs. Since a shared pair counts as only one electron for each atom, this would involve the loss of one-quarter of the extra stability due to a pair of *s* electrons, and the atom will strive to prevent this. On the other hand, the bonds will strive to be as strong as possible. In consequence a compromise is reached such as to minimize the energy for the molecule as a whole; the bond orbitals will have a small amount of *s* character and be intermediate between *p* bonds and tetrahedral bonds, with the unshared pair utilizing most of the *s* orbital. The bond strengths of these bonds will be between 1,732 and 2, and the angles between the bond directions will be increased somewhat from the *p*-bond value 90° toward the tetrahedral value 109°28'.

4-4. ORBITALS FOR INCOMPLETE *s-p* SHELLS

In boron trimethyl, $B(CH_3)_3$, only three of the four orbitals of the valence shell are used. If the best bond orbitals were utilized the C—B—C bond angles would be near 109°28'. However, the molecule obtains added stability by using the *s* orbital as completely as possible, and this tends to cause the *s* orbital to be divided among three bond orbitals, which are found by the simple theoretical treatment to be coplanar and to make angles of 120° with one another.* The boron trimethyl molecule is planar, with 120° angles, indicating that the bond orbitals are those obtained by dividing the *s* orbital among three.

The formation of a fourth bond by boron would strengthen the bonds (all bond orbitals becoming tetrahedral) and stabilize the molecule; we can thus understand the ability of boron trimethyl to add ammonia to

give the compound
$$H_3C-B-N-H$$
with H_3C and H above, H_3C and H below. The boron halogenides, whose

structures are discussed in Section 9-5, similarly add molecules containing unshared pairs to give products such as $Cl-B-N\equiv C-CH_3$, with Cl above and Cl below,

formed from boron trichloride and methyl cyanide. The electric dipole moment of ammonia-borane, H_3BNH_3, is 4.9 D (measured in dioxane solution); this value is a reasonable one for the structure

$$H-\overset{-}{B}-\overset{+}{N}-H.$$

with H, H above and H, H below.

* The three bond orbitals (taken in the *xy* plane) are
$$\frac{1}{\sqrt{3}}s + \frac{\sqrt{2}}{\sqrt{3}}p_x, \quad \frac{1}{\sqrt{3}}s - \frac{1}{\sqrt{6}}p_x + \frac{1}{\sqrt{2}}p_y, \text{ and } \frac{1}{\sqrt{3}}s - \frac{1}{\sqrt{6}}p_x - \frac{1}{\sqrt{2}}p_y.$$
Their bond strength is 1.991, only slightly less than that of tetrahedral orbitals.

In a molecule such as mercury dimethyl the two bond orbitals would be expected to use all the *s* orbital between them.*   The simple treatment shows that the two bonds would then be opposed.   This is substantiated by the observation of a linear configuration for gas molecules of $HgCl_2$, $HgBr_2$, HgI_2, CH_3HgCl, CH_3HgBr, and $Hg(CH_3)_2$, and also of a linear configuration of the molecules Hg_2Cl_2, Hg_2Br_2, and Hg_2I_2 (with electronic structures $: \ddot{X}—Hg—Hg—\ddot{X} :$) in crystals.   A similar configuration

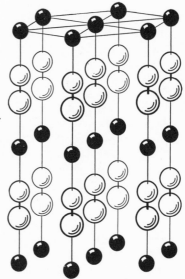

FIG. 4-4.—The arrangement of atoms of gold (small circles), carbon, and nitrogen in the hexagonal crystal AuCN.

is expected for bicovalent complexes of univalent copper, silver, and gold. It has been verified for the $[AuCl_2]^-$ ion and the $[Ag(CN_2)]^-$ ion, and also for AuCN crystal (Fig. 4-4).   In the AuCN crystal there are covalent bonds between both the nitrogen atom and the carbon atom of the cyanide group and the gold atom, so as to form very long —Au—C≡N—Au —C≡N—Au—⋯ molecules, which are packed in a hexagonal array.

4-5. CONCENTRATION OF BOND ORBITALS

The description of the bond orbitals of the carbon atom as sp^3 tetrahedral hybrid orbitals is satisfactory in many respects, but it can be im-

---

* The two corresponding bond orbitals (with bond directions taken along the *x* axis) are

$$\frac{1}{\sqrt{2}}(s + p_x) \quad \text{and} \quad \frac{1}{\sqrt{2}}(s - p_x);$$ their bond strength is 1.932.

proved. One improvement is that of concentrating the orbitals more closely about the bond direction by the introduction of some d and f character.

Concentration of bond orbitals was recognized in the bond orbitals of the hydrogen atoms in H_2^+ and H_2 as evaluated by minimizing the energy (Secs. 1-4 and 1-5). It was found that the best $1s$ orbital is not that for the free hydrogen atom; instead, the orbitals are shrunk toward the hydrogen nuclei, corresponding to effective nuclear charges 1.23 for H_2^+ and 1.17 for H_2. Moreover, much improvement is obtained by adding some $2p$ orbital (2 percent for H_2^+ and 1 percent for H_2), which further concentrates the orbital into the region of low potential energy for the electron, between the two nuclei.

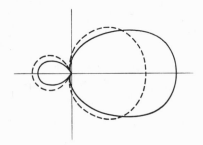

Fig. 4-5.—Tetrahedral bond orbital with 4 percent d character and 2 percent f.

We may accordingly expect that the bond orbitals of the carbon atom will be found on careful examination to be hybrids with some d and f character in addition to their principal sp^3 character. A simple calculation leads to about 4 percent d character and 2 percent f character. As seen from Figure 4-5, the orbital is significantly more concentrated in the bond direction than the sp^3 orbital (dashed curve). Its strength, 2.76, is 38 percent greater than that of an sp^3 orbital.

A bond formed by two such orbitals, with energy proportional to S^2, has bond energy nearly double (1.90 times) that of a bond formed by two sp^3 orbitals. The d and f character may have significant effect on many properties of bonds, such as bond angles.

4-6. RESTRICTED ROTATION ABOUT SINGLE BONDS

The single-bond orbitals discussed above are cylindrically symmetrical about the bond direction, and hence the energy of a molecule, insofar as it is determined by the bond orbital, should be independent of the orientation of the two parts of a molecule about the axis of a single bond. Other interactions, also between the two parts of a molecule such as ethane, might be expected not to depend much on this orientation, so that the molecule might show essentially free rotation about the single bond. This is in agreement with chemical experience—no case of isomerism corresponding to restriction of rotation about a pure single bond has been reported.

It has been found, however, that the forces restricting rotation about single bonds, though not large enough to permit the isolation of isomers, are large enough to be of significance in structural chemistry, as, for example, in the calculation of entropy values from structural information. It was shown by the American chemists J. D. Kemp and K. S. Pitzer in 1937 that the value of the entropy of ethane indicates very strongly that as the two methyl groups are rotated about the single carbon-carbon bond relative to one another the potential energy of the molecule changes by

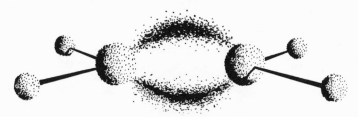

Fig. 4-6.—A representation of the ethylene molecule with the double bond shown as two bent single bonds.

about 3 kcal/mole, the potential function having three maxima and three minima in a complete rotation, corresponding to the trigonal symmetry of the methyl groups. Values close to 3 kcal/mole have been reported also for several other alkanes and substituted alkanes; for example, 3.30 for CH_3CH_2F and 3.18 for CH_3CHF_2. The minima of the potential

energy function correspond to the staggered configuration,

and the maxima to the eclipsed configuration,

4-7. ORBITALS AND BOND ANGLES FOR MULTIPLE BONDS

For a double bond, as in ethylene, two orbitals of each of the two bonded atoms are required. There are two alternative ways in which these orbitals have usually been described. In the first the two orbitals for each atom have been assumed to be essentially tetrahedral orbitals, extending toward two corners of a tetrahedron defining an edge shared with another tetrahedron representing the other atom with which the double bond is formed.   This leads to a description of the double bond, as involving two bent single bonds, that is closely similar to the one used by organic chemists for many decades (Fig. 4-6).   The nineteenth-century German chemist Baeyer, for example, explained the instability of the carbon-carbon double bond relative to two single bonds as resulting from the strain energy of bending the two bonds that constitute the double bond.

The other description of the double bond is in terms of a σ bond, formed by a σ orbital for each atom directed toward the other atom, and a π bond, formed by a π orbital (p_z orbital, with the nuclei lying in the xy plane) for each atom, as shown in Figure 4-7.

When the quantum mechanical equations are examined it is found that the two descriptions of the double bond are identical in the molecular-orbital treatment based on s-p hybrids.   They are not identical in the

FIG. 4-7.—A representation of the ethylene molecule with
the double bond shown as a sigma bond and a pi bond.

valence-bond treatment, especially when the bond orbitals are concentrated about their bond directions by the assumption of d and f character, as described in Section 4-5.   In the case of the bent-bond orbitals the d and f character increases the electron density in two regions, one on each side of the internuclear axis (near the tetrahedron corners determining the shared edge).   In the case of the σ-π description the d and f character increases the electron density in three regions, one on the internuclear axis and one on either side of it.   The greater separation of the electrons for the bent-bond structure with concentrated bond orbitals than for the σ-π structure may stabilize the bent-bond structure enough to make it the better approximation to use in discussing multiple bonds in general.   In addition, it has the advantage of being the more closely related to single bonds, whose properties are well known.

The bent-bond structure accounts in a simple way for some of the properties of the double bond and the triple bond, such as the bond lengths.   The carbon-carbon single-bond, double-bond, and triple-bond lengths are 1.54, 1.33, and 1.20 Å, respectively.   If the multiple bonds are represented by arcs with constant curvature, with length 1.54 Å and beginning in the tetrahedral directions, the calculated lengths are 1.32 Å for the double bond and 1.18 Å for the triple bond, in approximate agreement with the experimental values.   There is no similar way of discussing bond lengths for the σ-π structure.

Inasmuch as the tetrahedral bond orbitals are individually the best bond orbitals by the bond-strength criterion, the description of the carbon atom as having its bonds directed toward the corners of a regular tetrahedron would be expected to apply to a carbon atom forming two single bonds and one double bond as well as to one forming four single bonds. Hence for the bent-bond structure the value 125.27° is predicted between a single bond and a double bond of a carbon atom.   For the σ-π structure

TABLE 4-4.—EXPERIMENTAL VALUES OF SINGLE-BOND:
DOUBLE-BOND ANGLE FOR QUADRICOVALENT ATOMS

Compound	Method[a]	Angle	Value
Propylene	M	C—C=C	124.75° ± 0.3°
$F_2C=CH_2$	M	F—C=C	125.2° ± 0.2°
CCl_2O	M	Cl—C=C	124.3° ± 0.1°
$Cl_2C=CH_2$	M	Cl—C=O	123.2° ± 0.5°
CH_3CHO	M	C—C=O	123.9° ± 0.3°
Propynal, HCCCHO	M	C—C=O	123.8° ± 0.2°
HCOOH	M	O—C=O	124.5° ± 0.5°
Glycine	X	O—C=O	125.5° ± 0.3°
Alanine	X	O—C=O	125.6° ± 0.5°

[a] M denotes microwave spectroscopy of gas molecules and X denotes x-ray diffraction of crystals.

a smaller value might be predicted; for example, the orbitals for the σ bond and the two single bonds might be the trigonal orbitals described in Section 4-4, which give the value 120°.   Values close to 125.27° have been found by experiment for many molecules; some of the most reliable of the experimental values are given in Table 4-4.

Ethylene is an exception; the angle C=C—H is reported as 122.0° by electron diffraction and 121.3° by infrared spectroscopy; it is thus closer to the value corresponding to trigonal quantization than to that corresponding to tetrahedral quantization.   The low value, corresponding to a high value of the angle HCH (116°, 117.4°), may be the result of large van der Waals repulsion of the hydrogen atoms (Sec. 7-12).   A similar behavior is shown by formaldehyde, for which the H—C=O angle is 119.2° ± 1.0°.   This very low value for formaldehyde may be associated with the large amount of ionic character (totaling about 44 percent) of the carbon-oxygen bond.

The angle —N̈= in pyrimidines is about 11° less than the angle —C=.

Also, in *s*-triazine, $C_3N_3H_3$, which is a planar molecule with trigonal symmetry, the two angles have the values $113.2° \pm 0.4°$ and $126.8° \pm 0.4°$, respectively, with difference $-13.6°$, and in *s*-tetrazine, $C_2N_4H_2$, they have the values $115.9° \pm 0.7°$ and $127.4° \pm 0.7°$, respectively, with difference $-11.5°$. (In all of these planar six-membered rings the bond angles have average value 120°, and hence it is the difference that is significant.) We conclude that the —N= angle is about 12° less than the —C= angle (125.27°), and hence that its normal value is 113°.

The explanation of the deviation of the value from 125.27° (the tetrahedral value) is that the bond orbitals of the tricovalent nitrogen atom are not tetrahedral orbitals, but are orbitals with only about 5 percent of *s* character, plus small amounts of *d* and *f* character (Secs. 4-3 and 4-5). For these orbitals a value for the single-bond:double-bond angle intermediate between the values 90° for pure *p* orbitals and 125.27° for tetrahedral orbitals would be expected.

4-8. PARTIAL IONIC CHARACTER OF MULTIPLE BONDS

The expectation from the bent-bond description of multiple bonds is that each of the bent single bonds of the multiple bond would have the same amount of partial ionic character as an unstrained single bond between the two atoms. This expectation is borne out reasonably well by experiment. For example, for formaldehyde, H_2CO, the H—C bond is expected from the electronegativity difference of the atoms to have 4 percent ionic character and each of the C—O bonds to have 22 percent. The electric dipole moment is then calculated (H—C bond length 1.09 Å, C=O 1.23 Å, angles 120°) to be 2.81 D, somewhat larger than the experimental value, 2.27 D. If the reasonable assumption is made that for each C—O single bond the ionic-covalent ratio is 22/78 but that the structure with both bonds ionic makes no contribution, the calculated value of the moment is 2.34 D, in good agreement with experiment. Similar agreement is found also for other molecules; it is necessary, however, to be alert for the possibility of significant contribution by resonance structures, as discussed in later chapters of this book.

EXERCISES

4-1.—Verify the statement that the function given in Equation 4-4 is the best *sp* hybrid bond orbital by carrying out the processes of differentiating, equating to zero, and solving for a, as outlined in the text.

4-2.—Verify the statements that f_2, as given in Equation 4-5, is orthogonal to f_1 (Eq. 4-4), and that it is the best *sp* hybrid bond orbital (in the xz plane) orthogonal to f_1.

4-3.—Assign electronic structures to SCl_2, PCl_3, and $SiCl_4$. What are the orbitals used for bond formation and those used for unshared pairs in the outer electron shells of the atoms? What values would you expect for the bond angles?

4-4.—Would you expect boron trichloride, BCl_3, to have a pyramidal structure or a planar structure? Nitrogen trichloride, NCl_3? Assign bond orbitals to boron and nitrogen in these molecules.

4-5.—(a) What electronic structure and spatial configuration would you predict for diboron tetrachloride? (b) for dicarbon tetrachloride? Discuss the differences between the two molecules. (Ans. (a) Nonplanar, angle Cl—B—Cl 120°; (b) planar, angle Cl—C—Cl 113°.)

4-6.—Discuss the electronic structure of the $CdCl_2$ gas molecule. What is the nature of the cadmium bond orbitals? What is the value of the Cl—Cd—Cl bond angle?

4-7.—The molecule As_4S_4, in the mineral realgar and in the gas phase, has been assigned a normal covalent structure (covalence 3 for As, 2 for S). What electronic structure would you suggest for the molecule?

4-8.—The normal state of the gas molecule C_2 is diamagnetic (no unpaired electrons). What electronic structure would you assign to it? Discuss the use of the orbitals for bonds and for occupancy by unshared pairs.

4-9.—The gas molecule C_3 has a symmetrical linear configuration. Discuss its electronic structure.

4-10.—The ozone molecule, O_3, has a bent configuration, with bond angle 116.8°. Discuss its electronic structure.

CHAPTER 5

Complex Bond Orbitals; The Magnetic Criterion for Bond Type

THE hybrid bond orbitals discussed in the preceding chapter have been described as having only a small amount of d and f character. The bonds in many molecules and complex ions, especially those involving atoms of the transition elements, can be discussed in a simple way in terms of hybrid orbitals with a large amount of d character (and, in a few cases, f character). These bonds and a magnetic criterion for bond type are discussed in the following sections.

5-1. BONDS INVOLVING d ORBITALS

The first-row atoms can form no more than four stable bond orbitals. For the second-row atoms the s and p orbitals of the M shell are much more stable than the d orbitals, and in general contribute preponderantly to the bond orbitals, but the promotion energy for the d orbitals (which also are in the M shell) is small enough to permit these orbitals to take a larger part in bond formation than for the first row atoms.

The existence of compounds such as PF_5, PF_3Cl_2, PCl_5, $[PF_6]^-$, and SF_6 suggests that one or two $3d$ orbitals are here being used together with the $3s$ orbital and the three $3p$ orbitals (all hybridized to bond orbitals) for bond formation. It seems probable, however, that for fluo-

rides the completely covalent structures such as

$$\begin{matrix} F & & F \\ & \diagdown \diagup & \\ F\!-\!P & & \\ & \diagup \diagdown & \\ F & & F \end{matrix}$$

are of little

significance, and that the molecules instead resonate mainly among

$$\begin{array}{c} :\overset{\cdots}{\underset{\cdots}{F}}:^{-} \quad F \\ \diagup \end{array}$$

structures such as $\begin{array}{c} F\!-\!P^{+} \\ \diagup \quad \diagdown \\ F \quad\;\; F \end{array}$, and so on, involving at most four cova-

lent bonds. (The four covalent bonds resonate among the five positions, making all bonds in the molecule nearly equivalent in bond type.)

Heavier atoms such as tin form complexes $[MX_6]^{--}$ with chlorine, bromine, and even iodine; it is likely that some use is made of the d orbitals of the valence shell of the central atom in these complexes.

It is, however, the d orbitals of the shell with total quantum number one less than that of the valence shell that are of great significance for bond formation. In the transition elements the inner d orbitals have about the same energy as the s and p orbitals of the valence shell; and if they are not completely occupied by unshared electron pairs they play a very important part in bond formation. For the hexamminocobaltic ion, for example, structures such as

$$\begin{bmatrix} H_3N & \diagdown & \diagup & NH_3 \\ H_3N\!-\!Co\!-\!NH_3 \\ \diagup & & \diagdown \\ H_3N & & NH_3 \end{bmatrix}^{+++}$$

are written. It is seen on counting electrons that the cobalt atom (with atomic number 27) holds 24 unshared electrons in addition to the six pairs shared with nitrogen. The number of available orbitals is such that six of the stable orbitals (of the krypton shell) can be used for bond formation with enough remaining for the unshared pairs. This is seen from the following diagram:

The 24 unshared electrons occupy the orbitals $1s$, $2s$, three $2p$, $3s$, three $3p$, and three of the $3d$ orbitals, leaving two $3d$ orbitals, the $4s$ orbital, and the three $4p$ orbitals available for use as bond orbitals.

For the atoms of the first transition group (the iron group) there is little difference in energy of the $3d$ orbitals and the $4s$ and $4p$ orbitals, so that the question as to how these orbitals can be combined to form good bond orbitals becomes an interesting one. Similarly, the orbitals $4d$, $5s$, and

$5p$ have about the same energy for atoms of the palladium group, and $5d$, $6s$, and $6p$ for atoms of the platinum group. The following discussion of dsp hybridization applies to all three transition groups.

5-2. OCTAHEDRAL BOND ORBITALS

It is found on analysis of the problem that when only two d orbitals are available for combination with the s and p orbitals six equivalent bond orbitals of strength 2.923 (nearly as great as the maximum 3 for the best spd hybrid) can be formed, and that these six orbitals have their bond directions toward the corners of a regular octahedron. We accordingly conclude that complexes such as $[Co(NH_3)_6]^{+++}$, $[PdCl_6]^{--}$, and $[PtCl_6]^{--}$ should be octahedral in configuration. This conclusion is of course identical with the postulate made in 1893 by the Swiss chemist A. Werner to account for isomerism in complexes with different substituent groups, and verified also by the x-ray examination of $Co(NH_3)_6I_3$, $(NH_4)_2PdCl_6$, $(NH_4)_2PtCl_6$, and other crystals (see Fig. 5-1).

A polar graph of an octahedral bond orbital is shown in Figure 5-2, from which its great concentration in the bond direction, leading to large overlapping and the formation of a very strong bond, can be seen.

It is interesting to note that these considerations lead to an explanation of the difference in stability of cobalt(II) and cobalt(III) as compared with iron(II) and iron(III) in covalent octahedral complexes. The formation of covalent complexes does not change the equilibrium between bipositive and tripositive iron very much, as is seen from the values of the oxidation-reduction potentials, whereas a great change is produced in the equilibrium between bipositive and tripositive cobalt:

$$\text{Potential}$$

$$Fe^{++} = Fe^{+++} + e^-, \qquad -0.77 \text{ v.}$$
$$[Fe(CN)_6]^{----} = [Fe(CN)_6]^{---} + e^-, \qquad -0.36 \text{ v.} \qquad \left. \right\} -0.41 \text{ v.}$$

$$Co^{++} = Co^{+++} + e^-, \qquad -1.84 \text{ v.}$$
$$[Co(CN)_6]^{----} = [Co(CN)_6]^{---} + e^-, \qquad +0.83 \text{ v.} \qquad \left. \right\} -2.67 \text{ v.}$$

The effect is so pronounced that covalent compounds of cobalt(II) can decompose water with liberation of hydrogen, whereas the cobalt(III) ion decomposes water with liberation of oxygen, being one of the most powerful oxidizing agents known. The explanation is contained in Figure 5-3. In the ions Co^{++}, Co^{+++}, Fe^{++}, and Fe^{+++} there is room for all unshared electrons in the $3d$ orbitals and inner orbitals. When

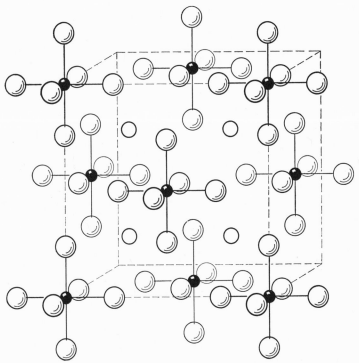

Fig. 5-1.—The structure of the cubic crystal K_2PtCl_6. Octahedral complexes $PtCl_6$ have their centers at the corners and the centers of the faces of the cubic unit of structure. The potassium ions are at positions $\frac{1}{4}\frac{1}{4}\frac{1}{4}$, etc.; that is, they are at the centers of the eight small cubes with edges one-half as great as those of the large cube. Only four of the eight potassium ions in the cube are represented in the drawing. The chlorine atoms have coordinates $u00$, $0u0$, $00u$, etc., in which u is a parameter determining the Pt—Cl bond length. Its value can be determined by analysis of the x-ray photographs of the crystal. The value of the parameter for most substances of this class is approximately 0.25. For this value of the parameter the chlorine atoms and potassium ions occupy the positions corresponding to cubic closest packing of spheres (Sec. 11-5).

octahedral bonds are formed in the covalent complexes, with use of two of the $3d$ orbitals, only three $3d$ orbitals are left for occupancy by unshared electrons. These are enough for bipositive and tripositive iron and for tripositive cobalt, but they can hold only six of the seven outer unshared electrons of bipositive cobalt. The seventh electron must accordingly occupy an outer unstable orbital, causing the complex to be unstable.

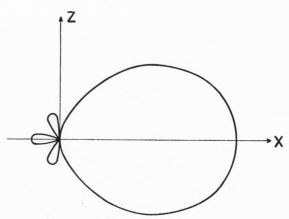

Fig. 5-2.—The angular dependence of an octahedral d^2sp^3 bond orbital with bond direction along the x axis.

The five d orbitals, in their angular dependence, are

$$
\left.
\begin{aligned}
d_{z^2} &= \sqrt{5/4}(3\cos^2\theta - 1) \\
d_{yz} &= \sqrt{15}\sin\theta\cos\theta\cos\phi \\
d_{xz} &= \sqrt{15}\sin\theta\cos\theta\sin\phi \\
d_{xy} &= \sqrt{15/4}\sin^2\theta\sin 2\phi \\
d_{x^2+y^2} &= \sqrt{15/4}\sin^2\theta\cos 2\phi
\end{aligned}
\right\}
\tag{5-1}
$$

The set of six equivalent octahedral orbitals formed from two d orbitals, the s orbital, and the three p orbitals is

$$
\left.
\begin{aligned}
\psi_1 &= \frac{1}{\sqrt{6}}s + \frac{1}{\sqrt{2}}p_z + \frac{1}{\sqrt{3}}d_{z^2} \\
\psi_2 &= \frac{1}{\sqrt{6}}s - \frac{1}{\sqrt{2}}p_z + \frac{1}{\sqrt{3}}d_{z^2} \\
\psi_3 &= \frac{1}{\sqrt{6}}s + \frac{1}{\sqrt{2}}p_x + \frac{1}{\sqrt{12}}d_{z^2} + \frac{1}{2}d_{x^2+y^2} \\
\psi_4 &= \frac{1}{\sqrt{6}}s - \frac{1}{\sqrt{2}}p_x + \frac{1}{\sqrt{12}}d_{z^2} + \frac{1}{2}d_{x^2+y^2} \\
\psi_5 &= \frac{1}{\sqrt{6}}s + \frac{1}{\sqrt{2}}p_y + \frac{1}{\sqrt{12}}d_{z^2} - \frac{1}{2}d_{x^2+y^2} \\
\psi_6 &= \frac{1}{\sqrt{6}}s - \frac{1}{\sqrt{2}}p_y + \frac{1}{\sqrt{12}}d_{z^2} - \frac{1}{2}d_{x^2+y^2}
\end{aligned}
\right\}
\tag{5-2}
$$

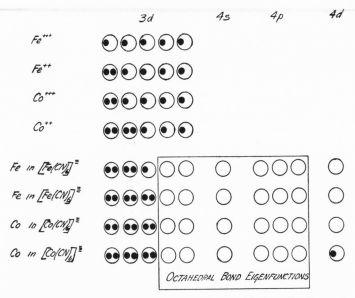

FIG. 5-3.—Occupancy of orbitals by electrons in hypoligating and hyperligating octahedral complexes of bipositive and tripositive iron and cobalt.

The orbital d_{z^2} has the angular dependence shown in Figure 5-4. It is cylindrically symmetrical about the z axis and consists of two positive lobes extending in the directions $+z$ and $-z$ and a negative belt about the xy plane. The nodal zones are at 54°44′ and 125°16′ with the z direction. The strength of the orbital is 2.236, which is $\sqrt{5}$.

The four other d orbitals described in Equation 5-1 differ in shape from d_{z^2}. The four are equivalent except for spatial orientation. The angular dependence of one of them (d_{xz}) is shown in Figure 5-5. It has four equivalent lobes, with extrema in four directions in the xz plane, at angles 90° and 180° with one another. The strength (value in these directions) is 1.936. The five d orbitals (unlike the three p orbitals) are therefore not equivalent in shape. Three (but not more) equivalent to d_{z^2} can be formed by linear combination, their axes of cylindrical symmetry making the nodal angles 54°44′ or 125°16′. Orbitals intermediate between d_{z^2} and $d_{x^2+y^2}$ can be obtained by linear combination (for example, $\frac{2}{3}\sqrt{2}d_{z^2} + \frac{1}{3}d_{x^2+y^2}$ has values 2.108 along $\pm z$, -0.409 along $\pm x$, and -1.699 along $\pm y$).

The best bond orbital that can be obtained by *spd* hybridization (for the method of determining the coefficients see Sec. 4-2) has the form

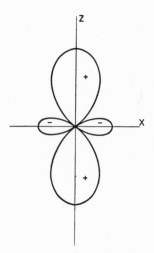

FIG. 5-4.—The angular dependence of the d_{z^2} orbital.

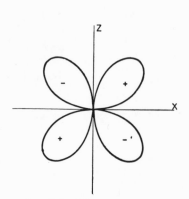

FIG. 5-5.—The angular dependence of the d_{xz} orbital.

$$\frac{1}{3}s + \frac{1}{\sqrt{3}}p_z + \frac{\sqrt{5}}{3}d_{z^2} \tag{5-3}$$

This orbital, as written above, has its maximum (strength 3.000) along z. Its nodal zones are at 73°9′ and 133°37′ with the bond direction. Three of these best bond orbitals (mutually orthogonal) can be constructed; their bond directions make the angles 73°9′ or 133°37′ with one another, with each of the three bond angles having independent choice between these two values (except that three bonds at 133°37′ cannot be formed).

The magnetic moment of octahedral complexes can often be used to distinguish between those in which there are d^2sp^3 octahedral bonds and those with a different electronic structure, in the way that will be discussed in Section 5-5. An alternative method of treatment of these complexes is mentioned in Section 5-8.

5-3. SQUARE BOND ORBITALS

In a covalent complex of bivalent nickel such as the nickel cyanide ion $[Ni(CN)_4]^{--}$ the 26 inner electrons of the nickel atom can be placed in pairs in the $1s$, $2s$, three $2p$, $3s$, three $3p$, and four of the $3d$ orbitals. This leaves available for use in bond formation the fifth $3d$ orbital as well as the $4s$ and three $4p$ orbitals. It is found on hybridizing these orbitals that four strong bond orbitals directed to the corners of a square can be formed.   The four orbitals (written with the bonds directed along $+x, -x, +y,$ and $-y$) are

$$
\left.
\begin{aligned}
\psi_1 &= \frac{1}{2}s + \frac{1}{\sqrt{2}}p_x + \frac{1}{2}d_{xy} \\[4pt]
\psi_2 &= \frac{1}{2}s - \frac{1}{\sqrt{2}}p_x + \frac{1}{2}d_{xy} \\[4pt]
\psi_3 &= \frac{1}{2}s + \frac{1}{\sqrt{2}}p_y - \frac{1}{2}d_{xy} \\[4pt]
\psi_4 &= \frac{1}{2}s - \frac{1}{\sqrt{2}}p_y - \frac{1}{2}d_{xy}
\end{aligned}
\right\}
\tag{5-4}
$$

They have the bond strength 2.694, much greater than that of sp^3 tetrahedral orbitals (2.000).   These four square orbitals are formed with use of only two of the $4p$ orbitals; the other p orbital might accordingly also be used by the nickel atom to form another (rather weak) bond.

From this argument these nickel complexes are expected to have a square planar configuration, rather than the tetrahedral configuration usually assumed for four groups about a central atom.   In 1931, when the argument was first presented, this configuration had not been recognized for any complexes of nickel.   The foregoing discussion is also applicable to the coordination complexes of palladium(II) and platinum(II), with suitable change in the total quantum numbers of the atomic orbitals.   For these complexes the square configuration had been deduced many years ago by Werner from the observed existence of isomers and had been later verified by the x-ray investigation of crystals of the chloropalladites and chloroplatinites (Fig. 5-6).

Evidence for the square configuration for $[Ni(CN)_4]^{--}$ and other complexes of quadriligated nickel(II) was provided in 1931 only by the magnetic properties of salts containing this ion and by the observed isomorphism of $K_2Ni(CN)_4 \cdot H_2O$ and $K_2Pd(CN)_4 \cdot H_2O$.   Since then many investigations have been carried out that show the presence of this configuration in nickel complexes.

The tetragonal crystals $Cs_2AgCl_2AuCl_4$ and $Cs_2AuCl_2AuCl_4$, with the structure shown in Figure 5-7, contain square complexes $[AuCl_4]^-$ of tripositive gold, as well as linear complexes $[AgCl_2]^-$ or $[AuCl_2]^-$ of unipositive silver or gold.

5-4. THE MAGNETIC CRITERION FOR BOND TYPE

The usefulness of the magnetic susceptibility of substances in giving information about their electronic structure was emphasized by G. N.

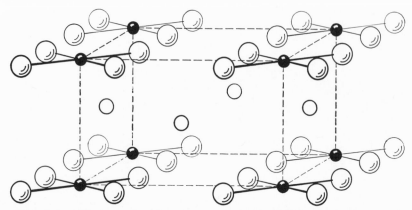

FIG. 5-6.—The structure of the tetragonal crystals K_2PdCl_4 and K_2PtCl_4. The small circles represent palladium or platinum atoms, those of intermediate size (unshaded) potassium ions, and the largest chlorine atoms. The four chlorine atoms about each palladium or platinum atom lie at the corners of a square.

Lewis in his early work on valence. In 1925 Welo and Baudisch discussed the magnetic properties of complex ions and suggested a simple rule: that the magnetic moment of a complex (as found by measuring its magnetic susceptibility—see App. VIII) is equal to that of the atom with the same number of electrons as the central atom of the complex, including two for each covalent bond that the central atom forms. For example, the ferrocyanide ion, $[Fe(CN)_6]^{----}$, has zero magnetic moment. The ion Fe^{++} has 24 electrons, to which we add 12 for the six covalent bonds to the cyanide ions, to obtain the total 36; this is the electron number for krypton, which is diamagnetic ($\mu = 0$).

This simple rule is satisfactory for many substances, but there are also many exceptions. For example, the complex $[Ni(CN)_4]^{--}$ is diamagnetic, although the rule would make it paramagnetic (resembling Se, $Z = 34$, with magnetic moment about 2.8 magnetons).

It has been found that the magnetic moments of complexes can be discussed in a generally satisfactory way by assigning the atomic electrons (the electrons that are not involved in bond formation) to the stable orbitals that are not used as bond orbitals. The assignment is made in the way corresponding to maximum stability, as given by Hund's rules for atoms (App. IV); in particular, electrons are introduced into equivalent orbitals in such a way as to give the maximum number of unpaired electron spins compatible with the Pauli exclusion principle. Observed values of the magnetic moment can often be used in selecting

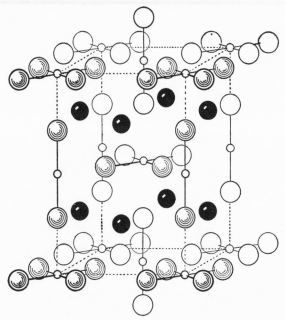

Fig. 5-7.—The structure of the tetragonal crystals $Cs_2AgAuCl_6$ and $Cs_2AuAuCl_6$. Large full circles represent cesium atoms, large open or shaded circles chlorine atoms, and small circles gold or silver atoms.

one from among several alternative electronic structures for a complex. Application of this magnetic criterion to octahedral and square complexes is made in the following sections.

5-5. THE MAGNETIC MOMENTS OF OCTAHEDRAL COMPLEXES

There are three kinds of electronic structures that may be expected for the octahedral complexes MX_6 of the iron-group transition elements (and also for those of the palladium and platinum groups).

The first kind is that in which no $3d$ orbitals are involved in bond formation; the bonds may be formed with use of the $4s$ orbital and the three $4p$ orbitals (four sp^3 bonds resonating among the six positions), or with use of these four orbitals and two $4d$ orbitals. For this structure all five $3d$ orbitals of M are available for occupancy by the atomic electrons, and the expected magnetic moment is close to that for the monatomic ion M^{+z}. In earlier discussions this kind of structure was described as essentially ionic; this description may, however, be misleading, and we shall here refer to complexes with this kind of structure as *hypoligated* complexes (the ligands are bonded less strongly than in complexes with the other structures).

In structures of the second kind, which occur only rarely, one of the $3d$ orbitals is used in bond formation, leaving four for occupancy by atomic electrons.

Octahedral structures of the third kind are those in which d^2sp^3 bonds are formed with use of two of the $3d$ orbitals, leaving only three for occupancy by atomic electrons. Complexes with these structures were formerly described as essentially covalent; here we shall describe them as *hyperligated* complexes (complexes with strong bonds).

The way in which the magnetic criterion can be used to distinguish between hypoligated and hyperligated octahedral complexes can be illustrated for iron(II). The Fe^{++} ion has six electrons outside the argon shell. For hypoligated complexes five $3d$ orbitals are available, and the stable disposition of the six electrons among the five orbitals leaves four unpaired, with one orbital occupied by a pair; the corresponding magnetic moment due to the spins of four electrons is 4.90 magnetons. The hydrated iron(II) ion, $[Fe(OH_2)_6]^{++}$, is observed to have $\mu = 5.25$, and hence this ion is a hypoligated octahedral complex. On the other hand, the hyperligated octahedral complexes of iron(II) must place the six electrons in three orbitals, and hence must have $\mu = 0$, as is observed for $[Fe(CN)_6]^{----}$.

The magnetic moments predicted for the normal states of the monatomic ions Fe^{++}, Co^{++}, and so on are due in part to spin and in part to orbital motion. Their values may be calculated for the predicted stable Russell-Saunders state (Chap. 2 and App. IV) as $g\sqrt{J(J+1)}$, where J is the total angular momentum quantum number and g is the Landé g-factor appropriate to the Russell-Saunders state (App. IV). For example, the normal state of Fe^{++} is $^5D_4$, for which $g = 1.500$ and $\mu = 6.70$. In complexes, however, the orbital magnetic moment of the complex is in large part quenched, and the moment approaches the value due to the spin alone, which is $\sqrt{n(n+2)}$, in which n is the number of electrons with unpaired spins. For $n = 4$ the spin moment is 4.90, as mentioned above. The experimental value for the hexahydrated iron(II) ion in solution and in several crystals is 5.25, showing that the orbital moment is largely quenched.

The value of the spin moment for iron-group ions rises to a maximum of 5.92, corresponding to five unpaired electrons, and then decreases, as shown in Table 5-1.

The observed values for the iron-group ions in aqueous solution are

TABLE 5-1.—MAGNETIC MOMENTS OF IRON-GROUP
IONS IN AQUEOUS SOLUTION

Ion	Number of $3d$ electrons	Number of unpaired electrons	Calculated spin moment[a]	Observed moment[a]
K^+, Ca^{++}, Sc^{+++}, Ti^{4+}	0	0	0.00	0.00
Ti^{+++}, V^{4+}	1	1	1.73	1.78
V^{+++}	2	2	2.83	2.80
V^{++}, Cr^{+++}, Mn^{4+}	3	3	3.88	3.7–4.0
Cr^{++}, Mn^{+++}	4	4	4.90	4.8–5.0
Mn^{++}, Fe^{+++}	5	5	5.92	5.9
Fe^{++}	6	4	4.90	5.2
Co^{++}	7	3	3.88	5.0
Ni^{++}	8	2	2.83	3.2
Cu^{++}	9	1	1.73	1.9
Cu^+, Zn^{++}	10	0	0.00	0.00

[a] In Bohr magnetons.

seen from the table to agree reasonably well with the theoretical values.
The deviations observed can be explained as resulting from contributions
of the orbital moments of the electrons.

In many crystalline salts of these elements values of μ are observed
that are close to those for the aqueous ions; some of these are given
in Table 5-2. For central atoms with more than three $3d$ electrons this
agreement substantiates the assignment of the octahedral complexes to
the hypoligated class.

TABLE 5-2.—MAGNETIC MOMENTS OF IRON-GROUP IONS IN SOLID COMPOUNDS

Substance	Calculated spin moment[a]	Observed moment[a]	Substance	Calculated spin moment[a]	Observed moment[a]
$CrCl_3$	3.88	3.81	$CoCl_2$	3.88	5.04
$CrSO_4 \cdot 6H_2O$	4.90	4.82	$(NH_4)_2Co(SO_4)_2 \cdot 6H_2O$		5.00
$MnCl_3$	5.92	5.75	$Co(N_2H_4)_2SO_3 \cdot H_2O$		4.31
$MnSO_4 \cdot 4H_2O$		5.87	$Co(N_2H_4)_2Cl_2$		4.93
$NH_4Fe(SO_4)_2$		5.86			
$(NH_4)_3FeF_6$		5.90	$NiCl_2$	2.83	3.3
			$Ni(N_2H_4)_2SO_3$		3.20
$FeCl_2$	4.90	5.23	$Ni(N_2H_4)_2(NO_2)_2$		2.80
$FeCl_2 \cdot 4H_2O$		5.25	$Ni(NH_3)_4SO_4$		2.63
$(NH_4)_2Fe(SO_4)_2 \cdot 6H_2O$		5.25			
			$CuCl_2$	1.73	2.02
			$Cu(NH_3)_4SO_4 \ H_2O$		1.81

[a] In Bohr magnetons.

The observation that an iron(II) complex contains four unshared electrons does not require that the bonds in the complex be of the extreme ionic type. As many as four rather weak covalent bonds could be formed with use of the $4s$ and $4p$ orbitals without disturbing the $3d$ shell, and a corresponding amount of covalent character of the bonds would not change the magnetic moment of the complex. Similarly the octahedral d^2sp^3 bonds could have some ionic character without relinquishing their hold on the two $3d$ orbitals. At some point in the change in bond type from the ionic extreme to the octahedral covalent extreme the discontinuity in the nature of the normal state will occur, and the argument given above permits us to describe the octahedral complexes with four unpaired electrons as hypoligated and those with no unpaired electrons as hyperligated.

The decision between hypoligation and hyperligation is determined by competition between two factors. The factor favoring hypoligation is the resonance interaction that stabilizes atomic states with a large number of unpaired electrons (large multiplicity, as given by Hund's first rule, Sec. 2-7). The factor favoring hyperligation is the bond energy, as determined by the bond-forming power of the ligands and the strength of the bond orbitals of the central atom.

In Table 5-3 there are given observed values of magnetic moments of some compounds containing octahedral complexes, not only of the iron-group elements but also of the palladium-group and platinum-group elements, to which the discussion is also applicable. It is seen that the octahedral complexes of iron with fluorine and with water are hypoligated, whereas those with the cyanide, nitrite, and dipyridyl groups are hyperligated. All of the complexes of cobalt(III) that have been investigated are hyperligated except that with fluorine, $[CoF^6]^{---}$, which is hypoligated. It is interesting that in the sequence $[Co(NH_3)_6]^{+++}$, $[Co(NH_3)_3F_3]$, $[CoF_6]^{---}$ the transition from hyperligation to hypoligation occurs between the second and third complex.

Bipositive cobalt forms hypoligating bonds with water and hyperligating bonds with nitrite groups.

All the octahedral complexes of the elements of the palladium and platinum groups that have been investigated are diamagnetic, showing the strong tendency of these elements to form hyperligating bonds.

The magnetic properties of prussian blue and similar substances are of unusual interest. X-ray investigations have shown that substances such as $KFeFe(CN)_6 \cdot H_2O$ form cubic crystals in which iron atoms lie at the points of a simple cubic lattice, each being connected with its six neighbors by CN groups extending along the cube edges (Fig. 5-8). The

TABLE 5-3.—OBSERVED MAGNETIC MOMENTS OF OCTAHEDRAL COMPLEXES
OF TRANSITION ELEMENTS

Hyperligated complexes	μ cal-culated	μ ob-served	Hypoligated complexes	μ cal-culated	μ ob-served
$K_4[Cr^{II}(CN)_6]$	2.83	3.3			
$K_3[Mn^{III}(CN)_6]$		3.0			
$K_4[Mn^{II}(CN)_6]$	1.73	2.0	$Mn^{II}(NH_3)_6Br_2$	5.92	5.9
$K_3[Fe^{III}(CN)_6]$		2.33	$(NH_4)_3[Fe^{III}F_6]$	5.92	5.9
$K_4[Fe^{II}(CN)_6]$	0.00	0.00	$(NH_4)_2[Fe^{II}F_5 \cdot H_2O]$		5.9
$Na_3[Fe^{II}(CN)_5 \cdot NH_2]$		.00	$[Fe^{II}(H_2O)_6](NH_4SO_4)_2$	4.90	5.3
$[Fe^{II}(dipyridyl)_3]SO_4$		.00			
$K_3[Co^{III}(CN)_6]$		.00			
$[Co^{III}(NH_3)_3F_3]$		.00	$K_3[Co^{III}Fe_6]$	4.90	5.3
$[Co^{III}(NH_3)_6]Cl_3$		.00	$[CoF_3(OH_2)_3] \cdot 1/2H_2O$		4.47
$[Co^{III}(NH_3)_5Cl]Cl_2$		.00			
$[Co^{III}(NH_3)_4Cl_2]Cl_2$		.00			
$[Co^{III}(NH_3)_3(NO_2)_3]$		.00			
$[Co^{III}(NH_3)_5 \cdot H_2O]_2(C_2O_4)_3$		.00			
$[Co^{III}(NH_3)_4CO_3]NO_3 \cdot 3/2H_2O.$		.00			
$K_2Ca[Co^{II}(NO_2)_6]$	1.73	1.9	$[Co^{II}(NH_3)_6]Cl_2$	3.88	4.96
$K_2[Pd^{IV}Cl_6]$	0.00	0.00			
$[Pd^{IV}Cl_4(NH_3)_2]$		.00			
$Na[Ir^{III}Cl_2(NO_2)_4]$		.00			
$[Ir^{III}(NH_3)_5NO_2]Cl_2$		.00			
$[Ir^{III}(NH_3)_4(NO_2)_2]Cl$		.00			
$[Ir^{III}(NH_3)_3(NO_2)_3]$		.00			
$K_2[Pt^{IV}Cl_6]$		.00			
$[Pt^{IV}(NH_3)_3]Cl_4$		.00			
$[Pt^{IV}(NH_3)_5Cl]Cl_3$		.00			
$[Pt^{IV}(NH_3)_4Cl_2]Cl_2$		.00			
$[Pt^{IV}(NH_3)_3Cl_3]Cl$		.00			
$[Pt^{IV}(NH_3)_2Cl_4]$		.00			

potassium ions and water molecules lie in the cubes outlined in this way. The magnetic susceptibility shows that half of the iron atoms, presumably those bonded to the carbon atoms of the six adjacent cyanide groups, form hyperligating bonds, whereas the other iron atoms form hypoligating bonds.

5-6. THE MAGNETIC MOMENTS OF TETRAHEDRAL AND SQUARE COORDINATED COMPLEXES

The bipositive nickel atom forming four covalent dsp^2 bonds has only four $3d$ orbitals available for the eight unshared $3d$ electrons, which must thus form four pairs, the square complex NiX_4 being diamagnetic. Bipositive nickel in a complex involving only the $4s$ and $4p$ orbitals (electrostatic bonds or weak covalent bonds) distributes the eight $3d$ electrons among the five $3d$ orbitals in such a way as to leave two electrons unpaired, the complex having a magnetic moment of 2.83 Bohr magnetons. From this argument it is seen that the assignment of nickel complexes to

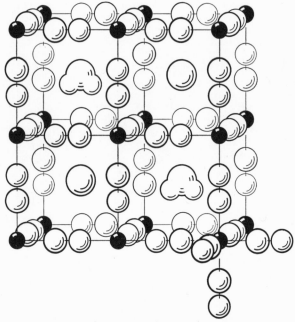

FIG. 5-8.—A drawing representing the front half of the cubic unit of structure of the crystal prussian blue, $KFeFe(CN)_6 \cdot H_2O$. The structure can be described by reference to the eight small cubes that constitute the cubic unit of structure. Alternate corners of the small cubes are occupied by iron(II) and iron(III) atoms. The cyanide groups lie along the edges of the small cubes; each cyanide group forms a single bond with two iron atoms, defining the edge of the cube. Water molecules and potassium ions alternate at the centers of the small cubes. The structure can be described as a three-dimensional latticework of iron atoms and cyanide groups defining cubical cells that contain the water molecules and potassium ions.

the tetrahedral and square coplanar classes can be made by magnetic measurements.

The crystals $K_2Ni(CN)_4$ and $K_2Ni(CN)_4 \cdot H_2O$, shown by isomorphism to contain the planar complex $[Ni(CN)_4]^{--}$, are diamagnetic.

On the other hand, the compounds $[Ni(NH_3)_4]SO_3$, $[Ni(N_2H_4)_2] \cdot (NO_2)_2$, $[Ni(C_2H_4(NH_2)_2)_2](SCN)_2 \cdot H_2O$, and $[Ni(C_5H_7O_2)_2]$ (nickel acetylacetone) are paramagnetic, with values of μ between 2.6 and 3.2.

The complexes of palladium(II) and platinum(II) are all diamagnetic. Diamagnetism has been verified for $PdCl_2 \cdot 2H_2O$, $PdCl_2 \cdot 2NH_3$, K_2PdCl_4, $K_2Pd(CN)_4$, K_2PdI_4, $K_2Pd(SCN)_4$, $K_2Pd(NO_2)_4$, palladium dimethylglyoxime, and even palladous nitrate in solution (probably containing the ion $[Pd(H_2O)_4]^{++}$). The crystalline substances $PdCl_2$,

PdI_2, $Pd(CN)_2$, $Pd(SCN)_2$ and $Pd(NO_3)_2$ are also diamagnetic. Their atomic arrangements are unknown, except that of $PdCl_2$, which contains ribbons of $PdCl_4$ squares with opposite edges shared, but it is probable that they all involve square-coordinated palladium.

5-7. THE ELECTRONEUTRALITY PRINCIPLE AND THE STABILITY OF OCTAHEDRAL COMPLEXES

Many factors affect the stability of complexes. One important factor, the multiple-bond character of the M—X bonds, will be discussed in Section 9-7.

Another important factor is the partial ionic character of the bonds. In general it may be said that stable complexes are those with structures such that each atom has only a small electric charge, approximating zero (that is, in the range -1 to $+1$). The electroneutrality principle, of which the foregoing statement is a special case, will be discussed further in Section 8-2.

Let us consider the cobalt(III) hexammoniate ion, $[Co(NH_3)_6]^{+++}$ If the Co—N bonds were ionic bonds the entire charge $3+$ would be located on the cobalt atom; and if they were extreme covalent bonds the cobalt atom would have the charge $3-$ and each nitrogen atom the charge $1+$ (Fig. 5-9). In fact, the bonds have partial ionic character such as to make the atoms nearly neutral. If it is assumed, as illustrated in Figure 5-10, that the Co—N bonds have 50 percent and the N—H bonds 17 percent ionic character, the cobalt and nitrogen atoms become neutral and each hydrogen atom has the charge $+\frac{1}{6}$. This distribution of the charge of the complex ion, over the surface of the nearly spherical group, corresponds to electrostatic stability; an electrically charged solid metal sphere has its charge entirely on its surface.

The assumed amount of ionic character of the N—H bond is that corresponding to its electronegativity difference, but that for the Co—N bond is larger (50 percent, whereas the electronegativity difference corresponds to 30 percent).

We may understand from an extension of the foregoing discussion why stable cationic complexes have a peripheral set of hydrogen atoms, as in the hydrates and ammoniates, and the stable anionic complexes have a peripheral set of electronegative atoms, as in $[Co(NO_2)_6]^{---}$, $[Fe(CN)_6]^{----}$, and $[Co(C_2O_4)_3]^{---}$.

The electronegativity principle provides an explanation of the stability of hydrated ions of the iron-group transition elements with oxidation number $+2$ or $+3$. The electronegativity values for the elements Ti to Ni lie in the range 1.5 to 1.8, corresponding to 52 to 63 percent of partial

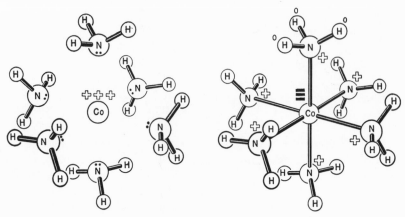

Fig. 5-9.—The representation of alternative extreme types of electronic structures for the octahedral complex ion $[Co(NH_3)_6]^{+++}$. On the left is a representation of the structure with extreme electrostatic bonds. The cobalt atom is represented as having a positive electric charge, $3+$. At the right is represented the structure in which normal covalent bonds are between the cobalt atom and the surrounding nitrogen atoms, as well as between the nitrogen atom and its three attached hydrogen atoms. This structure places the charge $3-$ on the cobalt atom and $1+$ on each nitrogen atom.

ionic character of the bonds to oxygen atoms, and hence to the transfer of 2.22 to 2.88 units of negative charge to the metal atom in the hexahydrated complex. This charge transfer would make the metal atom nearly neutral if its oxidation number were $+2$ or $+3$.

5-8. LIGAND FIELD THEORY

An interesting and useful method of theoretical treatment of certain properties of complexes and crystals, called the *ligand field theory*, has been applied with considerable success to octahedral complexes, especially in the discussion of their absorption spectra involving electronic transitions. The theory consists in the approximate solution of the Schrödinger wave equation for one electron in the electric field of an atom plus a perturbing electric field, due to the ligands, with the symmetry of the complex or of the position in the crystal of the atom under consideration. The theory is usually applied in such a way as to permit the evaluation from experimental quantities of parameters representing the strength of the ligand field and the magnitudes of the interactions of the d electrons in the complexes; there is difficulty, however, in the interpretation of these values in terms of structural features.

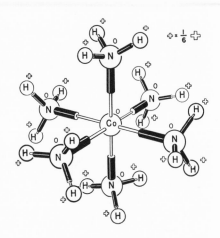

Fig. 5-10.—The distribution of charge in the complex ion $[Co(NH_3)_6]^{+++}$, with the cobalt-nitrogen bonds represented as having 50 percent ionic character and the nitrogen-hydrogen bonds as having 16.7 percent ionic character. This electronic structure leaves the cobalt atom and the nitrogen atoms with zero electric charge. The total charge of the complex, $3+$, is distributed over the eighteen hydrogen atoms.

In some respects the ligand field theory is closely related, at least qualitatively, to the valence-bond theory described in the preceding sections, and many arguments about the structure of the normal state of a complex or crystal can be carried out in either of the two ways, with essentially the same results.

For example, it has been found that CrF_2 crystallizes with the rutile structure (Fig. 3-2), but with four of the Cr—F bonds (lying in a plane) with length 2.00 ± 0.02 Å and the other two with length 2.43 Å (and hence presumably much weaker), whereas in other crystals (MgF_2, TiO_2) the six ligands of the metal atom are at essentially the same distance. The distortion of the coordination polyhedron can be explained in a straightforward way by the ligand field theory, or alternatively by the consideration of bond orbitals. The substance has paramagnetic susceptibility corresponding to four unpaired $3d$ electrons per chromium atom. These electrons utilize four of the five $3d$ orbitals. Hence it would be expected (Sec. 5-3) that the atom would make use of the remaining d orbital to form dsp^2 square bonds (with, of course, some partial ionic character).

CrF_3 forms a cubic crystal containing regular octahedral CrF_6 groups, each fluorine atom forming a joint corner of two octahedra; the Cr—F bonds all have length 1.90 Å. The regularity of these octahedra is expected; the three unpaired $3d$ electrons use only three of the $3d$ orbitals, leaving two available for formation of d^2sp^3 octahedral bonds.

In an environment with regular octahedral symmetry the five d orbitals can be divided into two sets. Two orbitals, d_{z^2} and $d_{x^2+y^2}$, interact in an equivalent manner along the x, y, and z axes, and the other three, d_{xy}, d_{yz}, and d_{yz}, interact in a different way with the field.   The latter three, which avoid the octahedral ligands, represent a triply degenerate state for a nonbonding electron that is more stable than the doubly degenerate state represented by the first two.

If only one of the orbitals d_{xy}, d_{yz}, d_{xz} is occupied, the structure no longer has regular octahedral symmetry.   If three are occupied, as in CrF_3, the regular symmetry is retained.   The fourth $3d$ electron in CrF_2 can be described as occupying the d_{z^2} orbital, and repelling the two fluorine atoms along $+z$ and $-z$.

5-9. CONFIGURATIONS FOR ATOMS WITH UNSHARED ELECTRON PAIRS

A considerable amount of information about the relative orientations of bonds formed by an atom that also possesses one or more unshared electron pairs has been gathered.

In a few cases an unshared electron pair seems to have no effect on bond directions.   This is observed for Se(IV) in the octahedral complex ion $[SeBr_6]^{--}$ and for Sb(III) in $[SbBr_6]^{---}$.

Usually, however, an unshared pair seems to occupy one of the corners of a coordination polyhedron and to replace the shared pair of a bond. The molecules NH_3, PCl_3, etc. have pyramidal configurations that might be described as involving bonds directed toward three corners of a tetrahedron with the fourth corner occupied by the unshared pair, and a similar description can be given for H_2O, $(CH_3)_2S$, and related molecules.

The extension of this postulate to atoms with five bonds and one unshared pair suggests that the bonds should be directed toward the five corners of a square pyramid, which with the unshared pair would form an octahedron. BrF_5 has this configuration.   The bromine atom lies about 0.15 Å below the base of the pyramid, so that the F—Br—F angles (from the apical fluorine atom to the basal atoms) are about 86°. The unshared electron pair thus occupies a larger volume about the bromine atom than the shared pairs.   This distortion from the regular octahedral configuration is the expected consequence of the large amount of s character of the orbital occupied by the unshared pair and the d and f character of the bond orbitals.

In the crystal $KICl_4$ the four chlorine atoms of the $[IC_4]^-$ complex are located at the corners of a square about the iodine atom; we may consider that the octahedron about iodine is completed by the two unshared electron pairs of the iodine atom, one above and one below the ICl_4 plane.

Our postulate suggests that the configuration of molecules such as $TeCl_4$ is similar to that of PCl_5 and related molecules; that is, that the four bonds and one unshared pair occupy the five corners of a trigonal bipyramid. The unshared pair would probably occupy one of the equatorial positions rather than one of the apical positions. Such a configuration has, indeed, been found for tellurium tetrachloride, with chlorine atoms at the two apices and at two of the three equatorial positions of a trigonal bipyramid, the unshared pair occupying the third.

The bromine trifluoride molecule can be similarly described as a trigonal bipyramid with fluorine atoms at the two apical positions and one equatorial position (and unshared pairs at the other two equatorial positions), the four atoms thus being coplanar.

We conclude from the foregoing examples that in general the configurations of molecules with unshared electron pairs are similar to those of molecules with only shared pairs in the valence shell, except that the unshared pairs occupy a larger volume than the shared pairs, thus causing a decrease in the values of the bond angles.

EXERCISES

5-1.—The hexafluorides of sulfur, selenium, and tellurium are known. Assign electronic structures and discuss the nature of the bond orbitals of the central atoms.

5-2.—Assign an electronic structure and spatial configuration to disulfur decafluoride, S_2F_{10}.

5-3.—Using the functions given in Equations 5-1, make a polar graph, resembling that of Figure 5-2 for an octahedral bond orbital, for the best *spd* orbital (Eq. 5-3). Verify that its strength is 3.000 and its nodal cones are at $73°9'$ and $133°37'$ with the bond direction.

5-4.—Describe the bond orbitals of the two kinds of gold atoms in the crystal $Cs_2AuAuCl_6$ (Fig. 5-7).

5-5.—Gold trichloride forms dimeric molecules Au_2Cl_6 in which two chlorine atoms are shared by the two gold atoms. Is the molecule planar or nonplanar? Describe its structure.

5-6.—Trimethylphosphine and gold tribromide interact to form the molecule $(CH_3)_3P$—$AuBr_3$. Assign an electronic structure to the molecule and discuss the arrangement of atoms about the phosphorus and gold atoms.

5-7.—Assign electronic structures to the silver dicyanide ion, $[Ag(CN)_2]^-$, the zinc tetracyanide ion, $[Zn(CN)_4]^{--}$, the auric tetracyanide ion, $[Au(CN)_4]$, and the ferricyanide ion, $[Fe(CN)_6]^{---}$. What spatial configurations do these ions have? How many unpaired electrons does each contain?

5-8.—The observed magnetic moment of the cobalt(II) tetraiodide ion is 5.0 Bohr magnetons. How many unpaired electrons does the cobalt complex have? What orbitals of the cobalt atom are used for unshared pairs and unpaired electrons? Would you expect the complex to have a planar configuration or a tetrahedral configuration?

5-9.—Assign an electronic structure to the iodine pentafluoride molecule. How many unshared pairs does the iodine atom have in its outer shell? What is the nature of the bond orbitals and unshared-pair orbitals? What is the spatial configuration of the molecule?

5-10.—Assign an electronic structure and expected spatial configuration to the xenon tetrafluoride molecule, and discuss the nature of the bond orbitals. (Ans. Square planar.)

5-11.—The PCl_5 molecule has the configuration of a trigonal bipyramid. The three equivalent P—Cl bonds in the equator can be described as using sp^2 hybrid bond orbitals of the phosphorus atom (see footnote in Section 4-4), and the two axial bonds as using hybrids of the p_z orbital and the d_{z^2} orbital. Formulate these hybrid orbitals and calculate their bond strength. (Ans. 2.226.)

5-12.—The molecule $TeCl_4$ has been observed to have a configuration with a nearly linear Cl—Te—Cl group, and the other two chlorine atoms in the plane perpendicular to this axis, with bond angle about 110°. How many unshared pairs does the tellurium atom have? Can you advance an explanation of the unusual spatial configuration? What other configuration would you consider a likely one for this molecule? (Ans. A trigonal pyramid with the tellurium atom in or near the base.)

CHAPTER 6

The Resonance of Molecules among Several Valence-Bond Structures

ONE of the most interesting and useful applications of the theory of resonance is in the discussion of the structure of molecules for which no one valence-bond structure is satisfactory. An introduction to this discussion is presented in the following sections.

6-1. RESONANCE IN NITROUS OXIDE AND BENZENE

For many molecules it is possible to formulate valence-bond structures that are so reasonable and that account so satisfactorily for the properties of the substances that they are accepted by everyone without hesitation. The structures given on the next page may be shown for illustration. The physical and chemical properties of substances and the configurations of molecules associated with structures of this type are well understood, and this understanding forms the basis for a large part of chemical reasoning.

It is sometimes found, however, that an unambiguous assignment of a single valence-bond structure to a molecule cannot be made: two or more structures that are about equally stable may suggest themselves, no one of which accounts in a completely satisfactory way for the properties of the substance. Under these circumstances some new structural concepts and symbols might be introduced; we might, for

example, use the symbol for benzene, without attempting to

interpret this symbol in terms of single and double bonds. With the development of the idea of quantum-mechanical resonance a more il-

Oxygen fluoride

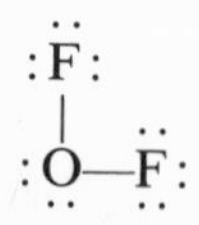

$$:\ddot{F}:$$
$$|\quad\ \ \cdot\cdot$$
$$:\ddot{O}-\ddot{F}:$$

Trimethylamine

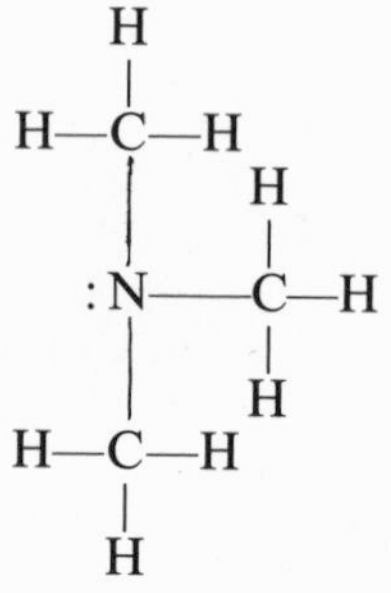

$$\begin{array}{c}
\text{H} \\
| \\
\text{H}-\text{C}-\text{H} \\
\end{array}$$

$$:\text{N}\underline{\quad\quad}\begin{array}{c}\text{H}\\ |\\ \text{C}-\text{H}\\ |\\ \text{H}\end{array}$$

$$\begin{array}{c}
\text{H}-\text{C}-\text{H} \\
| \\
\text{H}
\end{array}$$

Ethane

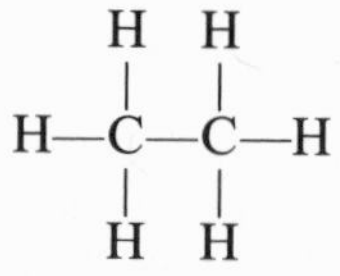

$$\begin{array}{cc}
\text{H} & \text{H} \\
| & | \\
\text{H}-\text{C}-\text{C}-\text{H} \\
| & | \\
\text{H} & \text{H}
\end{array}$$

Ethylene

$$\begin{array}{c}
\text{H} \qquad\qquad \text{H} \\
\diagdown \qquad\quad \diagup \\
\text{C}=\text{C} \\
\diagup \qquad\quad \diagdown \\
\text{H} \qquad\qquad \text{H}
\end{array}$$

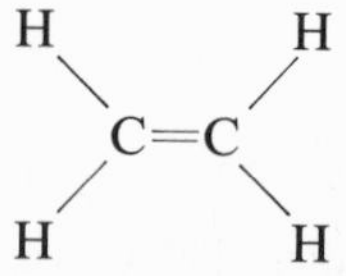

luminating and useful solution to this difficulty has been found: *the actual normal state of the molecule is not represented by any one of the alternative reasonable structures, but can be represented by a combination of them*, their individual contributions being determined by their nature and stability. The molecule is then described as *resonating among the several valence-bond structures.*

The resonance of molecules among various electronic structures has been discussed in detail in Chapter 3 for the case that the resonating structures differ in regard to bond type (ionic and covalent). The resonance under discussion in this chapter is not greatly different; it involves structures that differ in the distribution of bonds rather than in their type.

The nitrous oxide molecule may be used as an example. This molecule is linear, with the oxygen atom at one end. It contains 16 valence electrons; and it is seen that these can be assigned to the stable L orbitals of the atoms in any of the following reasonable ways:

$$A \qquad \overset{-}{:}\overset{..}{N}\!\!=\!\!\overset{+}{N}\!\!=\!\!\underset{..}{O}:$$

$$B \qquad \overset{-}{:}\underset{..}{N}\!\!=\!\!\overset{+}{N}\!\!=\!\!\overset{..}{O}:$$

$$C \qquad :N\!\!\equiv\!\!\overset{+}{N}\!\!-\!\!\underset{..}{\overset{..}{O}}\overset{-}{:}$$

Each of these three structures involves four covalent bonds (counting a double bond as two and a triple bond as three), and a separation of charge to adjacent atoms. (Structures *A* and *B* differ in that in *A* the double bond between N and N is formed with use of p_z orbitals and that between N and O with p_y orbitals, and in *B* they are reversed; see Sec. 4-7.) Other structures that might be written are recognized at once as being much less stable than these, such as

$$D \qquad \overset{--}{:}\underset{..}{N}\!\!-\!\!\overset{+}{N}\!\!\equiv\!\!\overset{+}{O}:$$

on which instability is conferred by the arrangement of electric charges, and

$$E \qquad \overset{-}{:}\overset{..}{N}\!\!=\!\!\overset{..}{N}\!\!-\!\!\overset{..}{\overset{+}{O}}:$$

$$F \qquad :\overset{..}{N}\!\!-\!\!\overset{..}{N}\!\!=\!\!\overset{..}{O}:$$

with instability arising from the smaller number of covalent bonds.

A decision cannot be made between structures *A*, *B*, and *C*, which are, indeed, so closely similar in nature that there can be no large energy difference between them. Moreover, they satisfy the other conditions for resonance: they involve the same number of unpaired electrons (zero), and they correspond to about the same equilibrium configuration of the nuclei (linear, for a central tetrahedral atom forming either two double bonds or a single bond and a triple bond). We accordingly expect the normal state of the molecule to correspond to *resonance among structures A, B*, and *C*, with small contributions by the other less stable structures, which can be neglected in our discussion. The molecule is more stable than it would be if either *A*, *B*, or *C* alone represented its normal state by an amount of energy equal to the resonance energy among the three structures. Its interatomic distances and force constants are not those corresponding to any one structure alone, but to resonance among them (Chap. 7). Its electric dipole moment is not large, but is close to zero, the opposed moments of the structures canceling each other; the experimental value, from the microwave spectrum, is $0.166 \pm 0.002\ D$, with the direction not known.

The value of the electric dipole moment provides an illustration of the significance of resonance as compared with tautomerism. If nitrous oxide gas were a tautomeric mixture of molecules of types A, B, and C, its dielectric constant would be large, since the molecules of each type would have large dipole moments and would make a large contribution to the dielectric constant of the gas. The frequency of resonance among the structures is, however, very large, of the order of magnitude of electronic frequencies in general, and the nuclei do not have time to orient themselves in an applied electric field in order to contribute to the dielectric constant of the medium before the electrons of the molecule have run through their phases, which results in a very small average electric moment.

The discussion in Section 1-3 about the element of arbitrariness in the concept of resonance may be recalled at this point with reference to the nitrous oxide molecule and the other molecules that are described in this chapter as resonating among several valence-bond structures. It is not necessary that the structures A, B, and C be used as the basis of discussion of the nitrous oxide molecule. We might say instead that the molecule cannot be satisfactorily represented by any single valence-bond structure, and abandon the effort to correlate its structure and properties with those of other molecules. By using valence-bond structures as the basis for discussion, however, with the aid of the concept of resonance, we are able to account for the properties of the molecule in terms of those of other molecules in a straightforward and simple way. It is for this practical reason that we find it convenient to speak of the resonance of molecules among several electronic structures.

It is to be emphasized again that in writing three valence-bond structures for the nitrous oxide molecule and saying that it resonates among them we are making an effort to extend the valence-bond picture to molecules to which it is not applicable in its original form, and that we are not required to do this but choose to do it in the hope of obtaining a satisfactory description of these unusual molecules, permitting us to correlate and "understand" the results of experiments on their chemical and physical properties and to make predictions in the same way as for molecules to which a single valence-bond structure can be assigned. Nitrous oxide does not consist of a mixture of tautomeric molecules, some with one and some with another of the structures written above; instead, all the molecules have the same electronic structure, this being of such a nature that it cannot be satisfactorily represented by any one valence-bond diagram but can be reasonably well represented by three. The properties of the molecule are essentially those expected for an average of the three valence-bond structures, except for the stabilizing effect of the resonance energy.

To represent the molecule we may use the symbol $\{:\overset{-}{\overset{..}{N}}{=}\overset{+}{N}{=}O:$, $:N{=}\overset{+}{N}{=}\overset{..}{O}:$, $:N{\equiv}\overset{+}{N}{-}\overset{..}{\overset{-}{O}}:\}$, the resonating structures being enclosed in brackets. I do not believe that it is wise to attempt to simplify the symbol further—to write, for example, N≡N=O, even though, as we shall see later, the N—N bond and the N—O bond have properties approaching those of a triple bond and a double bond, respectively (Chap. 8). If the formula N≡N=O were to be used, it would be confused with formulas for nonresonating molecules. This formula suggests that the nitrogen atom can form five covalent bonds, which is not true. Moreover, the formula carries with it no stereochemical implications—we do not know the relative orientation to expect for a double bond and a triple bond—whereas the resonating formula shows at once that the molecule is linear.

Benzene provides an interesting and important illustration of a resonating molecule. The two Kekulé structures for benzene, *A* and *B*,

are the most stable valence-bond structures that can be written for the known hexagonal planar configuration. Other structures, such as the Dewar structures

or the

Claus-Armstrong-Baeyer centric structure

correspond to diminished stability because of their weak bonds between distant atoms, and they need not be considered in a simple discussion. The Kekulé structures individually do not provide a satisfactory representation of the benzene molecule; the high degree of unsaturation that by comparison with hexene or cyclohexene would be expected for a molecule containing three double bonds is not shown by benzene, which instead is surprisingly stable and unreactive.   It is resonance that gives to benzene its aromatic properties.   The two Kekulé structures are equivalent, and have the same energy; they accordingly enter into complete resonance.   The molecule is stabilized in this way by the resonance energy of about 37 kcal/mole (Sec. 6-3).   The unsaturation of a compound containing a double bond is due, from the thermodynamic point of view, to the instability of a double bond relative to two single bonds, amounting to about 19 kcal/mole per double bond* or 57 kcal/mole for three double bonds. The resonance energy removes the greater part of this instability and gives to the molecule a degree of saturation approaching that of the paraffins.

The stereochemical properties of the benzene molecule can be predicted from the concept of resonance between the two Kekulé structures.   This resonance gives to each of the carbon-carbon bonds a large amount of double-bond character, with its stereochemical implications.   The bonds adjacent to a double bond are planar; accordingly the entire benzene molecule must be planar.   The six carbon-carbon bonds are equivalent; hence the carbon hexagon must be regular, and the carbon-hydrogen bonds must be directed radially.   All these statements have been verified experimentally in recent years by the study of electric dipole moments of benzene derivatives, of electron-diffraction photographs of benzene vapor, of x-ray data for crystalline benzene, and of the Raman and infrared spectra of benzene.

6-2. RESONANCE ENERGY

The assignment of a resonating structure to a molecule can sometimes be made on the basis of theoretical arguments, as in the two cases discussed above.   In general such an assignment should be supported by experimental evidence, such as that provided by chemical properties, resonance energies, interatomic distances, force constants of bonds, bond angles, electric dipole moments, and so forth.   If the reasonable valence-bond structures are not equivalent, an estimate of the magnitudes of the contributions of different structures to the normal state of a molecule may be made from this information.

Of these methods of studying resonance in molecules the most fruitful at present are the determination and interpretation of values of

---

* The values 147 and 83.1 kcal/mole for the energy of the $C=C$ and $C-C$ bonds, respectively, are given in Secs. 6-2 and 3-5.

interatomic distances, discussed in the following chapter, and the calculation of values of resonance energies from thermochemical data. It is to the latter that we now turn our attention.

Values of Bond Energies for Multiple Bonds.—In Section 3-5 there is given a table of values of bond energies for single bonds. In the construction of this table care was taken to make use of data for only those molecules to each of which an unambiguous assignment of a valence-bond formula could be made. This consideration of bond energies is extended in Table 6-1, which contains values for some multiple bonds, obtained by methods similar to those described in Section 3-5.

TABLE 6-1.—VALUES OF BOND ENERGIES FOR MULTIPLE BONDS

Bond	Bond energy	Compounds
$C=C$	147 kcal/mole	
$N=N$	95	
$O=O$	96	$^1\Delta$ state of O_2
$C=N$	147	*n*-Butylisobutylideneamine
$C=O$	166	Formaldehyde
	171	Other aldehydes
	174	Ketones
$C=S$	114	
$C\equiv C$	194	
$N\equiv N$	226	N_2
$C\equiv N$	207	Hydrogen cyanide
	213	Other cyanides

By the addition of the suitable quantities from Tables 3-4 and 6-1 an approximate value can be predicted for the heat of formation of a gas molecule from the elements in the state of monatomic gases, provided that the molecule in its normal state is well represented by a single electronic structure of the valence-bond type. For example, the heat of formation of acetylene from the elements in their standard states is -53.9 kcal/mole, and that from atoms is 393.7 kcal/mole. The sum of bond energies $2C-H + C\equiv C$ is 393 kcal/mole. The error of 1 kcal/mole is indicative of the degree of reliability of the bond energy values, which are averages of those found by consideration of the thermochemical data for many substances.

Empirical Values of Resonance Energies.—The tables of bond energies permit the calculation of values of the heats of formation of molecules to which a single valence-bond structure can be assigned that agree with the experimental values to within a few kcal/mole. On carrying out a similar calculation for a resonating molecule on the basis of any single valence-bond structure that can be formulated, it is found that *in every case the actual energy of formation of the molecule is greater than the calculated value;* that is, the molecule is actually more stable than it would be if it had the valence-bond structure assumed for it in making the bond-energy calculation. This result is required by the fundamental quantum-mechanical principle on which the concept of resonance is based (Sec. 1-3); it provides, however, a pleasing confirmation of the arguments used in the construction of the table of bond energies.

The difference between the observed heat of formation and that calculated for a single valence-bond structure for a molecule with use of the table of bond energies is an empirical value of the resonance energy of the molecule relative to the assumed valence-bond structure.

It is desirable that the structure used as the basis for the resonance-energy calculation be the most stable (or one of the most stable) of those among which resonance occurs. It is not always convenient for this choice to be made, for the following reason. The tabulated bond energies are designed for use only between atoms with zero formal charge; no simple method of calculating the heats of formation of molecules containing charged atoms has been devised, because of the difficulties introduced by the Coulomb energy terms for the separated charges. For this reason there is no empirical value available for the resonance energy of the nitrous oxide molecule; the stable structures involve atoms with formal charges.

It must be remembered that one of the conditions for resonance of molecules among several electronic structures is that the configuration of the molecule (the arrangement of the nuclei) remain constant during the electronic resonance; it is the composite electronic structure that provides a single potential function determining the equilibrium configuration and modes of oscillation for the molecule. It is not possible for an amide to resonate between the tautomeric structures

$$R-C\overset{\ddot{O}:}{\underset{\ddot{N}H_2}{\big<}} \quad and \quad R-C\overset{:\ddot{O}H}{\underset{NH}{\big<}} \; .$$

We use the structures

and

to describe the molecule.

The heat of formation of the benzene gas molecule from separated atoms is found from the heat of combustion (789.2 kcal/mole) and the heats of formation of the products of combustion, water and carbon dioxide, to have the value 1323 kcal/mole. The sum of the bond energies $6C-H + 3C-C + 3C=C$ gives the value 1286 kcal/mole for the heat of formation of a hypothetical molecule with the Kekulé structure or , involving noninteracting double bonds. The difference between these, 37 kcal/mole, is the resonance energy of the molecule.

In calculating resonance energies it is for simplicity and convenience only that the thermochemical data are converted into energies of formation of molecules from separated atoms and compared with sums of bond energies; the same results can be obtained by dealing directly with heats of formation from elementary substances in their standard states or with heats of combustion or of hydrogenation reactions or other reactions, the resonating substance being compared with suitable nonresonating substances. This may be illustrated by the calculation of the resonance energy of benzene from data obtained in the important series of direct measurements of heats of hydrogenation. The value expected for the heat of hydrogenation of a hypothetical molecule with a Kekulé structure involving noninteracting double bonds is 85.77 kcal/mole, three times the heat of hydrogenation of cyclohexene:

$$C_6H_{10} + H_2 \rightarrow C_6H_{12} + 28.59 \text{ kcal/mole.}$$

The value observed for the heat of hydrogenation of benzene is much less than this:

$$C_6H_6 + 3H_2 \rightarrow C_6H_{12} + 49.80 \text{ kcal/mole.}$$

The difference, 35.97 kcal/mole, is the resonance energy for benzene, which stabilizes the molecule relative to the individual Kekulé structures.   The agreement with the value found above, 37 kcal/mole, provides sound substantiation of the magnitude of the benzene resonance energy.

The empirical resonance-energy values given in Table 6-2 are discussed in the following sections of this chapter and in later chapters.

TABLE 6-2.—EMPIRICAL RESONANCE-ENERGY VALUES

Substance	Resonance energy (in kcal/mole)	Reference structure
Benzene, C_6H_6	37	
Naphthalene, $C_{10}H_8$	75	
Anthracene, $C_{14}H_{10}$	105	
Phenanthrene, $C_{14}H_{10}$	110	
Biphenyl, $C_{12}H_{10}$	5[a]	
Cyclopentadiene, C_5H_6	4	
Styrene, C_8H_8	5[a]	
Stilbene, $C_{14}H_{12}$	7[a]	
Phenylacetylene, C_6H_5CCH	10[a]	

[a] Extra resonance energy, not including that within the benzene ring.

TABLE 6-2.—(continued)

Substance	Resonance energy (in kcal/mole)	Reference structure
Phenol, C_6H_5OH	7[a]	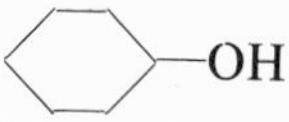 ⬡—OH
Aniline, $C_6H_5NH_2$	6[a]	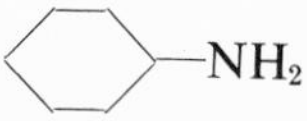 ⬡—NH_2
Benzaldehyde, C_6H_5CHO	4[a]	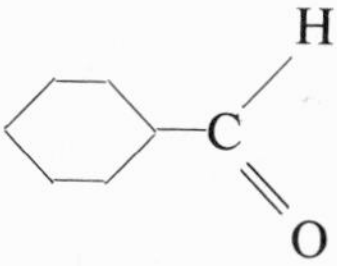 ⬡—C(H)=O
Phenyl cyanide, C_6H_5CN	5[a]	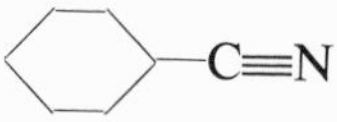 ⬡—C≡N
Pyridine, C_5H_5N	43	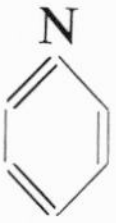 (pyridine ring structure)
Quinoline, C_9H_7N	69	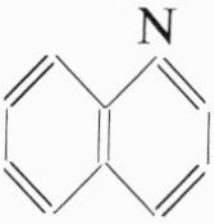 (quinoline ring structure)
Pyrrole, C_4H_5N	31	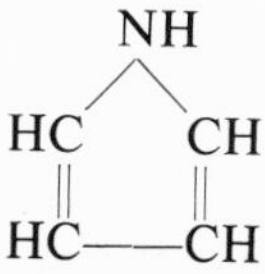 (pyrrole ring structure)
Furan, C_4H_4O	23	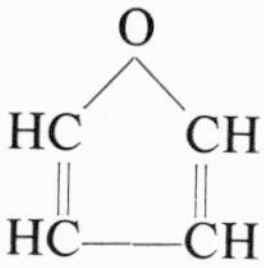 (furan ring structure)
Thiophene, C_4H_4S	31	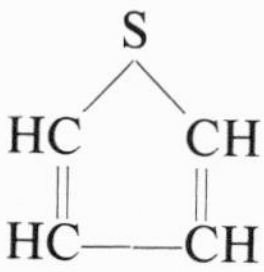 (thiophene ring structure)

TABLE 6-2.—(continued)

Substance	Resonance energy (in kcal/mole)	Reference structure
Acids, RCOOH	28	R—C, =O, OH
Esters, RCOOR'	24	R—C, =O, OR'
Amides, RCONH$_2$	21	R—C, =O, NH$_2$
Carbon monoxide, CO	83	C=O
Carbon dioxide, CO$_2$	36	O=C=O
Carbon oxysulfide, SCO	20	S=C=O
Carbon disulfide, CS$_2$	11	S=C=S
Alkyl cyanates, RNCO	7	R—N=C=O

6-3. THE STRUCTURE OF AROMATIC MOLECULES

In the foregoing discussion of the structure of benzene the stability and characteristic aromatic properties of the substance have been attributed to resonance of the molecule between the two Kekulé structures. A similar treatment, which provides a similar explanation of their outstanding properties, can be given the condensed polynuclear aromatic hydrocarbons.

For naphthalene the conventional valence-bond structure is the Erlenmeyer structure:

I

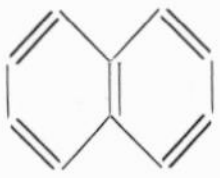

There are two other structures that differ from this only in a redistribution of the bonds:

II 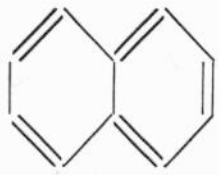   and   III

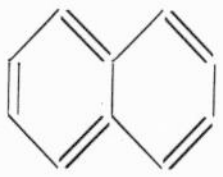

These three structures, the most stable valence-bond structures that can be formulated for naphthalene, are seen to have about the same energy and to correspond to about the same molecular configuration. It is to be expected then that they will be combined to represent the normal state of the naphthalene molecule, to which they should contribute about equally. Resonance among these three stable structures should stabilize the molecule to a greater extent than does the Kekulé resonance in benzene, involving two equivalent structures; it is seen from Table 6-2 that the resonance energy of naphthalene, 75 kcal/mole, is indeed much greater than that of benzene.

For anthracene four stable valence-bond structures can be formulated,

I 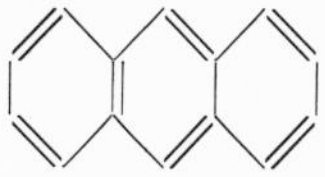   II

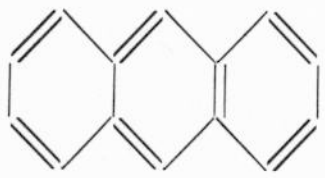

III 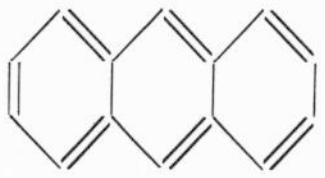   IV

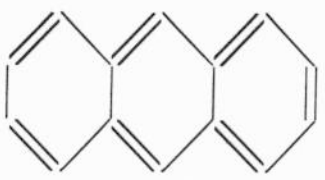

and for phenanthrene five,

I 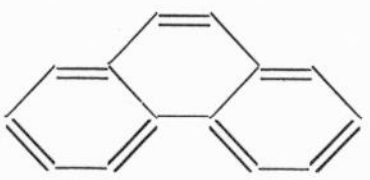   II

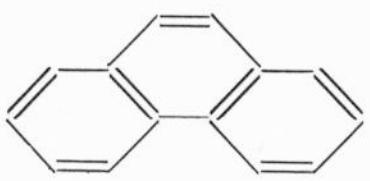

III 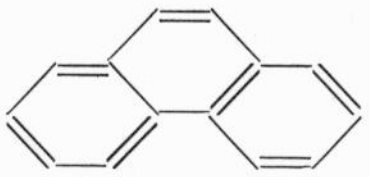   IV 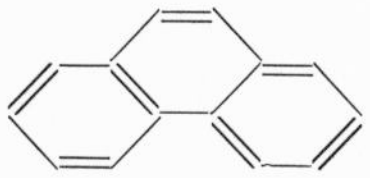   V

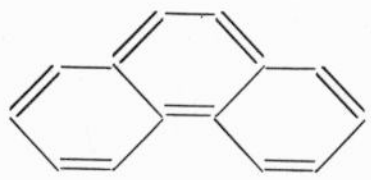

The observed values of the resonance energy are 105 kcal/mole for anthracene and 110 kcal/mole for phenanthrene. These are reasonable in comparison with those of benzene and naphthalene, and also with each other, the angular ring system having a larger number of stable resonating structures and a larger resonance energy than the linear ring system.

The higher condensed ring systems can be similarly represented as resonating among many valence-bond structures. The resonance energy increases in rough proportion to the number of hexagonal rings in the system. In addition, it is somewhat greater for the branched and angular ring systems than for the corresponding linear ones, the former resonating among more stable valence-bond structures than the latter (as in the case of phenanthrene and anthracene).

The configurations of the molecules are those expected for the resonating structures. Through resonance each bond acquires some double-bond character, which causes the adjacent bonds to strive to be coplanar. The molecules are thus brought into completely planar configurations, with 120° bond angles. This has been verified for naphthalene and anthracene and many larger aromatic hydrocarbons by careful x-ray studies.

The general chemical properties of the substances are also accounted for. The stabilization of the molecules by resonance gives them aromatic character in the same way as for benzene.

A simple consideration of the resonating structures leads to an explanation for observed differences in behavior of different carbon-carbon bonds in these molecules. In benzene we may say that each bond has $\frac{1}{2}$ double-bond character, since it occurs as a single bond in one Kekulé structure and as a double bond in the other. This does not mean that the bond behaves half the time as a double bond, but rather that it is a bond of a new type, very different from a double bond, and with properties intermediate between those of a double bond and a single bond. (The properties are not the average of those for the two bond types; consideration must also be given the stabilizing effect of the resonance energy.)

In naphthalene, anthracene, and phenanthrene the amounts of double-bond character, found by averaging the stable resonating structures, are as in the following diagrams. In naphthalene the 1,2 bonds have $\frac{2}{3}$ double-bond character and the 2,3 bonds $\frac{1}{3}$ double-bond character. These numbers cannot be given a simple quantitative interpretation in terms of chemical reactivity; they do demand, however, that qualitative relations be satisfied. The 1,2 bonds in naphthalene must be closer to

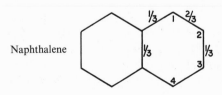

Naphthalene

Anthracene

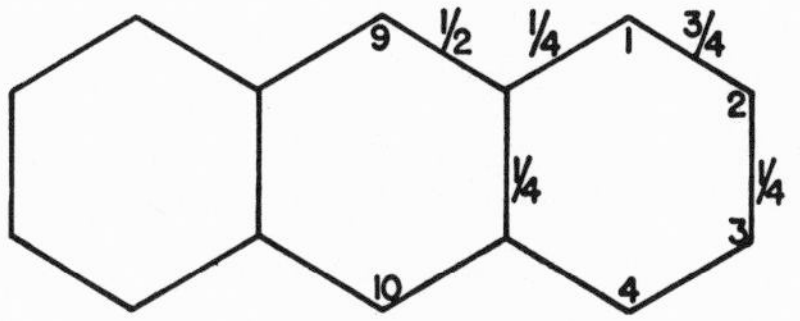

Phenanthrene

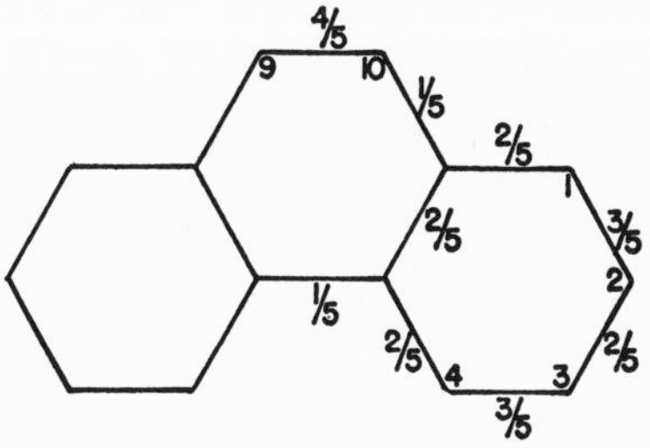

ordinary double bonds in their properties than are the benzene bonds, which in turn are much more like double bonds than are the 2,3 bonds in naphthalene, the last, indeed, having practically no double-bond properties. These statements are in agreement with general chemical experience. A hydroxyl group on carbon atom 2 of the system

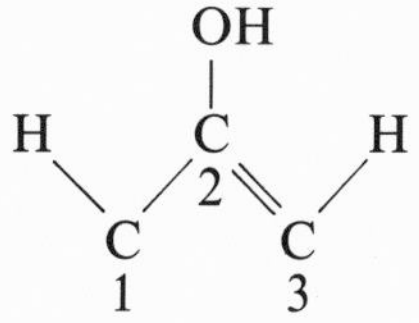

will induce substitution on carbon atom 3 on attack by certain reagents (bromine, diazomethane) rather than on carbon atom 1, the double bond serving as the path for the directing influence. This phenomenon can be used to test the extent to which different carbon-carbon bonds have the properties of a double bond. It has been found that with hydroxyl in position 2 of naphthalene reaction occurs readily in position 1, whereas even when position 1 is blocked with methyl reaction does not occur at position 3. This shows strong double-bond properties for the 1,2 bond and very weak ones for the 2,3 bond, as expected. Moreover, it has also been found that the 1,2 bonds in anthracene have stronger double-bond properties than the 1,2 bond in naphthalene, and that the double-bond properties of the 9,10 bond in phenanthrene are stronger still, in agreement with the amounts of double-bond character. For this reason phenanthrene, despite its greater thermodynamic stability, consequent to its greater resonance energy, is more reactive than anthracene.

The Quantitative Treatment of Resonance in Aromatic Molecules.— It has been found possible to carry out the quantitative discussion of resonance in aromatic molecules by simplifying the problem in the following way: Of the four valence orbitals of the carbon atom shown in Figure 4-1 before hybridization, three lie in the plane of the ring (s, p_x, and p_y, the plane of the ring being taken as the xy plane). These can be combined to give three bond orbitals that are coplanar and make $120°$ angles with one another,* and are thus adapted to the formation by the carbon atom of single covalent bonds to the two adjacent carbon atoms in the ring and to the attached hydrogen atom. It is assumed that this single-bond framework of the molecule,

$$
\begin{array}{c}
\text{H} \\
|\\
\text{H} \quad \text{C} \quad \text{H}\\
\diagdown \diagup \diagdown \diagup\\
\text{C} \qquad \text{C}\\
|\qquad\quad|\\
\text{C} \qquad \text{C}\\
\diagup \diagdown \diagup \diagdown\\
\text{H} \quad \text{C} \quad \text{H}\\
|\\
\text{H}
\end{array}
$$

remains unchanged; for each atom the fourth orbital and its electron then remain to be considered.

The fourth orbital is the p_z orbital shown in Figure 4-1. It possesses lobes above and below the plane of the ring. Let us assume that each of the six p_z orbitals is occupied by one electron (this involving neglect of ionic structures). The problem is to calculate the interaction energy of the six electrons in the six orbitals.

If there were only two orbitals and two electrons, as in the hydrogen molecule, the interaction energy would be just the resonance energy associated with the interchange of the two electrons between the two orbitals. This is the situation in ethylene; the two p_z electrons here convert the single bond into a double bond. Let us designate this p_z resonance energy by the symbol α.†

---

* These orbitals are given in a footnote of Sec. 4-4 for the s orbital divided equally among the three bonds. In benzene it is probable that the strong C—C bonds, with interatomic distances smaller than the single-bond value, use more of the s orbital than does the H—C bond.

† In this discussion α has been used to represent the magnitude of the resonance energy of two p_z electrons, taken with positive sign.

The resonance energy for the two Kekulé structures in benzene can be calculated in terms of α by neglecting all interactions except those between adjacent atoms in the ring. The way in which this calculation is carried out is described in Appendix V. The resonance energy for the two Kekulé structures is found to have the value 0.9 α, this being the extra stability of the ring relative to one of the Kekulé structures.

However, it is found on examination of the problem that consideration must also be given, in addition to the Kekulé structures *A* and *B*, to the three structures *C*, *D*, and *E* of the Dewar type:

The three structures *C*, *D*, and *E* are less stable than the Kekulé structures and make much smaller contributions to the normal state of the benzene molecule. They increase the resonance energy from 0.9α to 1.11α. By equating this to the empirical resonance energy of benzene, 37 kcal/mole, α is found to have the value 33 kcal/mole.

A similar treatment of naphthalene leads to the value 2.04α, which on equation to the empirical resonance energy 75 kcal/mole fixes α at 37 kcal/mole, in approximate agreement with the result for benzene. Calculations for anthracene and phenanthrene lead to 2.95α and 3.02α, respectively, for the resonance energy, giving $\alpha = 36$ and 35 kcal/mole on comparison with empirical values.

A second method of treatment, called the *molecular-orbital* treatment to differentiate it from the valence-bond treatment described above, has also been applied to the problem. With it the six electrons are not combined in pairs to form bonds, but move independently from atom to atom. The calculated resonance energies are expressed in terms of an energy quantity β, their values being 2.00β for benzene and 3.68β for naphthalene. These lead, on comparison with the empirical values, to $\beta = 20$ kcal/mole for both substances, the ratio for the two being given satisfactorily by this treatment as well as by the valence-bond treatment. For anthracene and phenanthrene the theory gives as values of the resonance energy 5.32β and 5.45β, corresponding again to $\beta = 20$ kcal/mole (within 0.5 kcal/mole) in each case.

There is, moreover, a reasonable relation between α and β. The first quantity is the energy of interchange of two p_z electrons, analogous to that of the hydrogen molecule, and the second is the energy of resonance of one electron between two p_z orbitals, analogous to that of the hydrogen molecule-ion.   The ratio of bond energies in H_2^+ and H_2 is 0.59, and that of β and α is 0.57; the agreement of these two ratios is excellent.

The valence-bond treatment described above involves neglect of the partial ionic character of the bonds in the benzene molecule, and the molecular-orbital treatment overemphasizes it.

The agreement of the two treatments with each other and with the empirical resonance-energy values makes it probable that the description of the structure of aromatic molecules given above will not need extensive revision in the future, although it may be subjected to further refinement.

More about the Molecular-orbital Method.—The molecular-orbital method of making quantum-mechanical calculations is somewhat simpler than the valence-bond method, and for this reason it has been used for most of the quantitative treatments of conjugated and aromatic molecules that have been carried out.   The following discussion of benzene from the molecular-orbital point of view may be compared with the valence-bond description of benzene as involving mainly two Kekulé structures in resonance.

In Figure 4-7 there is a representation of the ethylene molecule with a carbon-carbon σ bond and a carbon-carbon π bond.   The π bond involves a concentration of the two π electrons in regions above and below the plane of the molecule.   In the simplest valence-bond treatment the two π electrons remain on different carbon atoms (but interchange, in the Heitler-London way, as described in Section 1-5); in the simplest molecular-orbital treatment the two electrons are independent of one another, and thus are on the same carbon atom as often as on different carbon atoms (50 percent ionic character, 25 percent C^+C^- and 25 percent C^-C^+).   More refined calculations lead to an intermediate amount of ionic character; the refined valence-bond calculations and the refined molecular-orbital calculations give the same results.

In the simplest molecular-orbital treatment of the benzene molecule the orbital wave functions and resonance energy of single π electrons are evaluated.   Let us consider the wave function of one π electron in the benzene ring.   We might assign it to the $2p\pi$ orbital of a certain carbon atom.   Let this orbital wave function be represented by the letter a, as shown in Figure 6-1.   When the quantum-mechanical equations are examined, however, it is found that neither the function a nor any one of the equivalent $2p\pi$ orbital functions b, c, d, e, f (Fig. 6-1) is a satisfactory wave function for the π electron.   The hexagonal symmetry of the molecule requires instead that certain combinations of these six functions be taken as the wave functions.

A set of six acceptable one-electron wave functions given by the quantum-mechanical equations is the following:

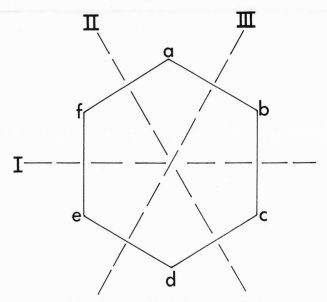

FIG. 6-1.—The three planes of symmetry (I, II, III)
referred to in the text.

$$B \quad \psi_6 = \frac{1}{\sqrt{6}} (a - b + c - d + e - f)$$

$$E'' \begin{cases} \psi_5 = \dfrac{1}{\sqrt{12}} (a - 2b + c + d - 2e + f) \\[2mm] \psi_4 = \dfrac{1}{\sqrt{12}} (2a - b - c + 2d - e - f) \end{cases}$$

(6-1)

$$E' \begin{cases} \psi_3 = \dfrac{1}{\sqrt{12}} (a + 2b + c - d - 2e - f) \\[2mm] \psi_2 = \dfrac{1}{\sqrt{12}} (2a + b - c - 2d - e + f) \end{cases}$$

$$A \quad \psi_1 = \frac{1}{\sqrt{6}} (a + b + c + d + e + f)$$

The corresponding values of the energy are 2β, β, $-\beta$, and -2β, as shown in Figure 6-2.

The most stable one-electron orbital is ψ_1 (symmetry symbol A). It is symmetric with respect to the vertical planes of symmetry of the benzene

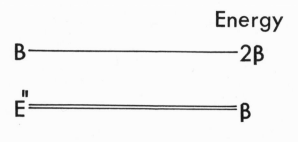

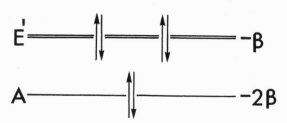

FIG. 6-2.—Energy values for the molecular
orbitals of benzene.

ring, and it corresponds to resonance of the π electron equally among all six carbon atoms. The resonance stabilizes the electron by the amount 2β (energy -2β; β is taken as positive).

The Pauli exclusion principle allows two electrons, with opposed spins, to occupy the molecular orbital ψ_1. Two others may occupy ψ_2, and two others ψ_3, as shown in Figure 6-2.

Thus the normal state of the benzene molecule is assigned the structure in which the six π electrons occupy the three molecular orbitals ψ_1, ψ_2, and ψ_3.

The total resonance energy is 8β (4β for the two electrons in ψ_1 and 4β for the four in ψ_2 and ψ_3). The resonance energy for the two π electrons of ethylene is 2β, and for a Kekulé structure of benzene might be expected to be 6β. Hence we conclude that the Kekulé resonance energy in benzene is 2β, according to simple molecular-orbital theory. This value of the resonance energy has been compared with that given by the valence-bond treatment in the preceding section.

The molecular orbital ψ_1 has been described above as involving symmetric resonance of the electron among the π orbitals of the six carbon atoms of the benzene ring. The least stable orbital, ψ_6 (not occupied in the normal state of the molecule), may be described in an equally simple way: it is antisymmetric with respect to reflection in each of the three vertical symmetry planes I, II, and III shown in Figure 6-1. An electron in this molecular orbital may be described as resonating equally but anti-symmetrically among the π orbitals of the six carbon atoms.

The molecular orbital ψ_2 is seen from its form (Equation 6-1) to have a single plane of antisymmetry, the plane marked I in Figure 6-1. Reflection in this plane (interchange of a and d, b and c, f and e) changes the sign of ψ_2. Similarly, the molecular orbital ψ_3 has a single plane of antisymmetry, the plane II. The functions ψ_2 and ψ_3 are seen to be identical except for orientation (rotation by 60°). This identity is expressed in the equality of their resonance energies.

We are now brought face-to-face with a complicating aspect of molecular-orbital theory. A third symmetry plane, III, is shown in Figure 6-1. It is equivalent to the planes I and II, and it is the plane of antisymmetry of the molecular orbital

$$\psi' = \frac{1}{\sqrt{12}} (a - b - 2c - d + e + 2f).$$

This molecular orbital is equivalent to ψ_1 and ψ_2, and has the same energy value. Why, then, are there not three orbitals E', with energy $-\beta$, shown in Figure 6-2? Why do not eight π electrons, rather than six, lead to stability for a hexagonal ring?

The answer to this question is that ψ_2, ψ_3, and ψ' are not independent solutions to the quantum-mechanical problem. The sum of ψ' and ψ_3 is seen to be ψ_2. There are only two *independent* molecular orbitals of symmetry type E', not three.

This complication is a minor one in quantum-mechanical calculations. It is, however, one of the features of the molecular-orbital description of the electronic structure of a molecule that have prevented the development of a qualitative molecular-orbital theory comparable in power, usefulness, and general applicability to the resonating-valence-bond theory that is presented in detail in this book.

EXERCISES

6-1.—The standard heat of combustion of methyl cyanide (gas) is 309.7 kcal/mole. (a) Calculate the standard heat of formation from C(graphite), $H_2(g)$, and $N_2(g)$. (b) The heat of formation from C(g), H(g), and N(g). (c) With the use of the single-bond energies from Table

3-3, evaluate the C≡N bond energy for this molecule. (Ans. 19.1, 593.6, 214.1 kcal/mole.)

6-2.—The standard heat of combustion (to carbon dioxide and liquid water) of formaldehyde (gas) is 134.1 kcal/mole and that of methanol (gas) is 179.3 kcal/mole. With use of the value for $H_2(g)$, 68.3 kcal/mole (Eq. 3-7), and the bond energies for single bonds (Table 3-3), evaluate the C=O bond energy. (Ans. 166.1 kcal/mole.)

6-3.—The heat of combustion of liquid pyridine, C_5H_5N, is 658.5 kcal/mole, and its heat of vaporization is 8.5 kcal/mole. (a) What is its heat of formation from elements in their standard states? (b) From $C(g)$, $N(g)$, and $H(g)$? (c) What is the sum of the bond energies for a single Kekulé structure? (d) The resonance energy? (Ans. 26, 1206, 1176, 30 kcal/mole.)

6-4.—Draw the Kekulé-like structures for the condensed aromatic hydrocarbon pyrene, $C_{16}H_{10}$. How much double-bond character do the various bonds have, on the assumption that these structures contribute equally? Would you expect pyrene to be more reactive or less reactive than phenanthrene?

Interatomic Distances and Their Relation to the Structure of Molecules and Crystals

7-1. INTERATOMIC DISTANCES IN NORMAL COVALENT MOLECULES: COVALENT RADII

As a result of the development of the x-ray method of studying the structure of crystals and the band-spectroscopic method and especially the electron-diffraction method of studying gas molecules, a large amount of information about interatomic distances in molecules and crystals has been collected. It has been found that the values of interatomic distances corresponding to covalent bonds can be correlated in a simple way in terms of a set of values of *covalent bond radii* of atoms, as described below.

The values found for the equilibrium distance between two atoms A and B connected by a covalent bond of fixed type (single, double, etc.) in different molecules and crystals are in most cases very nearly the same, so that it becomes possible to assign a constant value to the A—B bond distance for use in any molecule involving this bond. For example, the carbon—carbon distance in diamond (representing a single covalent bond) is 1.544 Å, and the values found in many other molecules are within ±0.01 Å of this value.

Similar constancy is shown by other covalent bond distances (with certain exceptions that will be discussed later). For the carbon—oxygen single bond, for example, the value 1.43 Å has been reported for methanol, ethanol, ethylene glycol, dimethyl ether, paraldehyde, metaldehyde, and many other molecules; this value is accepted as standard for the C—O bond.

Moreover, covalent bond distances are often related to one another in an additive manner; the bond distance A—B is equal to the arithmetic mean of the distances A—A and B—B. For example, the C—C distance in diamond is 1.544 Å and the Cl—Cl distance in Cl_2 is 1.988 Å. The arithmetic mean of these, 1.766 Å, is identical with the C—Cl distance 1.766 ± 0.003 Å found in carbon tetrachloride to within the probable error of the experimental value. In consequence, it becomes possible to assign to the elements *covalent radii* such that the sum of two radii is approximately equal to the equilibrium internuclear distance for the two corresponding atoms connected by a single covalent bond.

These covalent radii are for use in molecules in which the atoms form covalent bonds to a number determined by their positions in the periodic

TABLE 7-1.—COVALENT RADII FOR ATOMS

	C	N[a]	O[a]	F[a]
Single-bond radius	0.772	0.70	0.66	0.64 Å
Double-bond radius	.667			
Triple-bond radius	.603			
	Si	P	S	Cl
Single-bond radius	1.17	1.10	1.04	0.99
Double-bond radius	1.07	1.00	0.94	.89
Triple-bond radius	1.00	0.93	.87	
	Ge	As	Se	Br
Single-bond radius	1.22	1.21	1.17	1.14
Double-bond radius	1.12	1.11	1.07	1.04
	Sn	Sb	Te	I
Single-bond radius	1.40	1.41	1.37	1.33
Double-bond radius	1.30	1.31	1.27	1.23

[a] See also Table 7-3.

table—carbon four, nitrogen three, and so on. It is found empirically that the radii are applicable to covalent bonds with considerable ionic character; in some molecules, discussed in later sections, the partial ionic character plays an important part in determining the interatomic distances.

The radii are so chosen that their sums represent average internuclear distances for bonded atoms in molecules and crystals at room temperature. The atoms carry out thermal oscillations, which cause the internuclear distances to vary about their average values. At room temperature these are only slightly different from the values corresponding to the minima in the potential energy functions.

Values of the single-bond covalent radii of the nonmetallic elements are given in Table 7-1. These values, which were orginally obtained largely from x-ray diffraction studies of crystals, may be tested by comparison with the results of investigations of gas molecules as well as of crystals.

Comparison of the radii with half the interatomic distances in elementary molecules or crystals involving single bonds may be made as a check on the radii (Table 7-2). For the fourth-row elements, crystallizing with the diamond structure, and the halogens (other than fluorine) the

TABLE 7-2.—SINGLE-BOND DISTANCES AND RADII FOR ELEMENTS

Bond	Substance	Method[a]	One-half of observed distance	Assigned radius
C—C	Diamond	X-ray	0.772 Å	0.772 Å
Si—Si	Si(c)	X-ray	1.17	1.17
Ge—Ge	Ge(c)	X-ray	1.22	1.22
Sn—Sn	Sn(c)	X-ray	1.40	1.40
P—P	P_4(g)	ED	1.10	1.10
	P(c, black)	X-ray	1.09, 1.10	
As—As	As_4(g)	ED	1.22	1.21
	As(c)	X-ray	1.25	
Sb—Sb	Sb(c)	X-ray	1.43	1.41
S—S	S_8(g)	ED	1.04	1.04
	S_8(c)	X-ray	1.05, 1.02	
Se—Se	Se_8(c, α)	X-ray	1.17	1.17
	Se_8(c, β)	X-ray	1.17	
	Se(c, gray)	X-ray	1.16	
Te—Te	Te(c)	X-ray	1.38	1.37
F—F	F_2(g)	ED	0.718	0.64
	F_2(g)	Raman	.709	
Cl—Cl	Cl_2(g)	Sp	.994	.99
Br—Br	Br_2(g)	Sp	1.140	1.14
I—I	I_2(g)	Sp	1.333	1.33

[a] X-ray signifies the x-ray study of crystals, ED the electron-diffraction study of gas molecules, and Sp the spectroscopic study of gas molecules.

agreement is perfect, since these were the sources of the values in the table. The crystals P, As, Sb, Se, and Te also show reasonably good agreement. The electron-diffraction results for P_4, As_4, and S_8, obtained since the table was formulated, provide a good check of the corresponding radii.

The radius of the hydrogen atom in most molecules is 0.30 Å.

The dependence of the covalent radii of the elements on atomic number is shown in Figure 7-1. The relation is a simple one; for the first and second rows of the periodic table smooth curves can be drawn through the points, whereas for the other rows there is only a slight discontinuity between the quadrivalent atoms and their neighbors, which may be attributed to the change in the nature of the bond orbitals.

7-2. THE CORRECTION FOR ELECTRONEGATIVITY DIFFERENCE

The first values of covalent radii, as given in Table 7-1, were formulated before experimental values were available for F—F, O—O, and N—N single bonds.   An electron-diffraction study of F_2 then gave the F—F distance as 1.45 Å, whereas the accepted radius of fluorine would require 1.28 Å.   Similar discrepancies were then reported for O—O and

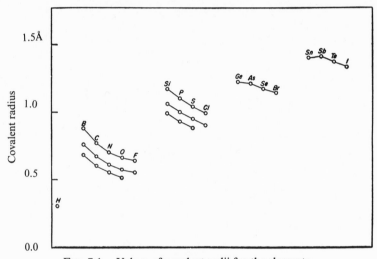

FIG. 7-1.—Values of covalent radii for the elements.

N—N.   Since the distances for many bonds between N, O, and F and other atoms are rather well given by the old radii, there are large deviations from additivity in the bond lengths.

It was suggested by Schomaker and Stevenson in 1941 that these deviations result from the partial ionic character of the bonds between unlike atoms.   They proposed that the radii for N, O, and F be taken to be those given by the N—N, O—O, and F—F distances (Table 7-3), and that in general the interatomic distance for a bond A—B be taken to be the sum of the radii for the atoms A and B with a correction term -0.09 Å $|x_A - x_B|$, in which $|x_A - x_B|$ is the absolute value of the difference in electronegativity of the two atoms.

There is at present uncertainty as to how to predict bond lengths in a reliable way.   In this book we shall assume that the length of a single bond between two atoms A and B can in most cases be reasonably well

TABLE 7-3.—SCHOMAKER-STEVENSON SINGLE-BOND
RADII OF FIRST-ROW ELEMENTS
(For other elements as in Table 7-1)

	B	C	N	O	F
Single-bond radius	0.81	0.772	0.74	0.74	0.72 Å
Double-bond radius	.71	.667	.62	.62	.60
Triple-bond radius	.64	.603	.55	.55	

calculated by use of the radii r_A and r_B as given for light atoms in Table 7-3 and for heavier atoms in Table 7-1, with the equation

$$D(A\text{—}B) = r_A + r_B - c|x_A - x_B| \qquad (7\text{-}1)$$

Here the Schomaker-Stevenson coefficient c is to be given the value 0.08 Å for all bonds involving one first-row atom (or two such atoms), the value 0.06 Å for bonds between Si, P, or S and a more electronegative atom (not of the first row), 0.04 Å for bonds between Ge, As, or Se and a more electronegative atom (not of the first row), and 0.02 Å for bonds between Sn, Sb, or Te and a more electronegative atom (not of the first row).

A comparison of a few calculated and observed bond lengths is given in Table 7-4. Similar agreement has been found for other bonds.

TABLE 7-4.—COMPARISON OF CALCULATED (EQUATION 7-1)
AND OBSERVED BOND LENGTHS

C—N	1.47 Å	C—O	1.43 Å	C—F 1.37 Å	Si—C	1.88 Å
$(CH_3)_3N$	1.47	CH_3OH	1.427	CH_3F 1.385	CH_3SiH_3	1.86
$C_6H_{12}N_4$	1.47	Many others	1.43		$(CH_3)_2SiH_2$	1.86
Many others	1.47				$(CH_3)_3SiH$	1.87
					$(CH_3)_4Si$	1.89
Cl—N	1.73 Å	Cl—O	1.69 Å	Cl—F 1.63 Å	O—F	1.42 Å
CH_3NCl_2	1.73	Cl_2O	1.70	ClF 1.63	OF_2	1.42

7-3. DOUBLE-BOND AND TRIPLE-BOND RADII

The experimental value for the carbon-carbon distance in ethylene, 1.334 ± 0.003 Å, leads to the double-bond radius 0.667 Å for carbon, as given in Table 7-1.

For the length of the carbon-carbon triple bond a number of reliable values in excellent agreement with one another are available. These include the value 1.204 Å for acetylene, 1.207 Å for methylacetylene,

1.211 Å for chloroacetylene, and 1.207 Å for methylchloroacetylene from infrared and microwave studies, and closely agreeing values from electron-diffraction studies. These lead to the value 0.603 Å for the triple-bond radius of carbon. The spectroscopic value 1.094 Å for $N\equiv N$ in N_2 gives 0.547 Å for the triple-bond radius of nitrogen.

In general the double-bond radii are about 0.105 Å less and the triple-bond radii about 0.17 Å less than the single-bond radii.

The usefulness of the multiple-bond radii in the discussion of the electronic structure of molecules will be illustrated in later sections.

7-4. INTERATOMIC DISTANCES AND RESONANCE

The resonance of the benzene molecule between the two Kekulé structures (the small contributions of other structures being neglected) can be considered to give each of the six carbon-carbon bonds 50 percent single-bond character and 50 percent double-bond character. We would expect that the carbon-carbon interatomic distance would lie between the single-bond value 1.544 Å and the double-bond value 1.334 Å—not midway between, but closer to the lower value, both because of the extra stabilization due to the resonance energy (a strong bond having smaller interatomic distance than a weak bond) and because of the greater effectiveness of the double-bond potential function (with its greater curvature of the neighborhood of its minimum, corresponding to its larger force constant) in determing the position of the minimum of the potential function for the resonating molecule. The observed value for benzene, 1.397 ± 0.001 Å, is only 0.07 Å greater than the double-bond distance.

It is to be expected that the bending of the bent bonds of the two

double bonds in a system $\overset{\diagdown}{\underset{\diagup}{}}C\!-\!C\overset{\diagup}{\underset{\diagdown}{}}$ away from their tetrahedral direc-

tions would make the forces of repulsion between them somewhat less than in a saturated molecule, and that for this reason the carbon-carbon single-bond distance in a conjugated system would be less than the normal value 1.544 Å. An estimate of the magnitude of this effect can be made by consideration of the C—H distances in saturated and unsaturated molecules. The C—H distance in methane, ethane, and other saturated molecules is about 1.100 Å; in ethylene, benzene, and other molecules in which the carbon atom forms a double bond it is about 1.085 Å, representing a decrease in the bond length of about 0.015 Å. In allene, $H_2C\!=\!C\!=\!CH_2$, the carbon-carbon double-bond length is 1.310 Å, 0.024 Å less than its normal value, and in glycine the carbon-carbon single bond (adjacent to a double bond with oxygen in the carboxylate ion) has length 1.523 Å, which is 0.021 Å less than the normal value. The average of these observed decreases in bond length is 0.020 Å, and we conclude that, as a result of the decreased repulsion of the bent bonds, the effective radius of the carbon atom, for either another double bond or the two single bonds that it can form in addition to the first double bond, is about 0.020 Å less than the normal radius.

We accordingly conclude that a pure single bond between two carbon

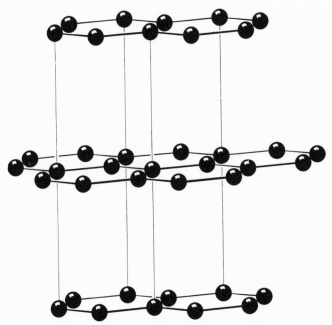

Fig. 7-2.—The arrangement of carbon atoms in the graphite crystal.

atoms forming double bonds with other atoms, as in 1,3-butadiene, $H_2C{=}CH{-}CH{=}CH_2$, would be decreased in length by 0.040 Å to 1.504 Å. In fact, the central carbon-carbon distance in the molecule is somewhat shorter still, about 1.46 Å. The further decrease in length may be attributed to partial multiple-bond character of the bond as discussed in later sections of this and the following chapter.

Similarly, the expected length of the central double bond in buta-triene, $H_2C{=}C{=}C{=}CH_2$, is 1.294 Å, a value 0.040 Å less than normal value, to correct for the bent-bond effect. The observed length of this bond is 1.284 Å, and that of the other two double bonds (with 1.314 Å expected) is 1.309 Å. These bond lengths show a small shortening from conjugation.

An empirical curve relating carbon-carbon interatomic distances with the amounts of single-bond and double-bond character for molecules resonating between structures some of which represent the bond as a single bond and some as a double bond could be used in interpreting observed values of the interatomic distances to obtain information as to the type of the bonds. The pure single-bond distance 1.504 Å (for use in a conjugated system of alternating single and double bonds) and the pure double-bond distance 1.334 Å provide the end points of the curve. A third point, at 50 percent double-bond character, is provided by the value 1.397 Å for benzene, and a fourth point by the value 1.420 Å for graphite. The structure of the graphite crystal is shown in Figure 7-2. It consists of hexagonal layers of molecules which are separated by a distance so large (3.40 Å) that there can be no covalent bonds between them; each of the layers is a giant molecule, and the superimposed layer molecules are held together only by weak van der Waals forces. The four valences of each carbon atom are used to form bonds with its three neighbors; the layer molecule resonates among many valence-bond structures such as

and in this way each carbon-carbon bond achieves one-third double-bond character.

Through these four points we draw a smooth curve, as shown in Figure 7-3, which we accept as representing the dependence of carbon-carbon interatomic distance on the amount of double-bond character for single-bond:double-bond resonance. The use of the curve in the discussion of the nature of the carbon-carbon bonds in resonating molecules is illustrated in the following chapter.

In view of the reasonable behavior of interatomic-distance values in general, it seems probable that by a suitable translation and change of vertical scale (to give the correct end points) the same function can be used for bonds between other atoms, and also for resonance involving triple bonds. These further uses of the curve are also illustrated in the following chapter.

7-5. THE CONDITIONS FOR EQUIVALENCE OR
NONEQUIVALENCE OF BONDS

It often happens that the most reasonable valence-bond structure that can be written for a molecule or crystal is less symmetrical than the known or predicted arrangement of the atomic nuclei. In this circumstance there is another valence-bond structure equivalent to the first and differing from it only in the distribution of the bonds (or there may be several other equivalent structures). An example is provided by

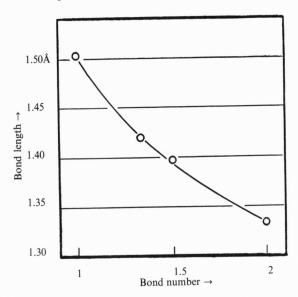

FIG. 7-3.—The relation between interatomic distance and the amount of double-bond character for single-bond:double-bond resonance of carbon-carbon bonds.

benzene, the two Kekulé structures being the most stable valence-bond structures for this molecule. Another example is sulfur dioxide, for which the reasonable structures $\overset{..}{S}{}^{+}\diagup\diagdown$ and $\overset{..}{S}{}^{+}\diagup\diagdown$ may be written; many other molecules of this type are discussed in the following chapters.

Let us consider a molecule A_2B, for which the two equivalent structures A—B—A (I) and A—B—A (II) may be written, each involving two bonds of which one is stronger than the other. We now ask whether the two A atoms in the molecules are to be considered as equivalent or not, and whether or not there are two different A—B bond lengths in the molecule.

This question needs to be discussed in detail. The principles of quantum mechanics require that the normal state of the isolated molecule that is observed over a long period of time have a resonance structure to which the equivalent structures I and II contribute equally. The interpretation of this resonance depends on the magnitude of the resonance energy. If the resonance energy is very large, no experiment can be devised to detect the individual structures I and II. The frequency of resonance is the resonance energy divided by Planck's constant h, and the minimum period of time during which an experiment could be carried out that would distinguish structure I from structure II is h divided by the resonance energy. For resonance between valence-bond structures in benzene and sulfur dioxide the resonance energy is so large that this period is about 10^{-15} seconds, and the bonds are made completely equivalent by resonance. There is only one value for the bond lengths.

If, on the other hand, the resonance integral is very small, it may be convenient to refer to the substance as containing tautomeric or isomeric molecules, with electronic structures that are represented essentially by I or II alone.

It is convenient for us to draw a rather broad line between resonance (in the sense of resonance of a molecule among alternative valence-bond structures) and tautomerism by the use of the ratio of the resonance frequency to the frequency of nuclear motion. If the resonance frequency is much greater than the frequency of oscillation of the nuclei, the molecule will be represented by the resonating structure {A—B—A, A—B—A} and the two bonds in the molecule will be equivalent, whereas if it is much less the two atoms A will oscillate for some time about equilibrium positions relative to B that are not equivalent, and will then interchange their roles.

The discussion can be made more definite by considering the forces between B and the two attached atoms. Structure I alone corresponds to a potential function that brings the equilibrium position of one atom (A' for the molecule A'—B—A) closer to B than that for A is, whereas structure II places A closer to B than A' is. (A and A' might, indeed, be isotopes, and hence physically distinguishable.) If the resonance energy is small, the molecule will oscillate for a time in a manner corresponding to a small distance A'—B and a larger distance B—A and then oscillate about new equilibrium positions, with B—A smaller than A'—B. This corresponds to tautomerism. If the resonance energy is sufficiently large, however, the potential function for nuclear oscillation will be changed, so that it has for each atom A a single minimum, and the two atoms A and A' will oscillate in equivalent fashion about equilibrium positions equidistant from B. The two bonds in the molecule are then equivalent. The magnitude of the resonance integral required to achieve this depends on (among other factors) the difference in the equilibrium configurations of the alternative structures. Thus the configurations of the carbon nuclei in benzene corresponding to the two Kekulé structures separately (with C—C = 1.54 Å and C=C = 1.33 Å) would place the carbon atoms only about 0.1 Å from their actual positions (with C—C = 1.39 Å). This distance (0.1 Å) is less than the usual amplitude of nuclear oscillation (about 0.2 Å), so that with each libration of the nuclei the molecule would pass through the configuration appropriate to each of the Kekulé structures. On the other hand, tautomerism may be expected when the stable configurations differ largely from one another, as, for example, with D and L configurations of complex molecules.

7-6. TETRAHEDRAL AND OCTAHEDRAL COVALENT RADII

Tetrahedral Radii.—In crystals with the diamond, sphalerite, and wurtzite arrangements (Figs. 7-4, 7-5, and 7-6) each atom is surrounded tetrahedrally by four other atoms. If the atoms are those of fourth-column elements or of two elements symmetrically arranged relative to the fourth column, the number of valence electrons is right to permit the formation of a tetrahedral covalent bond between each atom and its four neighbors. The diamond arrangement is shown by C, Si, Ge, and Sn, and the sphalerite or the wurtzite arrangement (or both) by many binary compounds.

In all of these crystals it is probable that the bonds are covalent bonds with some ionic character. In ZnS, for example, the extreme covalent structure

places formal charges 2− on zinc and 2+ on sulfur. It is probable that the bonds have enough ionic character in this crystal and in others of

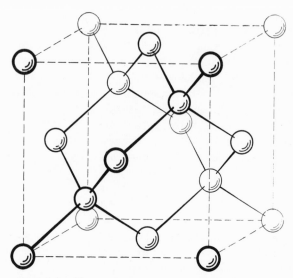

FIG. 7-4.—The arrangement of the carbon atoms in the diamond crystal. Each atom has four near neighbors, which are arranged about it at the corners of a regular tetrahedron.

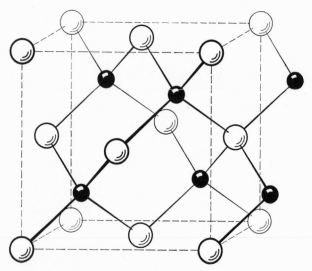

FIG. 7-5.—The arrangement of zinc atoms (small circles) and sulfur atoms (large circles) in sphalerite, the cubic form of zinc sulfide.

similar structure to make the actual charges of the atoms nearly zero; for ZnS this would require about 50 percent ionic character.

A set of values of tetrahedral covalent radii for use in crystals of these types is given in Table 7-5.   These values were obtained from the observed interatomic distances in crystals of these tetrahedral types and of other

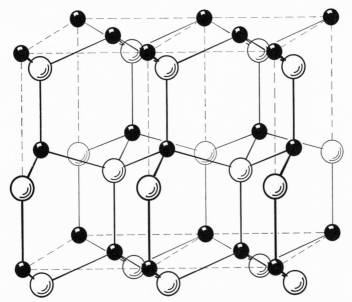

F<small>IG</small>. 7-6.—The arrangement of zinc atoms (small circles) and sulfur atoms (large circles) in wurtzite, the hexagonal form of zinc sulfide. The unit of structure outlined by dashes is the orthohexagonal unit, with edges at right angles to one another.   The lengths of the edges of the unit in the basal plane have the ratio $\sqrt{3}/1$, corresponding to the 120° angles of the hexagonal unit.

types in which the atom of interest forms four covalent bonds with neighboring atoms which surround it tetrahedrally.

Octahedral Radii.—In pyrite (Fig. 7-7) each iron atom is surrounded by six sulfur atoms, which are at the corners of a nearly regular octahedron, corresponding to the formation by iron of $3d^2 4s 4p^3$ bonds.   The iron-sulfur distance is 2.27 Å, from which, by subtraction of the tetrahedral radius of sulfur, 1.04 Å, the value 1.23 Å for the $d^2 sp^3$ octahedral covalent radius of bivalent iron is obtained (Table 7-6).

From similar data for other crystals with the pyrite structure or a closely related structure, values can be obtained for the octahedral radii

TABLE 7-5.—TETRAHEDRAL COVALENT RADII

	Be	B	C	N	O	F
	1.06	0.88	0.77	0.70	0.66	0.64
	Mg	Al	Si	P	S	Cl
	1.40	1.26	1.17	1.10	1.04	0.99
Cu	Zn	Ga	Ge	As	Se	Br
1.35	1.31	1.26	1.22	1.18	1.14	1.11
Ag	Cd	In	Sn	Sb	Te	I
1.52	1.48	1.44	1.40	1.36	1.32	1.28
	Hg					
	1.48					

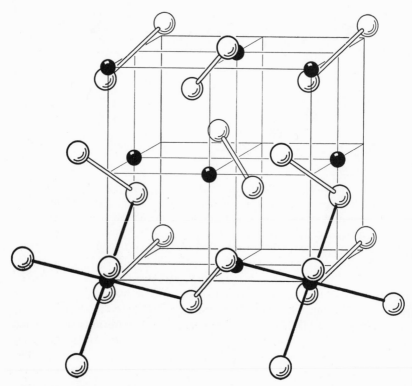

FIG. 7-7.—The arrangement of iron atoms (small circles) and sulfur atoms (large circles) in the cubic crystal pyrite, FeS_2. Each iron atom is surrounded octahedrally by six sulfur atoms, and each sulfur atom is surrounded tetrahedrally by one sulfur atom and three iron atoms.

of other transition-group elements. The elements Fe(II) and Co(III) in the indicated valence states are isoelectronic; it is interesting that there is very little difference in their radii, the decrease in radius with unit increase in atomic number being only 0.01 Å. The same very small decrease is shown in the two sequences Ru(II), Rh(III), Pd(IV) and Os(II), Ir(III), Pt(IV), which, moreover, have identical values of the radii.

For all of these atoms the number of electrons is such that all of the stable orbitals are occupied by unshared pairs or are used in bond formation. In CoS_2, $CoSe_2$, NiAsS, and $AuSb_2$ the atoms Co(II), Ni(III), and Au(IV) contain one more electron than can be fitted into the three

TABLE 7-6.—OCTAHEDRAL COVALENT RADII

Fe(II)	1.23 Å	Ru(II)	1.33 Å	Os(II)	1.33 Å
Co(III)	1.22	Rh(III)	1.32	Ir(III)	1.32
Ni(IV)	1.21	Pd(IV)	1.31	Pt(IV)	1.31
Co(II)	1.32			Au(IV)	1.40
Ni(III)	1.30				
Ni(II)	1.39				
Fe(IV)	1.20				

$3d$ orbitals ($5d$ for Au) that are left after the d^2sp^3 orbitals are usurped by the bonds. It is not known whether this extra electron is pushed into an outer orbital ($4d$) or whether a compromise is reached, the bonds relinquishing some $3d$ orbital to the electron. The effect of the extra electron is to produce an increase of 0.09 or 0.10 Å in the octahedral covalent radius for each of these atoms. The two extra electrons in Ni(II) produce a total increase of twice as much, 0.18 Å.

A deficiency of electrons, on the other hand, has, as might be expected, little effect on the radius. The value found for Fe(IV) is about 1.20 Å, only slightly less than that for Fe(II).

7-7. INTERATOMIC DISTANCES FOR FRACTIONAL BONDS

The carbon-carbon bond lengths for bond numbers 1, 2, and 3 are a linear function of the logarithm of the bond number. It has been found that a similar relation holds for values of n less than 1:

$$D(n) = D(1) - 0.60 \log n \qquad (7\text{-}2)$$

Here $D(n)$ is the bond length for bond number n (less than unity) and $D(1)$ is the bond length for $n = 1$, both in Ångström units.

The equation may be rewritten as

$$D(n) = D(1) + 0.60 \log (1/n) \tag{7-3}$$

We see that, since log 2 is 0.30, a half-bond ($n = 0.50$) is 0.18 Å longer than a single bond, and a quarter-bond is 0.36 Å longer than a single bond.

The use of this equation is illustrated in some of the exercises at the end of this chapter and in later sections of the book, especially Chapter 11.

7-8. VALUES OF SINGLE-BOND METALLIC RADII

In Chapter 11 there will be given a discussion of the observed interatomic distances in crystals of the metallic elements and an account of the derivation from them of a set of values of single-bond metallic radii. These values are shown in Table 7-7. They refer to single covalent bonds for which the bond orbitals have the same hybrid character as in the metals themselves, as discussed in Chapter 11. The relation be-

TABLE 7-7.—SINGLE-BOND METALLIC RADII

Li	Be	B											
1.225	0.889	0.81											
Na	Mg	Al	Si										
1.572	1.364	1.248	1.173										
K	Ca	Sc	Ti	V	Cr	Mn	Fe	Co	Ni	Cu	Zn	Ga	Ge
2.025	1.736	1.439	1.324	1.224	1.176	1.171	1.165	1.162	1.154	1.173	1.249	1.245	1.223
Rb	Sr	Y	Zr	Nb	Mo	Tc	Ru	Rh	Pd	Ag	Cd	In	Sn
2.16	1.914	1.616	1.454	1.342	1.296	1.271	1.246	1.252	1.283	1.330	1.413	1.497	1.399
Cs	Ba	La	Hf	Ta	W	Re	Os	Ir	Pt	Au	Hg	Tl	Pb
2.35	1.981	1.690	1.442	1.343	1.304	1.283	1.260	1.265	1.295	1.336	1.440	1.549	1.538

tween these radii and other radii (tetrahedral, octahedral) may be seen by a comparison of their values.

Use will be made of the single-bond metallic radii in some of the following chapters.

7-9. IONIC RADII AND VAN DER WAALS RADII

The structure of the sodium chloride crystal was determined by W. H. Bragg and W. L. Bragg in 1913, by the x-ray diffraction method. They found that the crystal does not contain diatomic molecules; instead, each atom has six neighboring atoms of the other kind, as shown in Figure 1-1. It is reasonable to assume that the crystal consists of sodium ions and chloride ions.

In the period around 1920 a detailed theory of the structure of ionic crystals was developed by Born, Haber, Landé, Madelung, and other investigators. Each ion in the crystal is considered to attract the six neighboring ions, with opposite electric charge, and also to attract or repel the more different ions in the crystal, through operation of the inverse-square Coulomb forces. In addition, a repulsive force, resulting from the interpenetration of electron shells, operates between each ion and the adjacent ions. A detailed account of the theory of ionic crystals is given in Chapter 13 of *The Nature of the Chemical Bond*.

It has been found possible to assign ionic radii to ions, as given in Table 7-8. For the alkali and halogenide ions these radii represent the relative extension in space of the outer electron shells, and they have such values as

TABLE 7-8.—IONIC RADII

Li^+	0.60 Å	Be^{++}	0.31 Å	O^{--}	1.40 Å	F^-	1.36 Å
Na^+	0.95	Mg^{++}	0.65	S^{--}	1.84	Cl^-	1.81
K^+	1.33	Ca^{++}	0.99	Se^{--}	1.98	Br^-	1.95
Rb^+	1.48	Sr^{++}	1.13	Te^{--}	2.21	I^-	2.16
Cs^+	1.69	Ba^{++}	1.35				

to cause their sums to be equal to interionic distances in crystals with the sodium chloride structure. For other crystals the observed interionic distances may be somewhat larger or smaller than the sums of the crystal radii. For example, in crystals in which there are eight anions arranged about a cation the observed distance is about 4 percent larger than the sum of the radii, and in crystals in which there are four anions about a cation the observed distance is about 5 percent smaller than the sum of the radii.

The observed Na—Cl distance in the sodium chloride crystal is 2.81 Å. This distance is equal to the sum of the ionic radii; the values of the ionic radii were selected in order to give this equality.

The description of the sodium chloride crystal as consisting of an arrangement of sodium ions and chloride ions is an extreme one; an alternative description may be given in terms of covalent bonds (with a large amount of ionic character) resonating among the Na—Cl positions. From this point of view the Na—Cl distance would be discussed in terms of the covalent radius of sodium, about 1.57 Å (the value of the single-bond metallic radius given in Table 7-7), and the covalent radius of chlorine, 0.99 Å.

Van der Waals Radii.—In a molecule of chlorine, with the electronic structure $:\overset{..}{\underset{..}{Cl}}:\overset{..}{\underset{..}{Cl}}:$, the covalent radius of chlorine may be described as representing roughly the distance from the chlorine nucleus to the pair of electrons that is shared with the other chlorine atom. In a crystal of the substance the molecules are attracted together by their van der Waals interactions and assume equilibrium positions at which the attractive forces are balanced by the repulsive forces that result from the interpenetration of the outer electron shells of the atoms in contact with one another. One-half the equilibrium internuclear distance between two chlorine atoms in such van der Waals contact is called the *van der Waals radius* or the *packing radius* of the chlorine atom.

The van der Waals radius of chlorine is larger than its covalent radius,

TABLE 7-9.—VAN DER WAALS RADII OF ATOMS

		H	1.2 Å		
N	1.5 Å	O	1.40	F	1.35 Å
P	1.9	S	1.85	Cl	1.80
As	2.0	Se	2.00	Br	1.95
Sb	2.2	Te	2.20	I	2.15

Radius of methyl group, $-CH_3$, 2.0 Å
Half-thickness of aromatic molecule, 1.70 Å

since it involves the interposition of two electron pairs between the atoms, rather than one. Moreover, the van der Waals radius of the chlorine atom is expected to be approximately equal to the ionic radius, inasmuch as the bonded chlorine atom presents the same aspect to the atoms in contact with it in directions away from the bond as the chloride ion, $:\overset{..}{\underset{..}{Cl}}:^-$, does in all directions. The observed chlorine-chlorine contact distances in many crystals lies close to the value 3.6 Å, and 1.80 Å is taken as the van der Waals radius of chlorine. This value and some other values are given in Table 7-9.

It is interesting to note that the van der Waals radii given in Table 7-9 are 0.75 to 0.83 Å greater than the corresponding single-bond covalent radii; to within their limit of reliability they could be taken as equal to the covalent radius plus 0.80 Å.

The effective radius of an atom in a direction that makes only a small angle with the direction of a covalent bond formed by the atom is smaller than the van der Waals radius in directions away from the bond. This might well be expected from the fact that the electron pair which would give the chloride ion, $:\overset{..}{\underset{..}{Cl}}:^-$, for example, its size in the direction toward the left is pulled in to form the bond in methyl chloride, $H_3C\!:\!\ddot{C}l\!:$. In consequence, atoms that are bonded to the same atom can approach one another much more closely than the sum of the van der Waals radii. In carbon tetrachloride the chlorine atoms are only 2.87 Å apart, and yet the properties of the substance indicate that there is no great strain resulting from the repulsion that should correspond to the van der Waals diameter 3.6 Å. Even in methylene chloride and chloroform, where the strain might be relieved by increasing the bond angle, the chlorine-chlorine distance is only 2.92 Å. We conclude that the nonbonded radius of an atom in directions close to the bond direction (within 35°) is about 0.5 Å less than the van der Waals radius; a unicovalent atom can be considered as a sphere that is whittled down on the side of the bond.

EXERCISES

7-1.—The electron-diffraction study of trimethylamine oxide, $(CH_3)_3NO$, has shown it to have a tetrahedral configuration with carbon-nitrogen bond length 1.49 ± 0.02 Å and nitrogen-oxygen bond length 1.44 ± 0.04 Å. Assign an electronic structure to the molecule. What values of the bond lengths would be predicted for this structure?

7-2.—The ozone molecule is observed to be bent, with bond angle 116.8°. Assign a resonating electronic structure to the molecule. Using the $O\!=\!O$ bond length 1.24 Å from Table 7-3 and a correction based upon the carbon-carbon bond length in ethylene and benzene, calculate a value of the bond length in ozone. (Ans. 1.30 Å.)

7-3.—The observed bond length in ozone is 1.278 ± 0.003 Å. Assuming that the difference between this value and the value calculated in Ex. 7-2 is the result of a difference in electronegativity for oxygen atoms with different formal charges ($+1$ and -1), evaluate the dependence of the electronegativity on formal charge. (Ans. $\Delta x = 0.27$ for O^+ and O^-.)

7-4.—Assign an electronic structure to methanethiol, H_3CSH, with your predicted values of bond lengths and bond angles. The experimental values, from microwave spectroscopy, are $C\!-\!S = 1.818$ Å, $S\!-\!H = 1.329$ Å, $C\!-\!H = 1.104$ Å, angles HCH $= 110.3°$ and HSC $= 100.3°$

7-5.—It is mentioned in Section 4-7 that the lengths of the carbon-carbon double bond and triple bond are approximately equal to the chords of arcs with length 1.544 Å, the single-bond value, and with the ends of the two or three arcs at the tetrahedral angle for each carbon atom. Use a similar assumption to calculate a value for the carbon-carbon internuclear distance in cyclopropane, C_3H_6. (Ans. 1.511 Å; experimental values are 1.524 ± 0.014 Å for cyclopropane and 1.513 ± 0.001 Å for both chlorocyclopropane and cyanocyclopropane.)

7-6.—The study of the structure of the ethylene oxide molecule, C_2H_4O, by microwave spectroscopy has led to the bond lengths C—C = 1.470 Å and C—O = 1.435 Å, with bond angle COC = 61.6°. Using the method of Exercise 7-5, with normal bond lengths (along circular arcs) 1.544 Å and 1.43 Å, respectively, and unstrained bond angles 109.5° for C and 90° for O, calculate values of the C—C and C—O chords. (Ans. 1.45 Å, 1.42 Å.)

7-7.—It is expected that the covalent radius of an atom would depend on the nature of the bond orbital. From the following observed M—H bond lengths evaluate the *p*-bond covalent radius for C, Si, Ge, and Sn: CH 1.120, CH_4 1.093, SiH 1.521, SiH_4 1.480, GeH 1.591, GeH_4 1.527, SnH 1.785, SnH_4 1.701 Å. (Ans. 0.799, 1.21, 1.28, 1.48 Å.)

7-8.—Assign electronic structures to the gas molecules $SnCl_2$, $SnBr_2$, and SnI_2. What value would you expect for the X-Sn-X bond angles? For the bond lengths? (See the preceding Exercise.) The observed values (by the electron-diffraction method) are angles about 95°, lengths 2.42, 2.55, and 2.73 Å, respectively; the observed bond lengths for the tetrahalogenides are 2.31, 2.44, and 2.64 Å, respectively.

7-9.—Assign an electronic structure to the gas molecule Si_2. What orbitals are used for bond formation and for unshared pairs? What bond length would you predict for the molecule? See Exercise 7-7. (Ans. 2.21 Å; the observed value, from band spectroscopy, is 2.252 Å.)

7-10.—Discuss the observed bond lengths 1.647 Å in AlH(*g*) and 1.602 Å in $(AlH)^+$. To what difference in structure do you attribute the difference in bond length?

7-11.—Using the method of Section 7-2 (correction for electronegativity difference), predict values for the normal covalent bond lengths Cl—F, Br—F, and I—F. The observed value in ClF is 1.628 Å. What is the nature of the bond orbitals? (Ans. 1.63 Å, 1.76 Å, 1.93 Å; nearly 100 percent *p* character.)

7-12.—The observed bond lengths in dichlorotris-2-chlorovinylstibine, $(CHClCH)_3SbCl_2$, are 2.15 ± 0.01 Å for the three Sb—C bonds, in the equatorial plane of the trigonal bipyramid, and 2.45 ± 0.01 Å for the Sb—Cl bonds. The observed Sb—Cl bond length in $SbCl_3$ is 2.33 Å. What is the effect of *d* character (Exercise 5-11) on the antimony radius?

7-13.—The ClF_3 molecule is observed to be planar. Two fluorine atoms, nearly on opposite sides of the chlorine atom, are at the distance 1.698 ± 0.005 Å; the third is in between (bond angle 87.5° to each of the other two), at the distance 1.598 ± 0.005 Å. Discuss the unshared-pair orbitals and bond orbitals in relation to the bond lengths (see Exercises 5-11 and 7-11).

7-14.—By extrapolating in the series Sb, Te, I, Xe obtain values of the electronegativity and the normal-valence radius of xenon. Use these values to calculate the Xe-F bond length for p bond orbitals of xenon and for orbitals with some d character (estimate the difference from ClF_3, Exercise 7-13). The observed values are 2.00 Å in XeF_2(linear) and 1.95 Å in XeF_4 (square planar). (Ans. 2.8, 1.29 Å, 1.91 Å, 2.01 Å.)

Types of Resonance in Molecules

WITH the background of information given in the preceding chapters about the nature of the phenomenon of the resonance of a molecule among several valence-bond structures and its relation to such properties as the energy of the molecule and its interatomic distances, we are now ready to begin the discussion of the structure of molecules to which a single valence-bond formula cannot be assigned. Some of these resonating molecules have already been mentioned as examples; in the selection of others for treatment the effort has been made to illustrate all of the principal types of resonance and to present substantiating evidence in each case.

8-1. THE STRUCTURE OF SIMPLE RESONATING MOLECULES

Carbon Monoxide.—The carbon monoxide molecule may be described as resonating among the four structures $:C:O:$, $:C::O:$, $:C::O:$, and $:C:::O:$. (The second and third structures differ in the use of p_y and p_z orbitals, as discussed for nitrous oxide in Section 6-1.) The resonance energy is very large: it is 83 kcal/mole, relative to a structure with a double bond (Table 6-2).

In the discussion of the internuclear distance in the molecule we make use of the normal covalent structures $:C—O:$, $:C=O:$, $:C=O:$, and $:C\equiv O:$, rather than the extreme covalent structures $:C:O:$, and so forth, because the empirical system of covalent radii is based upon the normal covalent structures, with the normal amount of ionic character. The expected bond lengths, given by the sums of the radii in Table 7-3 with the correction -0.08 Å for ionic character, are 1.43 Å for the first structure, 1.21 Å for the second and third, and 1.07 Å for the fourth. The observed value, 1.130 Å, is only 0.06 Å larger than the value for the structure $:\overset{-}{C}\equiv\overset{+}{O}:$, indicating that this structure makes a large contribution to the normal state of the molecule. The observed value of the electric dipole moment of the molecule is 0.112 D. This corresponds to resultant charges of only $+0.02e$ and $-0.02e$ on the atoms; there is some uncertainty about the direction of the moment, but it probably corresponds to a negative charge on the oxygen atom. It is shown in Exercises 8-3 and 8-4 that the assumption of independent resonance of the p_z and p_y electron pairs leads to about 60 percent as the contribution of the structure $:\overset{-}{C}\equiv\overset{+}{O}:$ required to account for the small dipole moment.

Carbon Dioxide and Related Molecules.—It is not surprising that so unconventional a molecule as carbon monoxide should have a resonating structure; but recognition of the fact that the carbon dioxide molecule, for which the valence-bond formula $O=C=O$ has been written ever since the development of valence theory, is not well represented by this structure alone and that other valence-bond structures also make important contributions must have come as a surprise to everyone.

The carbon-oxygen distance in this molecule is known to be 1.159 Å. If one structure $O=C=O$ alone represented the molecule the distance should be 1.18 Å, the double-bond length with adjacent-bent-bond correction. There are, however, two such structures, $:\overset{..}{O}=C=\overset{}{O}:$ and $:\overset{}{O}=C=\overset{..}{O}:$, differing in the planes of the double bonds. In addition, resonance might occur with two other structures, $:\overset{+}{O}\equiv C-\overset{..\,-}{O}:$ and $:\overset{-\,..}{O}-C\equiv\overset{+}{O}:$. If there were independent resonance of the xy and xz bonds the bond lengths would be somewhat less, approximately 1.16 Å. This value agrees with the observed value, and we conclude that the normal state of the carbon dioxide molecule can be described as composed to the extent of about 25 percent each of the four structures $:\overset{..}{O}=C=\overset{}{O}:$, $:\overset{}{O}=C=\overset{..}{O}:$, $:\overset{+}{O}\equiv C-\overset{..\,-}{O}:$, and $:\overset{-\,..}{O}-C\equiv\overset{+}{O}:$.

The observed resonance energy, relative to the ketonic type of double bond, is 33 kcal/mole.

Resonance of the same type as in carbon dioxide would be expected in carbon oxysulfide and carbon disulfide. The observed interatomic distances $C-O = 1.164$ Å and $C-S = 1.559$ Å in SCO and $C-S = 1.553$ Å in CS_2, agree with the expected values $C-O = 1.16$ Å and $C-S = 1.56$ Å.

8-2. THE ADJACENT-CHARGE RULE AND THE
ELECTRONEUTRALITY RULE

In Section 6-1 nitrous oxide was considered to resonate among three structures A, B, and C, which are so similar in nature as to contribute about equally to the normal state of the molecule. There is, however, a fourth structure, D, that must be discussed:

$$A \qquad :\overset{-\,..}{N}\!\!=\!\!\overset{+}{N}\!\!=\!\!\underset{..}{O}:$$

$$B \qquad :\overset{-}{N}\!\!=\!\!\overset{+}{N}\!\!=\!\!\overset{..}{O}:$$

$$C \qquad :N\!\!\equiv\!\!\overset{+}{N}\!\!-\!\!\underset{..}{\overset{..\,-}{O}}:$$

$$D \qquad :\overset{-\,-..}{N}\!\!-\!\!\overset{+}{N}\!\!\equiv\!\!\overset{+}{O}:$$

It is analogous to the fourth structure for carbon dioxide, which has the same number of electrons as nitrous oxide, and might be of importance for the latter molecule also. Resonance among the four structures, contributing equally, leads to the values N—N = 1.15 Å and N—O = 1.11 Å; that is, to an N—O distance smaller than the N—N distance, which is contrary to observation: N—N = 1.126 Å, N—O = 1.186 Å. The observed values are those expected for resonance among the first three structures.

We can attribute the lack of importance of structure D to the instability resulting from the charge distribution, which gives adjacent atoms electric charges of the same sign. The *adjacent-charge rule*, which states that structures that place electric charges of the same sign on adjacent atoms make little contribution to the normal states of molecules, has been further substantiated by observations on covalent azides. In the ionic crystals NaN_3 and KN_3 the azide ion is linear and symmetrical, each of the end atoms being 1.15 ± 0.02 Å from the central one. Resonance among the structures A, B, C, and D,

$$A \qquad :\overset{-\,..}{N}\!\!=\!\!\overset{+}{N}\!\!=\!\!\overset{-}{N}:$$

$$B \qquad :\overset{-}{N}\!\!=\!\!\overset{+}{N}\!\!=\!\!\overset{..\,-}{N}:$$

$$C \qquad :\overset{-\,-..}{N}\!\!-\!\!\overset{+}{N}\!\!\equiv\!\!N:$$

$$D \qquad :N\!\!\equiv\!\!\overset{+}{N}\!\!-\!\!\overset{..\,-\,-}{N}:$$

contributing equally, leads to agreement with the observed value, whereas structure A and B would require the value 1.17 Å. The covalent molecule methyl azide, on the other hand, has the configuration

$$N \xrightarrow{\text{1.24 Å}} N \xrightarrow{\text{1.10 Å}} N$$

1.47 Å $\diagup$ 120°

H_3C

the distances having probable errors of 0.02 Å. A similar configuration for the covalent azide group has been found in cyanuric triazide, $C_3N_3(N_3)_3$, in which the two N—N distances have the values 1.26 Å and 1.11 Å, and in hydrazoic acid, HN_3, with distances 1.240 Å and 1.134 Å and bond angle H—N—N = 112.7°. These values of the bond lengths are incompatible with resonance among the structures A, B, C, and D,

$A \qquad R—\overset{..}{N}=\overset{+}{N}=\overset{-}{N}:$

$B \qquad R—N=\overset{+}{N}=\overset{..}{\underset{..}{N}}:^{-}$

$C \qquad R—\overset{-..}{\underset{..}{N}}—\overset{+}{N}≡N:$

$D \qquad R—\overset{+}{N}≡\overset{+}{N}—\overset{..}{\underset{..}{N}}:^{--}$

but agree well with equal resonance between A and C, the calculated values being 1.25 Å and 1.12 Å. The significance of the adjacent-charge rule is seen from the fact that the elimination of structure D for the covalent azide and not for the azide ion is the result of the positive formal charge given to the nitrogen atom by the formation of a covalent bond.

Another structural feature of importance is the bond angle R—N—N. This angle has the value 116° for structure A (unstrained), 108° for C, and 180° for D (the value 116° applies also to B, but with the plane of the molecule normal to that for A) (Sec. 4-7). An average value would be expected for resonance among several structures. The observed values, 120° ± 10° in methyl azide, 114° ± 3° in cyanuric triazide, and 112.7° ± 0.5° in hydrogen azide, are in agreement with the value expected for resonance between A and C, about 112°.

The electroneutrality rule may also be applicable in the discussion of these molecules. This rule (Sec. 5-7) states that in general the electronic structure of substances is such as to cause each atom to have essentially zero resultant electric charge. Exceptionally large charges may result from the partial ionic character of bonds between atoms with great difference in electronegativity, if there is no way in which the charges can be reduced. The electroneutrality rule may be said to account for the very small electric dipole moments of CO and NNO, 0.112 D and 0.116 D, respectively. A structure such as *D* (above) for NNO and the covalent azides would, if it made a considerable contribution, confer a large negative charge on the end nitrogen atom. Moreover, the structure itself, with a double negative formal charge on one atom as well as adjacent charges of like sign on two other atoms, has two features leading to its instability and hence to a decrease in its contribution to the normal state of the molecule.

8-3. THE NITRO AND CARBOXYL GROUPS; ACID STRENGTHS

Resonance between the two equivalent structures $R-\overset{+}{N}\overset{\ddot{O}:}{\diagdown\underset{\ddot{O}:}{}}$ and

$R-\overset{+}{N}\overset{\overset{..}{O}:^-}{\diagup}$, with perhaps a small contribution by $R-\overset{++}{N}\overset{\overset{..}{O}:^-}{\diagup}$, is ex-

pected for the nitro group. This would lead to the tetrahedral value 125°16′ for the O—N=O bond angle and to the value 1.27 Å for the N—O distance, the three atoms of the group and the atom of R attached to nitrogen being coplanar, with the two oxygen atoms symmetrically related to the R—N axis. The observed value of the angle in *p*-dinitrobenzene is 124°, and that of the N—O bond length is 1.23 Å.

In nitryl chloride, NO_2Cl, the values are 130°35′ ± 15′ and 1.202 ± 0.001 Å, respectively (microwave spectroscopy). Both values indicate that there is a significant contribution of the structure

$\underset{:O}{\overset{:\ddot{O}}{\diagdown}}\overset{+}{N}\diagup$ Cl^-. The N—Cl bond length, 1.840 ± 0.002 Å, is 0.11 Å larger

than that for a single bond, indicating that the contribution of this structure is 24 percent.

Whereas in the nitro group the two resonating structures are equivalent, they are made nonequivalent in the carboxyl group and its esters, becoming equivalent again in the corresponding ions:

$$A \qquad R—C \overset{\displaystyle \ddot{O}:}{\underset{\displaystyle \ddot{O}—H}{\Big\backslash}} \qquad\qquad A' \qquad R—C \overset{\displaystyle \ddot{O}:}{\underset{\displaystyle \ddot{O}:^-}{\Big\backslash}}$$

$$B \qquad R—C \overset{\displaystyle \ddot{O}:^-}{\underset{\displaystyle \overset{+}{O}—H}{\Big\backslash}} \qquad\qquad B' \qquad R—C \overset{\displaystyle \ddot{O}:^-}{\underset{\displaystyle \ddot{O}:}{\Big\backslash}}$$

The lack of equivalence of structures A and B does not inhibit their resonance very thoroughly, however, since the corresponding resonance energy is still large, having the value of 28 kcal/mole for acids and 24 kcal/mole for esters.

The predicted configuration for the carboxylate ion group is that with the angle O—C=O equal to 125°16′ and each C—O bond length equal to 1.27 Å. (The single-bond and double-bond lengths are 1.41 Å and 1.21 Å, respectively.) The experimental values lie close to these; for example, for the formates of sodium, calcium, strontium, and barium the average values are 125.5° ± 1° and 1.25 ± 0.01 Å, respectively.

For formic acid two electron-diffraction studies have given the values O=C—OH = 123° ± 1°, C=O = 1.22 ± 0.01 Å, and C—OH = 1.36 ± 0.01 Å, and these values have been supported by several infrared and microwave spectroscopic investigations. Nearly the same values have been reported also for many other carboxylic acids. The bond numbers calculated from these bond lengths are about 1.85 and 1.15, respectively; that is, the presence of the hydrogen atom causes structure A to make an 85 percent and structure B only a 15 percent contribution. Essentially the same resonance is found in esters: for methyl formate, for example, the bond lengths in the carboxylate group are C=O = 1.22 ± 0.03 Å and C—OCH$_3$ = 1.37 ± 0.04 Å.

The concept of resonance provides an obvious explanation of some of the characteristic properties of the carboxyl group, the most striking of which is its acid strength. If the electronic structure of a carboxylic

acid were $R—C \overset{\displaystyle O}{\underset{\displaystyle OH}{\Big\backslash}}$, its acid strength would differ only by a rather

small amount from that of an alcohol. The double-bonded oxygen atom would attract electrons from the carbon atom, which in turn would exert the same influence on the hydroxyl oxygen, leaving it with a resultant positive charge. This would repel the proton, and an increase in the acid constant would be produced in this way, through operation of the *inductive effect*. Resonance with structure *B* provides a much more effective way of placing a positive charge on the hydroxyl oxygen, however, and the high acid strength of the carboxyl group can be attributed in the main to this effect.

The acid constant of phenol, 1.7×10^{-10}, is much larger than that of the aliphatic alcohols. This we attribute to resonance with the structures *F*, *G*, and *H*,

O—H   O—H   O—H

F   *G*   *H*

which give the oxygen atom a positive formal charge. The inductive effect of the ring is negligible; accordingly the increase in acid constant by a factor of about 10^6 from aliphatic to aromatic alcohols indicates that the resonance energy of the phenolate ion among the structures I to V

:O: :O: O: O: O:

I   II   III   IV   V

is about 8 kcal/mole greater than that for phenol. This is to be expected, since these five structures are closely similar in nature, differing only in the position of the negative charge, whereas for the unionized molecule the structures *F*, *G*, and *H*, with separated charges, are much less stable than the conventional structures and contribute only a small amount (7 kcal/mole—Table 6-2) to the resonance energy.

8-4. THE STRUCTURE OF AMIDES AND PEPTIDES

During the last two decades great progress has been made in the investigation of the structure of amides and peptides, because of their importance to the structure of proteins.

The principal resonance structures of amides, *A* and *B*,

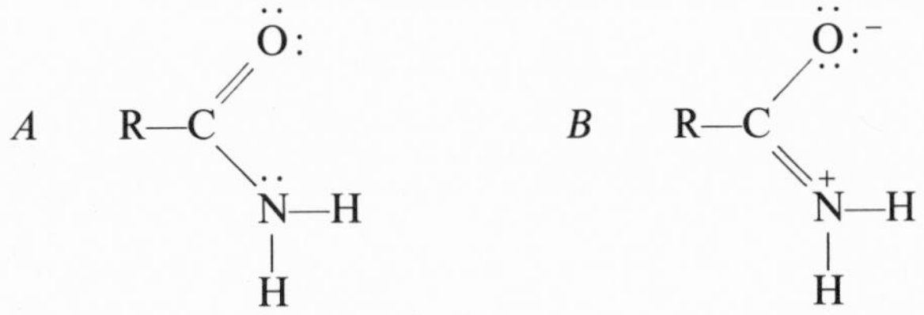

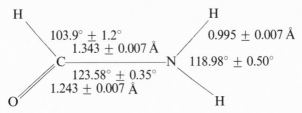

are not equivalent, and it is expected that *A* contributes somewhat more than *B* to the structure of the group.   The resonance energy is about 21 kcal/mole (Table 6-2).   The amides are very weak bases; the resonance with structure *B* is nearly completely inhibited by addition of a proton to the nitrogen atom.   The corresponding calculated value for the base constant, 1×10^{-20}, is so small as to be without significance, except to show that the amides do not form salts with acids by adding a proton to the amino group.

The structure of the amide group can be illustrated by the formamide molecule, which has been subjected to a careful study by microwave spectroscopy.   The molecule is completely planar, as required for resonance of *A* and *B*.   Its dimensions are given in the following diagram:

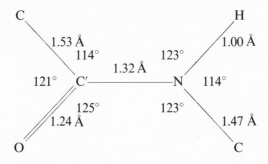

These dimensions are essentially the same as those that are assigned to the peptide group from analysis of the results of a number of careful x-ray structure determinations of crystals of amino acids, simple peptides, and related substances:

C
1.53 Å
114°
121°   C′———————N   114°
1.32 Å
123°
125°   123°
1.24 Å   1.47 Å
O   C

H
1.00 Å
123°

The value of the O=C'—N bond angle is close to the tetrahedral value 125°16'. The bond lengths are about as expected for resonance between structures A and B: the C'—N bond length, 1.32 Å, is 0.13 Å less than would be expected for a single bond adjacent to a double bond, showing that there is a considerable contribution by the resonance structure B. This contribution is evaluated as about 40 percent. For 60 percent A and 40 percent B the bond lengths are C—O = 1.26 Å and C—N = 1.34 Å; there may also be some contribution of multiple bonds involving the p orbitals normal to the plane of the group, correlated with the ionic aspect of the adjacent bond.

8-5. THE CARBONATE, NITRATE, AND BORATE IONS AND RELATED MOLECULES

Carbonic acid and its derivatives resonate among the three structures A, B, and C, the resonance being complete for the ion and somewhat inhibited in the acid and its esters.

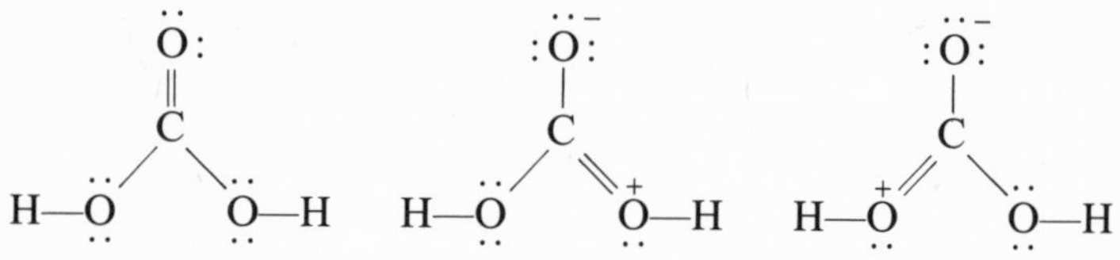

The resonating structure requires that the carbonate ion be planar with bond angles 120°, and three C—O distances equal to 1.31 Å. The trigonal planar configuration of the ion was found in the original x-ray study of calcite, carried out by W. L. Bragg in 1914, and has been verified since by examination of other carbonate crystals. The value calculated for the C—O distance is in satisfactory agreement with that found in recent reinvestigations of calcite, 1.30 ± 0.01 Å.

For the nitrate ion, with the same type of structure as the carbonate ion, a similar configuration is expected and observed:

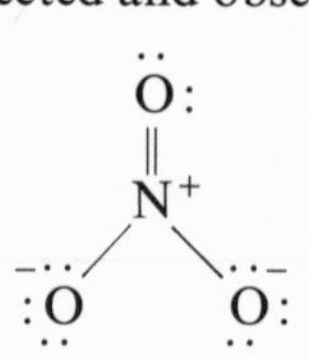

The borate group in boric acid is observed to have a planar trigonal configuration with the B—O distance 1.360 ± 0.005 Å. Similar BO_3 groups occur in many salts of boric acid.

8-6. RESONANCE IN CONJUGATED SYSTEMS

For a molecule such as butadiene-1,3, $CH_2=CH—CH=CH_2$, it is customary to write one valence-bond formula involving alternating single and double bonds and to take cognizance of the difference in properties from a molecule containing isolated double bonds by saying that here the double bonds are conjugated. From the new point of view the phenomenon of conjugation is attributed to resonance between the ordinary structure and certain structures involving one less double

bond; $\overset{\cdot}{C}H_2—CH=CH—\overset{\cdot}{C}H_2$ for butadiene, and to a smaller extent

$C^+H_2—CH=CH—\overset{\cdot\cdot}{C}H_2{}^-$, etc. These structures are less stable than the ordinary structure and contribute only a small amount to the normal state of the molecule, giving the 2,3 bond a small amount of double-bond character.

The quantum-mechanical treatment of this problem indicates that the single bonds in a conjugated system have about 20 percent double-bond character and that the extra resonance energy resulting from the conjugation of two double bonds is about 5 to 8 kcal/mole. The calculations also show that a double bond and a benzene nucleus are approximately equivalent in conjugating power.

The thermochemical data for biphenyl, phenylethylene, and stilbene (Table 6-2) correspond to a value of about 5 kcal/mole for the conjugation energy of a double bond and a benzene ring or of two benzene rings.

In butadiene-1,3 and cyclopentadiene the value found for the carbon-carbon distance for the bond between the conjugated double bonds is 1.46 Å, corresponding to 15 percent double-bond character. The same amount of double-bond character is also indicated by the following x-ray values for the bond between two benzene rings or a benzene ring and a double bond: stilbene $(C_6H_5—CH=CH—C_6H_5)$, 1.44 Å; biphenyl, 1.48 Å; *p*-diphenylbenzene, 1.46 Å.

This amount of double-bond character should give to the bond in some part the properties of a double bond; in particular, the conjugated systems should tend to remain planar. Chemical evidence for cis and

trans isomers of the type $H_2C=C\begin{smallmatrix}H\\\\ \diagup\\\\ \diagdown\\\\ C=CH_2\\\\ \diagup\\\\ H\end{smallmatrix}$ and $\begin{smallmatrix}H_2C\\\\ \diagdown\diagdown\end{smallmatrix}\begin{smallmatrix}CH_2\\\\ \diagup\diagup\end{smallmatrix}$ over C—C, H below has not been forthcoming; the restriction of rotation about the central bond is not great enough to prevent easy interconversion of these molecular species.   It is great enough, however, to cause the conjugated molecules to retain in general the planar equilibrium configuration, and this configuration has been verified by various physical techniques, such as x-ray diffraction, electron diffraction, and spectroscopy.   In the gas phase the trans molecules are found in greater number than the cis molecules, and in crystals the configuration is usually trans (about the single bonds).

8-7. RESONANCE IN HETEROCYCLIC MOLECULES

For pyridine, pyrazine, and related six-membered heterocyclic molecules Kekulé resonance occurs as in benzene, causing the molecules to be planar and stabilizing them by about 40 kcal/mole.   The interatomic distances observed in these molecules, C—$C = 1.40$ Å, C—$N = 1.33$ Å, and N—$N = 1.32$ Å, are compatible with this structure.   The resonance energy found for quinoline, 69 kcal/mole, is about the same as that of naphthalene.

Borazole, $B_3N_3H_6$, is an analog of benzene.   The molecule is a planar hexagon, with a hydrogen atom bonded to each of the ring atoms.   The observed B—N bond length, 1.44 ± 0.02 Å, is larger than expected for resonance between two Kekulé structures (1.33 Å), indicating that structures with an unshared pair on the nitrogen atom make an important contribution to the normal state.   If the Kekulé structures contribute to the extent required for electroneutrality of the atoms, with the bonds having 22 percent of partial ionic character, the B—N bond number would be 1.28; this value agrees with the observed bond length.

For the five-membered heterocyclic molecules furan, pyrrole, and thiophen, with the conventional structure

$$
\begin{array}{ccc}
HC & \!\!\!\!\!\text{———}\!\!\!\!\! & CH \\
\| & & \| \\
HC & & CH \\
& \diagdown \quad \diagup & \\
& \overset{}{\underset{\cdot\cdot}{X}}: &
\end{array}
$$

I

resonance is expected to occur with structures of the types

$$
\begin{array}{ccc}
HC & \!\!\!\!\!\text{═══}\!\!\!\!\! & CH \\
| & & | \\
\underset{\cdot\cdot}{HC^-} & & CH \\
& \diagdown \quad \diagup\!\!\diagup & \\
& \underset{\cdot\cdot\,+}{X} &
\end{array}
$$

II, III

and

$$
\begin{array}{ccc}
\text{HC} & \!\!\!\!\!\!\!\!\!\!\text{---}\!\!\!\!\!\!\!\!\!\! & \overset{..}{\text{CH}^-} \\
\| & & | \\
\text{HC} & & \text{CH} \\
& \diagdown\!\!\!\diagup & \\
& \text{X} & \\
& \overset{..\,+}{} &
\end{array}
$$

IV, V

The thermochemical data for these substances give the values 23, 31, and 31 kcal/mole, respectively, for the energy of this resonance. It is interesting that the extent of the resonance, as indicated by the magnitude of the resonance energy, increases with decrease in electronegativity of X; the very electronegative oxygen atom has a smaller tendency to assume the positive charge accompanying structures II to V than has the less electronegative nitrogen or sulfur atom. This conclusion is further substantiated by the observed interatomic distances, $C\text{---}O = 1.37$ Å, $C\text{---}N = 1.42$ Å, and $C\text{---}S = 1.74$ Å in furan, pyrrole, and thiophen, respectively; these correspond to about 23 percent total contribution of structures II to V for furan, 24 percent for pyrrole, and 28 percent for thiophen.

8-8. HYPERCONJUGATION

For methyl cyanide (and other alkyl cyanides) the structure

$$
\begin{array}{c}
\text{H} \\
\diagdown \\
\text{H}\text{---}\text{C}\text{---}\text{C}\!\equiv\!\text{N}: \\
\diagup \\
\text{H}
\end{array}
$$

may be accepted as a first approximation. There is evidence that a significant contribution, totaling about 20 percent, is made also by the several structures

$$
\begin{array}{c}
\text{H}^+ \\
\\
\text{H}\text{---}\text{C}\!=\!\text{C}\!=\!\overset{..\,-}{\text{N}}: \\
\diagup \\
\text{H}
\end{array}
$$

. The differences in electronegativity of the atoms indicate that each of the H—C bonds should have about 4 percent ionic character, with hydrogen positive, and each of the three bent bonds of the C≡N triple bond about 7 percent, with nitrogen negative. If these ionic aspects of the bonds were synchronized, the electron pair on the methyl carbon atom and the freed orbital of the cyanide carbon atom could form the second half of a carbon-carbon double bond, as represented in the structure given above. The observed electric dipole moment of methyl cyanide is 3.44 D, far larger than the sum of the moments of the methyl group and the cyanide group, about 1.5 D.   If the observed moment is attributed to the conjugated structures, their contribution is calculated to total 24 percent.   Also, the C—C distance in the molecule is 1.459 Å, which corresponds to about 17 percent double-bond character, and hence to a 17-percent contribution of these conjugated structures, in approximate agreement with the dipole-moment value.   Resonance of this sort, involving the breaking of a single bond (in this case an H—C bond), is called *hyperconjugation*.

Hyperconjugation affects many properties of hydrocarbons and other molecules.   Its effects are in general somewhat smaller than those of conjugation; they correspond to resonance energies of 1 or 2 kcal/mole (instead of 5 or 10), changes in bond length by 0.01 or 0.02 Å, and transfer of 0.01 or 0.02 units of electric charge.   These structural changes are, however, great enough to have significant effect on many of the physical and chemical properties of substances.

For toluene, for example, the value 0 for the electric dipole moment would be expected if the methyl group were attached to the ring by a normal single bond and the C—H bonds of the group and the ring had the same amount of ionic character.   The observed value, 0.37 D, indicates that structures of the type

contribute to a total extent of about 2.5 percent.   Correspondingly the heats of hydrogenation of alkylolefines are less than those of the corresponding olefines by about 2 kcal/mole per methyl group adjacent to the double bond.

EXERCISES

8-1.—It is stated in Section 8-1 and Table 6-2 that the resonance energy of the carbon monoxide molecule relative to the structure C≡O is 83 kcal/mole.   (a) Using thermochemical information given in Section 3-5, calculate the enthalpy change for the reaction $C(g) + O(g) \rightarrow CO(g)$. (b) With use of the ketone value for the C=O energy (Table 6-1), evaluate the resonance energy.

8-2.—The ketone value of the C=O energy applies to the quadricovalent carbon atom, not to the bicovalent carbon atom, with an unshared pair. Comparison with N=N and O=O (Table 6-1) suggests 96 kcal/mole as a rough value for the :C=C: bond energy. (a) Using this value and the energy correction for partial ionic character (assumed to apply to each single-bond half of the double bond), obtain a value for the :C=O̤: bond energy. (b) Calculate the corresponding value of the resonance energy for the carbon monoxide molecule. (Ans. 142 kcal/mole, 115 kcal/mole.)

8-3.—Assuming that the p_z and p_y electron pairs of the carbon monoxide molecule resonate independently, show that the contribution 60.0 percent of the structure :C≡O̤:⁺ to the normal state of the molecule corresponds for each electron pair to 77.4 percent service as a bonding pair and 22.6 percent service as an unshared pair. Evaluate the contributions of the structures :C—O̤:, :C=O̤:⁺, and :⁺C—O̤:⁻ to the normal state, on the basis of these assumptions. (Ans. 17.5%, 17.5%, 5.1%.)

8-4.—Assuming each carbon-oxygen bond to have 22 percent ionic character, as given in Table 3-7 for electronegativity difference 1, evaluate the electric charge on the oxygen atom for each of the four structures of Ex. 8-1. Also evaluate the resultant charge on the oxygen atom for the resonating structure described in Ex. 8-1. (Ans. $+0.34$, -0.44, -1.12, -0.012.)

8-5.—The heats of combustion of gaseous methane, ethane, hydrogen cyanide, and methyl cyanide are 210.8, 368.4, 158.3, and 309.7 kcal/mole, respectively. Calculate the enthalpy change for the reaction

$$HCN(g) + C_2H_6(g) \rightarrow CH_3CN(g) + CH_4(g).$$

Note that this value may be interpreted as the resonance energy of hyperconjugation in methyl cyanide. (Ans. 6.2 kcal/mole.)

8-6.—The heats of combustion of gaseous formaldehyde, acetaldehyde, and acetone are 134.1, 285.0 and 434.0 kcal/mole, respectively. By the method of Exercise 8-5 evaluate the hyperconjugation resonance energy in acetaldehyde and acetone. Would you consider these values to be compatible with the observed C—C bond lengths, 1.501 ± 0.005 Å for acetaldehyde and 1.515 ± 0.005 Å in acetone? (Ans. 6.7, 15.3 kcal/mole.)

8-7.—The ring *s*-triazine, $C_3H_3N_3$, has CN and N alternating. What resonating structure would you assign to it? What values do you predict for the bond angles in the ring (Sec. 4-7)? For the carbon-nitrogen bond lengths, using the values C—C in C_2H_6, 1.534 Å, in C_6H_6, 1.397 Å, C—N in CH_3NH_2, 1.474 Å?   (Ans. About 126°, 114°; 1.337 Å; observed values 127°, 113°, 1.338 Å.)

8-8.—By use of the standard heats of combustion of gaseous methyl formate (239.8 kcal/mole), methane (210.8 kcal/mole), dimethyl ether (347.6 kcal/mole), and formaldehyde (Ex. 8-1), evaluate the ester resonance energy.   (Ans. 31.1 kcal/mole.)

8-9.—From the principle of resonance the resonance energy of dimethyl carbonate would be expected to be about twice as great as for a simple ester; the double bond can resonate from its normal position into either of the two methoxy positions.   The heat of combustion of $OC(OCH_3)_2(g)$ is 349.7 kcal/mole.   From this value and information given in Exercises 8-1 and 8-2 calculate the dimethyl carbonate resonance energy.   (Ans. 58.0 kcal/mole.)

CHAPTER 9

The Structure of Molecules and Complex

Ions Involving Bonds with Partial

Double-Bond Character

FROM the discussion in the preceding chapters several significant conclusions have been drawn about the structure of molecules and complex ions involving bonds between atoms of the heavier elements—those beyond the first row of the periodic system—and atoms such as the halogens or oxygen and groups such as hydroxyl, amino, carbonyl, cyano, or nitro. It has been seen that the heavier atoms are not rigorously restricted by the octet rule, but can make use of d orbitals in bond formation; that electron donors such as the halogen and oxygen atoms and the hydroxyl and amino groups held by a single bond are able under certain circumstances to swing another pair of electrons into position for bond formation, thus giving some double-bond character to the bond; and that electron acceptors such as the cyano and nitro groups held by a single bond are able to provide an orbital for a pair of electrons from the rest of the molecule, to give some double-bond character to the bond. By application of these ideas, with recourse to experimental information to settle doubtful points, a detailed description of the structure of molecules and complex ions of the heavier elements can be formulated, as described in the following sections.

9-1. THE STRUCTURE OF SILICON TETRACHLORIDE AND
RELATED MOLECULES

For about 75 years the silicon tetrachloride molecule (which we select as an example) was assigned the simple valence-bond structure A. G. N. Lewis in his 1916 paper introduced the practice of showing the unshared

$$A \qquad \underset{\underset{\text{Cl}}{|}}{\overset{\overset{\text{Cl}}{|}}{\text{Cl}\!-\!\text{Si}\!-\!\text{Cl}}} \qquad\qquad A' \qquad :\!\ddot{\underset{\cdot\cdot}{\text{Cl}}}\!-\!\underset{\underset{\cdot\cdot}{:\ddot{\text{Cl}}:}}{\overset{\overset{\cdot\cdot}{:\ddot{\text{Cl}}:}}{\text{Si}}}\!-\!\ddot{\underset{\cdot\cdot}{\text{Cl}}}\!:$$

electron pairs of the valence shells (structure *A'*), and the recognition of the partial ionic character of covalent bonds (Chap. 3) showed that the Si—Cl single bond can be described as having the amount of ionic character (Si^+Cl^-) that corresponds to the difference in electronegativity of silicon and chlorine (about 30 percent—Sec. 3-9). Structure *A* is analogous to the structures of carbon tetrachloride and silicon tetramethyl, in which the central atom uses its sp^3 tetrahedral bond orbitals to form four single bonds with its ligands.

When the structure of silicon tetrachloride was determined, it was found that the configuration of the molecule is that of the regular tetrahedron, as expected, but that the Si—Cl distance, 2.01 Å $\pm$ 0.02 Å, is much smaller than the sum of the covalent radii, 2.16 Å. A part of the 0.15 Å decrease in bond length can be attributed to the partial ionic character of the bond, as discussed in Section 7-2. The bond shortening calculated by Equation 7-1 is 0.08 Å. The remaining shortening, 0.07 Å, is attributed to partial double-bond character of the bond. It corresponds to about 23 percent of double-bond character.

This amount of double-bond character is to be expected from consideration of the principle of electroneutrality (Sec. 8-2). The 30 percent partial ionic character of the Si—Cl bond that corresponds to the difference in electronegativity of the atoms would place the charge $+1.2$ on the silicon atom in the $SiCl_4$ molecule. This electric charge would be reduced to zero if each bond had 30 percent double-bond character, or to $+0.2$ (a value approximating electroneutrality) if each bond had 25 percent double-bond character. This amount of double-bond character (and the same amount of partial ionic character for each bond) is given by resonance among the six equivalent structures of type *B*:

$$B \qquad :\!\ddot{\underset{\cdot\cdot}{\text{Cl}}}\!-\!\underset{\underset{\cdot\cdot}{:\ddot{\text{Cl}}:}}{\text{Si}}\!=\!\overset{+}{\ddot{\text{Cl}}}\!: \qquad \text{with } \overset{\cdot\cdot\,-}{:\!\ddot{\text{Cl}}\!:}\text{ above}$$

It is probably significant that for these structures only the four stable orbitals of the silicon valence shell need to be used. The bond-angle strain is considerably less than for pure sp^3 orbitals, since d character can be introduced with little promotion energy. Some contribution may be made also by the six structures of type C:

$$C \quad \overset{\displaystyle :\overset{\cdot\cdot}{\underset{\cdot\cdot}{Cl}}:^{-}}{\underset{\displaystyle :\overset{\cdot\cdot}{\underset{\cdot\cdot}{Cl}}:^{-}}{\overset{+}{:}Cl=Si=\overset{\cdot\cdot}{Cl}:^{+}}}$$

9-2. THE OXIDES AND OXYGEN ACIDS OF THE HEAVIER ELEMENTS

The older conventional valence-bond formulas for an ion such as the sulfate ion,

$$A \quad \overset{\displaystyle O^{-}}{\underset{\displaystyle O}{\overset{|}{\underset{\parallel}{O=S-O^{-}}}}}$$

involving single and double covalent bonds from the central atom to the surrounding oxygen atoms in numbers determined by the position of the central atom in the periodic table, have now fallen into general disuse, in consequence of the suggestion, originally made by Lewis in his 1916 paper and accepted by most subsequent investigators, that the octet rule is to be applied to the sulfur atom and other second-row and heavier atoms, and that only four covalent bonds are to be represented in the electronic structures of the sulfate ion and similar ions:

$$B \quad \overset{\displaystyle :\overset{\cdot\cdot}{O}:^{-}}{\underset{\displaystyle :\overset{\cdot\cdot}{O}:^{-}}{\overset{-\cdot\cdot}{:}O-\overset{|^{++}}{S}\overset{\cdot\cdot}{O}:^{-}}}$$

On considering the question of the structure of these ions from the resonance point of view, we see that structure B, although it makes some contribution, is not of overwhelming importance, that other structures involving double bonds between the central atom and oxygen are significant, and that the available evidence indicates that the older valence-bond formulas such as A, with the double bonds resonating among the oxygen atoms, making them equivalent, and with the bonds considered to have partial ionic character, represent the ions somewhat more satisfactorily than the extreme structures of the type of B.

The observed values of interatomic distances in the tetrahedral ions of the ortho-oxygen acids of the second-row elements in crystals of their salts are 1.61 Å for SiO_4^{----}, 1.54 Å for PO_4^{---}, 1.49 Å for SO_4^{--}, and 1.44 Å for ClO_4^-. These values are 0.16, 0.19, 0.21, and 0.25 Å, respectively, less than the single-bond values (Sec. 7-2). Hence structure B alone is unsatisfactory. We may well expect that the bivalent oxygen atom in these ions will strive to share four valence electrons with the central atom, and that structures of the types C, D, E, and F might contribute largely to the normal state of the ions:

$$C \quad \ddot{\ddot{O}}\!-\!\overset{\displaystyle :\ddot{O}:^-}{\underset{\displaystyle :\ddot{O}:^-}{\overset{|}{\underset{|}{S}}}}\!\!\!\overset{+}{=}\!\!\ddot{O}: \qquad D \quad :O\!=\!\overset{\displaystyle :\ddot{O}:^-}{\underset{\displaystyle :\ddot{O}:^-}{\overset{|}{\underset{|}{S}}}}\!=\!\ddot{O}: \qquad E \quad :O\!=\!\overset{\displaystyle :\ddot{O}:}{\underset{\displaystyle \ddot{O}:}{\overset{|}{\underset{\|}{S}}}}\!=\!\ddot{O}: \qquad F \quad :O\!=\!\overset{\displaystyle :\ddot{O}}{\underset{\displaystyle \ddot{O}:}{\overset{\|}{\underset{\|}{S}}}}\!=\!\ddot{O}:$$

The shortening of the bond length by 0.25 Å for the perchlorate ion corresponds to about 100 percent double-bond character (50 percent for the p_y double bond and 50 percent for the p_z double bond; the $p_y p_z$ double bond is about 0.04 Å shorter than a p_y or p_z double bond). We accordingly assign a structure of type F to this ion. For the silicate ion the observed shortening corresponds to type D, with 50 percent double-bond character. The bonds in the phosphate ion correspond to resonance among the structures of types D and E (about 65 percent double-bond character), and in the sulfate ion to resonance among those of type E (75 percent double-bond character). These amounts of double-bond character are found to be in agreement with the electroneutrality principle (Sec. 5-7), when the partial ionic character of the bonds is taken into consideration.

It has been shown by neutron diffraction that in orthorhombic KH_2PO_4 the phosphorus atom has two oxygen atoms and two OH groups ligated to it. The corresponding P—O distances, 1.508 Å and 1.583 Å, correspond to 90 percent and 50 percent of double-bond character, respectively. A similar distortion (with one short bond, 1.52 Å, and three longer ones, 1.57 ± 0.02 Å) has been reported in crystalline phosphoric acid.

Very little accurate structural information about esters of the oxygen acids of the heavier elements has been reported. The molecule of tetramethyl orthosilicate, $Si(OCH_3)_4$, has Si—C = 1.64 ± 0.03 Å, C—O = 1.42 ± 0.04 Å, and angle Si—O—C = 113° ± 2°. These values are approximately those expected from the foregoing considerations; the amount of double-bond character of the Si—O bonds is indicated by the bond length to be about the same as for the silicate ion, and the Si—O—C bond angle lies between the value for two single bonds, about 108°, and a double bond and a single bond, 114°.

The pyro, meta, and other poly acids of the second-row atoms contain MO_4 tetrahedra with shared corners (oxygen atoms). As expected, the M—O bond lengths for the shared oxygen atoms are greater than for the others. Thus in the triphosphate ion of the $Na_5P_3O_{10}$ crystal the P—O bond lengths to the shared oxygen atoms are 1.61 ± 0.03 Å (central phosphorus atom) and 1.68 ± 0.03 Å (outer phosphorus atoms), and those for the eight unshared oxygen atoms are 1.50 ± 0.03 Å. These values correspond to 35 percent, 15 percent and 85 percent of double-bond character, respectively. The bond angle O—P—O for the bonds to the shared oxygen atoms is 98° and the angle P—O—P is 121°.

In the diphosphate (pyrophosphate) ion in $Na_4P_2O_7 \cdot 10H_2O$ the P—O bond lengths to the shared oxygen atom are 1.63 Å (25 percent double-bond character) and to the unshared oxygen atoms 1.47 ± 0.02 Å.

Many minerals can be described as salts of polysilicic acids, with SiO_4 tetrahedra sharing corners with one another.

Oxides of the Heavier Elements.—The structures of the oxides of the heavier nonmetallic elements are similar to those of the oxygen acids. In sulfur dioxide the S—O distance is 1.432 ± 0.001 Å and bond angle 119.5°. The bond length is approximately that expected for a double bond to

each sulfur atom (1.45 Å), corresponding to the structure

$$\overset{\displaystyle \ddot{O}:}{\underset{\displaystyle \ddot{O}:}{\overset{\displaystyle \|}{\underset{\displaystyle \diagdown}{:S}}}} \ \cdot$$

The value 22 percent for partial ionic character of the bonds leads to the calculated value 3.1 D for the electric dipole moment; the observed value, 1.59 D, indicates, as does the bond length, that the bonds have some triple-bond character.

Sulfur trioxide, for which the structure

$$\overset{\displaystyle :\overset{-\,\cdot\cdot}{O}:}{\underset{\displaystyle :\underset{\cdot\cdot}{O}:}{\overset{\displaystyle \diagdown}{\underset{\displaystyle \diagup}{\overset{++}{S}{=}\overset{\cdot\cdot}{O}:}}}}$$

in resonance with other structures may be written, has, as expected, a planar structure with bond angles 120°. This S—O bond length is 1.43 ± 0.02 Å, equal, to within experiment error, to that in SO_2, and indicating the structure

$$:\overset{..}{O}$$

$$\overset{:\overset{..}{O}}{\underset{:\underset{..}{O}}{\diagdown}}S=\overset{..}{O}:, \text{ with some triple-bond resonance.}$$

Sulfur trioxide easily polymerizes to form the trimer S_3O_9 and also an infinite asbestos-like polymer. In these polymers each sulfur atom is surrounded by a tetrahedron of four oxygen atoms, two of which are shared with other tetrahedra. The S—O bond lengths for the unshared oxygen atoms are 1.40 Å for the trimer and 1.41 Å for the in-

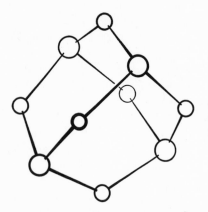

FIG. 9-1.—The structure of the molecules P_4O_6 and As_4O_6. Large circles represent phosphorus or arsenic atoms, small circles oxygen atoms.

finite polymer. These values correspond to bond number about 2.5 and zero charge on the oxygen atoms. For the shared oxygen atoms the bond lengths are between 1.59 Å and 1.63 Å, corresponding to bond number about 1.2 and zero charge on the oxygen atoms.

The sulfur bond angles, about 125° for the two unshared oxygen atoms and 100° for the two shared oxygen atoms, reflect the larger amount of multiple-bond character for the bonds to the unshared atoms.

The molecules P_4O_6, P_4O_{10}, and As_4O_6 have interesting configurations. In P_4O_6 and As_4O_6 the four phosphorus or arsenic atoms are at the corners of a tetrahedron, each bonded to three oxygen atoms along the tetrahedron edges (Fig. 9-1). The values of the P—O and As—O distances, 1.65 and 1.74 Å, respectively, indicate 22 percent and 10 percent, respectively, of double-bond character for the bonds. This makes itself evident also in the values of about 126° observed for the P—O—P and As—O—As bond angles. The P_4O_{10} molecule is closely similar to the P_4O_6 molecule in structure, with the addition of an oxygen atom to each phosphorus atom, completing the PO_4 tetrahedra (Fig. 9-2). These unshared oxygen atoms are at the surprisingly small distance 1.39 Å from the adjacent phosphorus atoms. In the $P_4O_6S_4$ molecule, which has a similar structure, the P—S distance is also very small, having the value 1.85 Å. The P—O distance, 0.34 Å less than the single-bond length, corresponds to a triple bond. The partial ionic character of the bonds, 39 percent, then leads to the charge -0.17 on the unshared oxygen atom. The P—S distance is close to the value

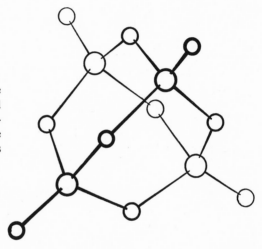

FIG. 9-2.—The structure of the molecules P_4O_{10} and $P_4O_6S_4$, showing the positions of attachment of the four oxygen or sulfur atoms to the P_4O_6 framework.

1.87 Å mentioned above (in the discussion of $PSCl_3$, etc.) as corresponding to electrical neutrality for the sulfur atom. The phosphorus bond angles in P_4O_{10}, 116.5° between the triple bond to the unshared oxygen atom and the bond (about 25 percent double-bond character; bond length 1.62 Å) to a shared oxygen atom, and 102.5° for two bonds to shared oxygen atoms, show the expected effect of the difference in character of the bonds.

Similar structural features have been found in many other oxides of the heavier metals.

9-3. THE STRUCTURE AND STABILITY OF CARBONYLS AND OTHER COVALENT COMPLEXES OF THE TRANSITION METALS

The problem of the stability of the complexes of the transition metals was for many years a puzzling one. Why is the cyanide group so facile in the formation of complexes with these elements, whereas the carbon atom in other groups, such as the methyl group, does not form bonds with them? Why do the transition metals and not other metals (beryllium, aluminum, etc.) form cyanide complexes? In the ferrocyanide ion, $[Fe(CN)_6]^{----}$, for example, the iron atom has a formal charge of -4, on the assumption that it forms six covalent bonds with the six ligands; how can this large negative charge be made compatible with the tendency of metals to lose electrons and form positive ions?

The answers to these questions and other questions about the transition-metal complexes have been provided by a new idea about their structure, developed in 1935 to account for the bond lengths observed in the nickel tetracarbonyl molecule. This idea is that atoms of the transition groups are not restricted to the formation of single covalent bonds, but can form multiple covalent bonds with electron-accepting ligands by making use of the $3d$ (or $4d$, $5d$) orbitals and electrons of the transition metal.

A possible structure for nickel tetracarbonyl is structure A:

$$\begin{array}{c}
\overset{\cdot\cdot}{O} \\
\mid\mid\mid \\
C \\
\mid \\
A \qquad :O\equiv C-Ni-C\equiv O: \\
\mid \\
C \\
\mid\mid\mid \\
\underset{\cdot\cdot}{O}
\end{array}$$

With this structure the nickel atom has achieved the krypton electron configuration: its outer shell contains five unshared pairs (in the five $3d$ orbitals) and five shared pairs (occupying the $4s4p^3$ tetrahedral bond orbitals). The Ni—C bond length expected for this structure is about 2.16 Å, as found by use of the tetrahedral radius 1.39 Å obtained by extrapolation from the adjacent values in Table 7-5 (Cu, 1.35 Å; Zn, 1.31 Å).

When an investigation of the structure of the molecule was carried out, by the electron-diffraction method, it was found that the molecule has the tetrahedral configuration predicted for structure A, but that the internuclear distance is surprisingly small, only 1.82 ± 0.03 Å.

The small distance suggests that the bonds have multiple-bond character, corresponding to resonance of structure A with other structures of types B, C, D, and E:

$$
B \quad \underset{\underset{\ddot{O}}{\overset{\overset{\ddot{O}}{\|}}{\underset{\|}{C}}}{\overset{\overset{\cdot\cdot}{O}}{\overset{\|}{C}}} \quad :O\!\!\equiv\!\!C\!-\!Ni\!=\!C\!=\!\ddot{O}:
$$

$$
C \quad :\underset{\cdot\cdot}{O}\!=\!C\!-\!Ni\!=\!C\!=\!\ddot{O}:
$$

$$
D \quad :\underset{\cdot\cdot}{O}\!=\!C\!=\!Ni\!=\!C\!=\!\ddot{O}:
$$

$$
E \quad :\underset{\cdot\cdot}{O}\!=\!C\!=\!Ni\!=\!C\!=\!\ddot{O}:
$$

The double bonds Ni=C are formed by use of the $3d$ orbitals and associated electrons of the nickel atom. For example, for the structures of type C the six bond orbitals of the nickel atom are d^2sp^3 hybrids, and the other three $3d$ orbitals are occupied by unshared pairs, and for structure E there are eight d^4sp^3 bond orbitals and one unshared pair.

There is uncertainty in the determination of the amount of double-bond character of the bonds, in part because of the dependence of the nickel radius on the amount of d character of the bond orbitals. For structures C we may use the d^2sp^3 value 1.21 Å (as given for Ni(IV) in Table 7-6); with the correction -0.12 Å for 50 percent double-bond character this gives the Ni—C bond length 1.86 Å. Similarly, for structures D the d^3sp^3 radius 1.15 Å (Table 7-7) with correction -0.17 Å for 75 percent double-bond character gives 1.74 Å. The observed value lies between these two. The electronegativity principle suggests about 79 percent of double-bond character (which gives zero charge for the nickel atom, with the assumption that all bonds have 12 percent of ionic character, corresponding to the C—Ni electronegativity difference 0.7). We conclude that the nickel-carbon bonds in nickel tetracarbonyl have a large amount of double-bond character, and that it is this structural feature that accounts for their stability.

For iron pentacarbonyl, $Fe(CO)_5$, a trigonal bipyramidal structure has been reported. The value found for the Fe—C distances, 1.84 Å, shows that the bonds in this molecule also have considerable double-bond character.

The electron-diffraction investigation of $Cr(CO)_6$, $Mo(CO)_6$, and $W(CO)_6$ has shown that the molecules are regular octahedra, with $Cr—C = 1.92$, $Mo—C = 2.08$, and $W—C = 2.06$ Å (all ± 0.04 Å). These values are about 0.10 Å less than those for single bonds, indicating that the bonds have some double-bond character.

The discovery that the iron-group elements can form bonds which have in part the character of multiple bonds by making use of the orbitals and electrons of the $3d$ subshell, while surprising, need not be greeted with skepticism; the natural formula for a compound RCO is that with a double bond from R to C, and the existence of the metal carbonyls might well have been interpreted years ago as evidence for double-bond formation by metals. The double-bond structure for nickel tetracarbonyl (structure E) was in fact first proposed by Langmuir in 1921, on the basis of the electroneutrality principle, but at that time there was little support for the new idea.

The single-bonded structures are not to be ignored; they seem to play a determinative part with respect to the stereochemical properties of the central atom, as discussed in Chapter 5. Nickel tetracarbonyl and its isosteres, for example, are tetrahedral in configuration, whereas the nickel cyanide complex ion $[Ni(CN)_4]^{--}$, in which the nickel-carbon bonds also have some double-bond character, is square, this difference being that predicted by discussion of the nature of the orbitals used in the formation of single bonds.

In many metal carbonyls containing two or more metal atoms there are metal-metal bonds. The structures of some of these molecules will be discussed in Chapter 11. The metal cyclopentadienyls and similar molecules involving fractional metal-carbon bonds will be discussed in Chapter 10.

The Cyano and Nitro Complexes of the Transition Elements.—The structural formula usually written for the ferrocyanide ion,

$$
A \quad
\begin{bmatrix}
& & \text{N} & & \\
& & \text{C} & \text{CN} & \\
& & | & \diagup & \\
\text{NC}—&\text{Fe}&—\text{CN} & & \\
& \diagup & | & & \\
\text{NC} & & \text{C} & & \\
& & \text{N} & &
\end{bmatrix}^{----}
$$

with single covalent bonds from the iron atom to each of the six carbon atoms, is seen to be surprising in that it places a charge of 4− on the iron atoms, whereas iron tends to assume a positive charge, as in the ferrous ion, and not a negative charge.   Now the cyano group is an electronegative group, and the Fe—C bonds accordingly have some ionic character, which, however, can hardly be great enough to remove the negative charge completely from the iron atom.   As suggested by the discussion of the metal carbonyls in the previous section, we assume that the cyano group in this complex can function as an acceptor of electrons, and that the bonds resonate among the following types:

$$A \quad \text{Fe} \quad (\text{CN})^-$$

$$B \quad \overset{-}{\text{Fe}}:\text{C}:::\text{N}:$$

$$C \quad \text{Fe}::\text{C}::\overset{\cdot\cdot\,-}{\text{N}}:$$

The first of these represents an electrostatic bond between the iron atom and the cyanide ion, the second a single covalent bond from iron to carbon, and the third a double covalent bond, with use of another $3d$ orbital of the iron atom, with its pair of electrons.   The first and the third of these place a negative charge on the cyanide group, and the second leaves the group neutral.   Resonance among these with the second structure contributing only about one-third would make the iron atom in the complex electrically neutral, the negative charge 4– being divided among the six cyanide groups.   The magnitude of the contribution of the third structure could be found from the value of the Fe—C distance, which, however, has not been accurately determined.

It is interesting to note that by using all of the $3d$, $4s$, and $4p$ orbitals of the iron atom the valence-bond structure B

can be written for the ferrocyanide ion.   This structure (which is, of course, in resonance with the equivalent structures obtained by redistributing the bonds) gives the iron atom a negative charge of only unity, dividing the residual charge 3– among the six nitrogen atoms, each of which then has the charge $\frac{1}{2}$; and it is probable that the ionic character of the bonds is great enough to transfer further negative charge also to the nitrogen atoms, making the iron atom neutral or even positive. The structures of this type, involving some iron-carbon double bonds, are without doubt of greater significance to the normal state of the complex ion than the conventional structure A written at the beginning of this section; it may well be convenient, however, to continue to represent the complex ion by the conventional structure, just as for convenience the benzene molecule is often represented by a single Kekulé structure.

For other anionic cyanide complexes of the transition elements, such as $[Fe(CN)_6]^{---}$, $[Co(CN)_6]^{---}$, $[Mn(CN)_6]^{4-}$, $[Cr(CN)_6]^{4-}$, $[Ni(CN)_4]^{--}$, $[Zn(CN)_4]^{--}$, and $[Cu(CN)_2]^{-}$, and the analogous complexes of the elements of the palladium and platinum groups, similar structures involving partial double-bond character of the metal-carbon bond can be written.

The nitrosyl group and the nitro group also are able to accept an additional pair of binding electrons, and the bonds in complexes such as $(Fe(CN)_5NO]^{--}$, $[Co(NH_3)_5NO]^{++}$, and $[Co(NO_2)_6]^{---}$ have to a considerable extent the character of the structures

$$M\!\!=\!\!\overset{+}{N}\!\!=\!\!\overset{..}{\overset{..}{O}}: \quad \text{and} \quad M\!\!=\!\!\overset{+}{N}\Big\langle{\overset{\textstyle \overset{..}{O}:^{-}}{\underset{\textstyle \underset{..}{O}:^{-}}{}}}$$

For a complex such as $[Co(NH_3)_6]^{+++}$, containing six ammino groups, structures involving metal-nitrogen double bonds cannot be formulated. The stability of these complexes is to be attributed to the large amount of ionic character of the single bonds between the metal atom and its ligands, as discussed in Section 5-7. The atoms and groups that occur in the octahedral complexes of cobalt are in the main strongly electronegative; they include NH_3, OH_2, $(OH)^{-}$, $(O_2)^{--}$ (peroxide), $H_2NCH_2CH_2NH_2$ (ethylenediamine), $(C_2O_4)^{--}$ (oxalate), $(NO_3)^{-}$, $(SO_4)^{--}$, and others. The atoms bonded to cobalt in all of these groups have about the same electronegativity (that of N^{+} in $M\!-\!N^{+}H_3$, for example, being not much different from that of O in $M\!-\!OH$, etc.). The somewhat less electronegative chlorine and bromine atoms can also be introduced, but only to a limited extent (occupying a maximum of two of the six positions), whereas the still less electronegative iodine atom cannot be introduced.

To summarize: we attribute the stability of the octahedral complexes of cobalt to the removal of the negative charge assigned to the central atom on the basis of a normal covalent single-bonded structure from it to the surrounding electronegative groups; in the case of cyano group, and to a smaller extent the nitrosyl and nitro groups, the transfer of charge is also accomplished in part by the formation of double bonds from the cobalt atom to the attached groups.

The iron-group elements are electropositive, tending to form positive ions; and this property is reflected in the nature of the complexes that they form. The metals of the palladium and platinum groups, on the other hand, have little tendency to form positive ions, but prefer to remain neutral or even to become negative; this characteristic is indicated by their position (2.2) in the electronegativity scale. In consequence these elements can form covalent octahedral complexes not only with cyanide, ammonia, hydroxide, and related groups but also with chlorine, bromine, and even iodine atoms. In the hexachloroplatinate ion, $[PtCl_6]^{--}$, the ionic character of the bonds removes some of the negative charge from platinum to chlorine; but in the hexaiodo-osmiate ion, $[OsI_6]^{----}$, the bonds to the weakly electronegative iodine atoms can have little ionic character and a good part of the negative charge would be left on the central atom; some of the negative charge may be removed by the contribution of double-bond structures involving a fifth outer orbital of the halogen atom.

EXERCISES

9-1.—It is mentioned in Section 9-5 that the bonds in the silicate ion, the phosphate ion, the sulfate ion, and the perchlorate ion are 0.16, 0.19, 0.21, and 0.25 Å shorter, respectively, than the single-bond values, and that 0.25 Å corresponds to 100 percent of double-bond character. By a suitable change of the vertical scale in Figure 7-3, use this figure to estimate the amount of double-bond character for the bonds in the first three ions. (Ans. 50, 65, 75%.)

9-2.—Use the results of the preceding exercise and the partial ionic character from Table 3-7 to evaluate the charge on the central atom of the four tetrahedral ions. (Ans. $+1.00$, $+0.97$, $+0.54$, -0.52.)

9-3.—Discuss the electronic structure of the triphosphate ion, $P_3O_{10}^{5-}$, mentioned in Section 9-2. Assuming that the covalence of each of the three phosphorus atoms is the same as in the orthophosphate ion (6.6, corresponding to 65 percent of double-bond character for each of the four bonds), that the eight bonds to unshared oxygen atoms have the same amount of double-bond character, and that each shared oxygen atom has covalence 2.5, evaluate double-bond character of the three kinds of phosphorus-oxygen bonds.

9-4.—Discuss the electronic structures of the disulfate ion, $S_2O_7^{--}$, and the diphosphate ion, $P_2O_7^{----}$. Can you suggest an explanation of the fact that disulfate ion reacts with water very rapidly, to form the ortho ion SO_4^{--}, whereas diphosphate ion reacts rather slowly?

9-5.—(a) Assign an electronic structure to Cl_2O. Note that the observed bond length, 1.70 ± 0.02 Å, agrees with the value obtained by use of Equation 7-1. (b) The electron-diffraction study of dichlorine heptoxide has led to the values 1.42 ± 0.01 Å for six and 1.72 ± 0.03 Å for two chlorine-oxygen bonds. Discuss the electronic structure of the molecule in relation to these values.

9-6.—In the perchloric acid molecule the observed chlorine-oxygen bond lengths have the values 1.64 ± 0.02 Å for the oxygen atom with hydrogen attached and 1.42 ± 0.02 Å for the other three oxygen atoms. Discuss the electronic structure of the molecule. Can you suggest an explanation of the difference between the larger bond length in this molecule and in Cl_2O_7?

9-7.—It is mentioned in Section 9-3 that the nickel atom in $Ni(CO)_4$ has zero charge when the bonds to carbon have 79 percent of double-bond character. (a) What amount of double-bond character would make the iron atom in $Fe(CO)_5$ neutral? (b) Would make the Cr atom in $Cr(CO)_6$ neutral? (Note that the electronegativity of chromium corresponds to 19 percent ionic character for the Cr—C bond.) (c) Can these amounts of double-bond character be achieved for $Fe(CO)_5$ and $Cr(CO)_6$? If not, what are the maximum amounts and the corresponding electronic structures?

9-8.—The elements Cr, Mn, Fe, Co, and Ni have nearly the same covalent radius (about 1.17 Å for the single-bond metallic radius—Table 7-7). The observed M—C bond lengths are 1.82 Å in $Ni(CO)_4$, 1.84 Å in $Fe(CO)_5$, and 1.92 Å in $Cr(CO)_6$. Discuss these values in relation to the results of the preceding Exercise.

9-9.—The cobalticyanide ion, $[Co(CN)_6]^{---}$, is usually assigned a structure in which the cobalt atom forms single bonds with the six surrounding carbon atoms. (a) To what formal charges on Co, C, and N does this structure correspond? (b) To what charges with consideration of the amounts of ionic character corresponding to the electronegativity difference? (c) What is the resonating electronic structure that makes the amount of double-bond character of the cobalt-carbon bonds a maximum, and what is the amount of double-bond character? (d) What charges does this structure place on the atoms? (e) What combination of the structures (a) and (c) makes the cobalt atom electrically neutral? To what amount of double-bond character for the cobalt-carbon bonds does it correspond? (Ans. (e) 33 percent.)

9-10.—The gas molecule Cu_3Cl_3 has been shown by electron-diffraction investigation to have a planar ring configuration, with angle CuClCu about 90°, angle ClCuCl about 150°, and bond length 2.16 Å. Discuss its electronic structure, with use of the covalent radii in Tables 7-1 and 7-7. What is the nature of the bond orbitals of chlorine and of copper?

9-11.—(a) Using the radii in Tables 7-1 and 7-7 and the electronegativity correction (Equation 7-1), calculate the expected length of a single bond between silver and chlorine. (b) The observed value found by spectroscopic study of AgCl vapor is 2.250 Å. To what amount of double-bond character does it correspond? (Use the curve in Figure 7-3; note that in the range of bond number 1.00 to 1.30 it is approximately a straight line with slope -0.37 Å.) (c) Draw the two electronic structures that in resonance describe the molecule. To what values of the electric charges on the two atoms do they correspond, individually and in the ratio corresponding to (b)? (Ans. 2.31 Å; 22 percent; ± 0.26, ∓ 0.52, ± 0.09.)

CHAPTER 10

The One-Electron Bond and the
Three-Electron Bond; Electron-
deficient Substances

IN a few molecules and crystals it is convenient to describe the interactions between the atoms in terms of the one-electron bond and the
three-electron bond. Each of these bonds is about half as strong as a
shared-electron-pair bond; each might be described as a half-bond.
There are also many other molecules and crystals with structures that
may be described as involving fractional bonds that result from the
resonance of bonds between two or more positions. Most of these
molecules and crystals have a smaller number of valence electrons than
of stable bond orbitals. Substances of this type are called *electron-
deficient substances*. The principal types of electron-deficient substances are discussed in the following sections (and in the next chapter,
on metals).

10-1. THE ONE-ELECTRON BOND

The one-electron bond in the hydrogen molecule-ion is about half as
strong as the electron-pair bond in the hydrogen molecule ($D_0 = 60.95$
kcal/mole for H_2^+, 102.62 kcal/mole for H_2—Secs. 1-4, 1-5); and, since
the same number of atomic orbitals is needed for a one-electron bond
as for an electron-pair bond, it is to be expected that in general molecules
containing one-electron bonds will be less stable than those in which
all the stable bond orbitals are used in electron-pair-bond formation.
Moreover, there is a significant condition that must be satisfied in order
for a stable one-electron bond to be formed between two atoms; namely,
that the two atoms be identical or closely similar (Sec. 1-4). For these
reasons one-electron bonds are rare—much rarer, indeed, than three-
electron bonds, to which similar restrictions apply.

Of the 33 excited states of the H_2 molecule that have been reported, 20 have internuclear distance within ± 0.03 Å of the value for H_2^+, 1.06 Å; it is therefore probable that these states can be described as corresponding to an H_2^+ ion, with a one-electron bond, and a second electron in an outer orbit, with only a small bonding or antibonding effect.

Similar excited states have been observed for diatomic molecules of the alkali metals. They may be interpreted as involving a molecule-ion, such as Li_2^+, with a one-electron bond, plus a loosely-bound outer electron. The internuclear distances are about 0.3 Å greater than for the corresponding normal states: 2.94 Å for Li_2^+ (2.672 Å for Li_2), 3.41 Å for Na_2^+ (3.079 Å for Na_2), and 4.24 Å for K_2^+ (3.923 Å for K_2). The values of the bond energies for the one-electron bonds, as indicated by the vibrational levels, are about 60 percent of those for the corresponding electron-pair bonds.

The only other substances in which one-electron bonds are important are the ferromagnetic metals. It will be pointed out in the following chapter that in these substances the interaction of the spins of atomic electrons and those of bonding electrons causes some of the pairs of bonding electrons to be split into unpaired bonding electrons with parallel spins.

10-2. THE THREE-ELECTRON BOND

Lewis in his 1916 paper and in his book on valence emphasized the fact that there exist only a few stable molecules and complex ions (other than those containing atoms of the transition elements) for which the total number of electrons is odd. He pointed out that in general an "odd molecule," such as nitric oxide or nitrogen dioxide, would be expected to use its unpaired electron to form a bond with another such molecule, and that the monomeric substance should accordingly be very much less stable than its dimer; and he stated that the method by which the unpaired electron is firmly held in the stable odd molecule was not at that time understood. Since then the explanation of the phenomenon has been found, as the result of the application of quantum mechanics to the problem; the stability of odd molecules is the result of the power of certain pairs of atoms to form a new type of bond, the *three-electron bond*.

The Conditions for Formation of a Stable Three-Electron Bond.— Let us consider the normal state of a system of three electrons and two nuclei or kernels, A and B, each with one stable bond orbital. There are only two essentially different ways of introducing the three electrons into the two available orbitals, I and II:

I   A: ·B

II   A·   :B

The exclusion principle permits only two electrons, which must have opposed spins, to occupy either one of the orbitals; the third electron must occupy the other orbital.

It is found on carrying out the energy calculations that structure I alone does not correspond to the formation of a stable bond; it leads instead to repulsion or at best to only a very weak attraction between the atoms. Structure II alone also leads to a similar type of interaction. If, however, the atoms A and B are identical or are closely similar, so that the two structures have nearly the same energy, then resonance will occur between them, which will stabilize the molecule and lead to an interaction between the atoms corresponding to the formation of a stable bond. This bond, corresponding to resonance of the type {A: ·B, A· :B}, may be called the *three-electron bond* and represented by the symbol A⋯B. It is found by calculation and by experiment to be about one-half as strong as an electron-pair bond (that is, to have half as great a value of the bond energy). The system of two molecules A⋯B, each containing a stable three-electron bond in addition to another bond between A and B, has accordingly about the same energy as A̤—B—B—A̤, involving an additional covalent bond; and we can expect that in some cases the heat of formation of the dimer will be positive and in others it will be negative, with corresponding differences in stability of the two forms. This is in accord with the results of observation: nitric oxide, to which we assign a structure involving a three-electron bond, does not form a stable dimer in the gas phase, whereas the similar substance nitrogen dioxide does form its dimer, dinitrogen tetroxide.

In order that there may be resonance between structures I and II and the formation of a stable three-electron bond the atoms A and B must be identical or similar; the conditions for formation of the bond are thus the same as those of the one-electron bond discussed in Section 1-4, and the two bonds show the same dependence of bond energy on the energy difference of the resonating structures. It is found on examination of the energy quantities that a stable three-electron bond might be formed between unlike atoms which differ by not much more than 0.5 in electronegativity, that is, between oxygen and fluorine, nitrogen and oxygen, nitrogen and chlorine, chlorine and oxygen, etc. Three-electron bonds between oxygen and fluorine, oxygen and oxygen, nitrogen and oxygen, and chlorine and oxygen have been recognized in stable molecules, and others are indicated also by spectroscopic data.

It may be pointed out that the one-electron bond, the electron-pair bond, and the three-electron bond use one stable bond orbital of each of two atoms, and one, two, and three electrons, respectively.

The Helium Molecule-Ion.—The simplest molecule in which the three-electron bond can occur is the helium molecule-ion, He_2^+, consisting of two nuclei, each with one stable $1s$ orbital, and three electrons. The theoretical treatment of this system has shown that the bond is strong, with bond energy about 55 kcal/mole and with equilibrium internuclear distance about 1.09 Å. The experimental values for these qualities, determined from spectroscopic data for excited states of the helium molecule, are about 58 kcal/mole and 1.080 Å, respectively, which agree well with the theoretical values. It is seen that the bond energy in $He \cdots He^+$ is about the same as that in $H \cdot H^+$, and a little more than half as great as that of the electron-pair bond in $H:H$.

10-3. THE OXIDES OF NITROGEN AND THEIR DERIVATIVES

Nitric Oxide.—Nitric oxide is the most stable of the odd molecules. For the first of the two structures I and II

$$\text{I} \quad :\!\overset{\displaystyle .}{\text{N}}\!\!=\!\!\overset{\displaystyle ..}{\text{O}}: \qquad\qquad \text{II} \quad \overset{\displaystyle -..}{:\!\text{N}}\!\!=\!\!\overset{\displaystyle .\,+}{\text{O}}:,$$

we would expect great ease of polymerization to stable molecules of the type

$$:\!\overset{\displaystyle ..}{\text{O}}\!\!=\!\!\text{N}: \\ | \\ :\!\text{N}\!\!=\!\!\underset{\displaystyle ..}{\text{O}}:,$$

and structure II, because of its unfavorable charge distribution, should be somewhat less stable than I. The unfavorable charge distribution is, however, partially neutralized by the ionic character of the double bond, and the difference in stability of I and II is small enough to permit nearly complete resonance between them. We accordingly assign to the molecule the structure $:\text{N}\!\!\triangleq\!\!\text{O}:$, involving a double bond and a three-electron bond between the two atoms. Of the four valence orbitals of each atom one is used for the unshared pair of electrons, two for the double bond, and the fourth for the three-electron bond.

The properties of the molecule are accounted for by this structure. The extra energy of the three-electron bond stabilizes the molecule relative to structure I to such extent that the heat of the reaction $2NO \rightarrow N_2O_2$ is small, and the substance does not polymerize in the gas phase.

This structure, which may be described as involving a $2\frac{1}{2}$ bond, is expected to lead to a bond length intermediate between that for a double bond and that for a triple bond. The N—O single-bond length is 1.44 Å (Sec. 7-2), and the double-bond and triple-bond lengths may be taken as 0.04 Å less than for N=N and N≡N, and hence equal to 1.20 Å and 1.06 Å, respectively. This triple-bond value agrees well with the experimental value 1.062 Å for NO^+, which has the structure :N≡O:. The observed distance for NO is 1.151 Å, somewhat larger than that expected for a $2\frac{1}{2}$ bond; it corresponds to the bond number 2.31. We conclude that the difference in electronegativity of the two atoms decreases the contribution of structure II to such an extent that the three-electron bond is about a one-third bond, rather than a one-half bond.

A study of the hyperfine structure of the electron spin magnetic resonance spectrum, resulting from the interaction with the nuclear spins, has led to the conclusion that structure I contributes 65 percent and structure II 35 percent, and that the odd electron occupies a $2p\pi$ orbital with 2.5 percent s character.

The electric dipole moment of the molecule is small, about 0.16 D. Structure I would lead to a moment with the oxygen atom negative, because of the partial ionic character of the bonds; this moment is neutralized by the contribution of structure II.

Dinitrogen Dioxide.—Crystals of nitric oxide contain its dimer, with the form of a rectangle with short edge 1.12 ± 0.02 Å and long edges 2.40 Å. The long edges represent very weak bonds. It is not unlikely that there is some mobility of an electron from one NO to the other in the dimer, and that its structure can be represented by the resonance structures A, B, and C:

$$:\overset{\cdots}{N}=\overset{+}{O}: \qquad :N≡\overset{+}{O}: \qquad :\overset{-}{N}=\overset{\cdots}{O}:$$

$$A \qquad\qquad B \qquad\qquad C$$

$$:\overset{\cdots}{O}=\overset{\cdots}{N}: \qquad :O=\overset{\cdots}{N}: \qquad :\overset{+}{O}≡N:$$

The structures B and C have no odd electrons, and for resonance with them A must have the spins of the two odd electrons opposed. Hence the substance should be diamagnetic—as it has been observed to be. The residual entropy at low temperature, approximately $R\ln2$ per mole of N_2O_2, can be explained as resulting from a disorder in the crystal, each N_2O_2 rectangle having two possible orientations.

The Nitrosyl Halogenides.—Nitrosyl fluoride, chloride, and bromide, ONF, ONCl, and ONBr, have been studied by the electron-diffraction method and by microwave spectroscopy. Their configuration is non-linear. The N—O distance is 1.14 ± 0.02 Å. Although a reasonable electronic structure, I,

$$\text{:}\overset{..}{X}\diagdown\overset{..}{N}{=}\overset{..}{O}\text{:}$$

I

can be formulated for these molecules, this seems not to be correct, for the observed N—F, N—Cl, and N—Br distances, 1.52 ± 0.03, 1.96 ± 0.01, and 2.14 ± 0.02 Å, are very much greater than the expected single-bond values (Sec. 7-2), 1.38, 1.73, and 1.86 Å, respectively. It seems probable that these molecules resonate between structure I and the ionic structure II (with a small contribution also from structure III, representing conjugation of the double bond and an electron pair of the halogen atom),

$$\text{:}\overset{-}{\underset{..}{X}}\text{:} \qquad \text{:}N{\equiv}O\overset{+}{\text{:}}$$

$$\overset{+}{\text{:}}\underset{..}{X}\diagup\overset{N{-}\overset{..}{O}\text{:}^{-}}{}$$

II   III

and that the ionic bond gives rise to the increase in the N—X distance.

A study of BrNO by microwave spectroscopy has yielded values of the bond lengths and bond angle in agreement with the electron-diffraction values (N—O = 1.15 ± 0.06 Å, N—Br = 2.14 ± 0.06 Å, angle BrNO = $114° \pm 5°$). The fine structure due to coupling of the electric quadrupole moment of the bromine nucleus with the electrons has been interpreted as showing that structure II contributes 39 percent to the normal state of the molecule, structure I 49 percent, and structure III, representing conjugation, 12 percent.

Nitrogen Dioxide.—To nitrogen dioxide we assign the resonating structure

$$\left\{ N\diagup\overset{..}{O}\text{:} \diagdown\overset{..}{O}\text{:} \quad , \quad N\diagup\overset{..}{O}\text{:} \diagdown\overset{..}{O}\text{:} \right\}$$

in which one oxygen atom is held to nitrogen by a double bond and one by a single bond plus a three-electron bond.

The N—O distance is intermediate between that in NO_2^+, 1.154 Å, and that in NO_2^-, 1.236 Å. An infrared study of NO_2 has yielded the values 1.188 ± 0.004 Å for N—O and 134.1° ± 0.25° for the angle ONO, in agreement with the less accurate electron-diffraction values.

10-4. THE SUPEROXIDE ION AND THE OXYGEN MOLECULE

On oxidation the alkali metals are converted into oxides to which the formula R_2O_4 and the name alkali tetroxide were assigned until recently, in the belief that the substances were analogous to the tetrasulfides and contained the O_4^{--} anion with structure

$$\overset{-\ ..}{:O:}$$
$$\underset{..}{:}\overset{..}{O}\text{—}\overset{..}{O}:$$
$$\overset{|\ -}{:O:}$$

With the discovery of the three-electron bond it was seen that these alkali oxides might contain the ion O_2^-, with the structure

$$[:O\cdots O:]^-,$$

involving a single bond and a three-electron bond between the two identical atoms. This suggestion was verified by the measurement of the magnetic susceptibility of the potassium compound. The superoxide ion O_2^- contains one unpaired electron, corresponding to the observed paramagnetism, which gives $\mu = 2.04$ Bohr magnetons, the theoretical value for the $^2\Pi$ state being about 1.85; whereas the O_4^{--} ion would be diamagnetic.

For the normal state of the oxygen molecule we would expect the structure

$$A \qquad :\overset{..}{O}{=}\overset{}{O}:$$

with a double bond. The normal molecule has, however, the term symbol $^3\Sigma$, showing it to contain two unpaired electrons; in consequence of this, the substance is strongly paramagnetic. It seems probable that the first excited state of the molecule, the $^1\Delta$ state, is represented by this double-bonded structure, and that the normal state, which is more stable by 22.4 kcal/mole, corresponds to a structure in which the two atoms are held together by a single bond and two three-electron bonds. The numbers of electrons and orbitals permit this structure, B,

$$B \qquad :O\vdots\vdots O:$$

to be formed, each oxygen atom using one of its four valence orbitals for an unshared pair, one for a single bond, and two for the two three-electron bonds.

Since the bond energy of a three-electron bond is about one-half that of a single bond, structure *B* would be expected to have about the same stability as structure *A*. There is another interaction to be considered, however—the coupling of the two three-electron bonds. Each of these involves one unpaired electron spin. The two unpaired spins can combine to give either a singlet state, by opposition, or a triplet state, by remaining parallel; one of these will be stabilized by the corresponding interaction energy and the other destabilized. Theoretical arguments lead to the conclusion that the triplet state should be the more stable, as observed. If the two odd electrons are somewhat unsynchronized they will be during one phase of their motion on the same oxygen atom, and their interaction will then be larger than when they are on different atoms. By Hund's first rule (Sec. 2-7) the interaction is such as to make the triplet more stable than the singlet. Strong support for these ideas is provided by the existence of a $^1\Sigma$ state 37.8 kcal/mole less stable than the normal state; this is to be identified as the state with structure *B* with unfavorable mutual interaction of the two three-electron bonds (opposed spins of the two odd electrons). The average energy of the normal state and this state is close to that of the double-bonded state.

10-5. OTHER MOLECULES CONTAINING THE THREE-ELECTRON BOND

A few molecules in addition to those discussed in the preceding sections can be assigned structures involving one or two three-electron bonds. The normal states of the molecules SO, S_2, Se_2, and Te_2 are $^3\Sigma$ states, like that of the normal oxygen molecule, and it is probable that the electronic structures with a single bond plus two three-electron bonds are satisfactory for these molecules. The observed values of interatomic distances, 1.493, 1.888, 2.152, and 2.82 Å, respectively, are about those expected.

The anion Cl_2^- has been reported in potassium chloride crystals irradiated with x-rays at the temperature of liquid nitrogen. It may be assigned the structure $:\!\overset{..}{Cl}\!\cdots\!\overset{..}{Cl}\!:^-$, and the bond length may be predicted to have the value 2.16 Å.

The cation Cl_2^+, to which we assign the structure $:\!Cl\!\cdots\!\overset{..}{Cl}\!:^+$, has been studied spectroscopically. It has bond length 1.89 Å; this value is slightly larger than the value expected for a single bond plus a three-electron bond, 1.86 Å.

The Cl—O distance in the odd molecule ClO_2 has been found to be 1.491 ± 0.014 Å. This value is compatible with the structure

$$
\left\{
\begin{matrix}
\overset{\cdot\cdot}{O}: & :\overset{\cdot\cdot}{O}: \\
\diagup\cdot\cdot\cdot & \diagup \\
:Cl & , & :Cl \\
\diagdown & \diagdown\cdot\cdot\cdot \\
:\underset{\cdot\cdot}{O}: & \underset{\cdot\cdot}{O}:
\end{matrix}
\right\}
, \text{ involving resonance of the three-electron bond}
$$

between the Cl—O positions. The OClO bond angle is $116.5° \pm 2.5°$.

10-6. ELECTRON-DEFICIENT SUBSTANCES

Electron-deficient substances are substances in which the atoms have more stable orbitals than electrons in the valence shell. An example is boron. The boron atom has four orbitals in its valence shell, and three valence electrons.

A characteristic feature of the structure of most electron-deficient substances is that the atoms have ligancy that is not only greater than the number of valence electrons but is even greater than the number of stable orbitals. Thus most of the boron atoms in the tetragonal form of crystalline boron have ligancy 6. Also, lithium and beryllium, with four stable orbitals and only one and two valence electrons, respectively, have structures in which the atoms have ligancy 8 or 12. All metals can be considered to be electron-deficient substances (Chap. 11).

Another generalization that may deserve to be called a structural principle is that an electron-deficient atom causes adjacent atoms to increase their ligancy to a value greater than the orbital number. For example, in the boranes, discussed in the following section, some of the hydrogen atoms, adjacent to the electron-deficient atoms of boron, have ligancy 2.

The structure of tetragonal boron has been determined with care. There are 50 boron atoms in the unit of structure. All but two of them are in icosahedral groups of 12, as shown in Figure 10-1. In the B_{12} icosahedron each boron atom forms five bonds with adjacent atoms. The icosahedra and the two additional boron atoms per unit (interstitial atoms) are arranged in such relative positions that each icosahedral boron atom also forms one more bond, extending in the direction directly out from the center of the icosahedron. Thus each of the icosahedral boron atoms has ligancy 6; the interstitial atoms have ligancy 4. The bonds (8 per unit) formed by the interstitial atoms are expected to have bond number about $\frac{3}{4}$, and the others (140 per unit) to have bond number slightly less than $\frac{1}{2}$ (0.465, when correction is made for the slightly stronger bonds formed with the interstitial atoms). The icosahedral boron atoms may be described as forming three single bonds each of which resonates between two positions.

The expected half-bond boron-boron distance is twice the single-

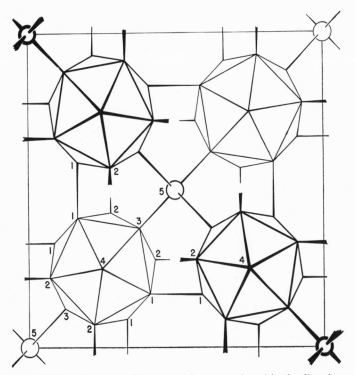

Fig. 10-1.—Structure of tetragonal boron as viewed in the direction of the c axis. One unit cell is shown. Two of the icosahedral groups (light lines) are centered at $z = \frac{1}{4}$, and the other two (heavy lines) at $z = \frac{3}{4}$. The interstitial boron atoms (open circles) are at $(0, 0, 0)$ and $(\frac{1}{2}, \frac{1}{2}, \frac{1}{2})$. Numbers identify the various structurally nonequivalent boron atoms. All of the extra-icosahedral bonds are shown with the exception of B_4—B_4, which is formed parallel to the c axis from each icosahedron to the icosahedra in cells directly above and below.

bond radius 0.81 Å plus the half-bond correction 0.18 Å (Sec. 11-4). This value, 1.80 Å, agrees well with the experimental value, 1.797 ± 0.015 Å. For the other bonds the observed value is 1.62 ± 0.02 Å.

Similar icosahedral B_{12} groups are found in other modifications of boron and also in the compound $B_{12}C_3$, in which there are linear C_3 groups.

As another example we may discuss the crystals MB_6, in which M represents Ca, Sr, Ba, Y, La, Ce, Pr, Nd, Gd, Er, Yt, or Th. The structure, shown in Figure 10-2, involves a boron framework with atoms M in the interstices. Each boron atom forms bonds with five other boron atoms, four in its B_6 octahedron and the fifth in an adjacent octahedron. The five bonds have the same length, which for CaB_6 has the experi-

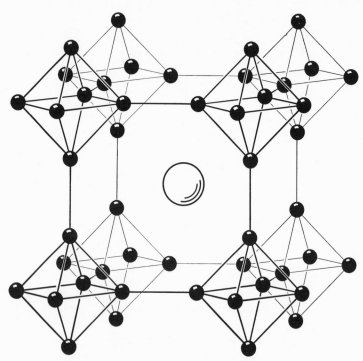

Fig. 10-2.—The atomic arrangement in the cubic crystal calcium hexaboride, CaB_6.

mental value 1.72 ± 0.01 Å. Nearly the same value is found in CeB_6, and similar values are found in the other compounds, ranging from 1.69 Å for YB_6 to 1.77 Å for BaB_6. These values reflect the sizes of the atoms M (the radius for ligancy 12 is 1.797 for Y, 1.970 for Ca, 2.215 Å for Ba—Table 11-1).

It is probable that the atoms M form bonds with one another, and that the boron atoms use their valence electrons in forming boron-boron bonds. The bond number of these bonds would then be 0.60, with the expected B—B bond length 1.75 Å. It is also not improbable that there is some transfer of valence electrons from M to the boron framework. If one electron were transferred, the B—B bond number would be 0.633, with expected bond length 1.74 Å.

10-7. THE STRUCTURE OF THE BORANES

Boron forms a series of hydrides of surprising composition. The simple substance BH_3 has not been prepared; instead, hydrides of various compositions occur, including B_2H_6, B_4H_{10}, B_5H_9, B_5H_{11}, B_6H_{10}, B_9H_{15}, and $B_{10}H_{14}$.

The structural problem presented by these substances is not a simple one; the fundamental difficulty is that there are not enough valence electrons in the molecules to bind the atoms together with electron-

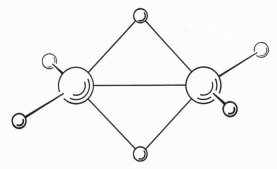

FIG. 10-3.—The configuration of atoms in diborane, B_2H_6.

pair bonds. In B_2H_6, for example, there are twelve valence electrons; all twelve would be needed to hold the six hydrogen atoms to boron by covalent bonds, leaving none for the boron-boron bond.

Diborane, B_2H_6, has the configuration shown in Figure 10-3. This configuration has been verified by spectroscopic and other physical evidence. The molecular dimensions were obtained by a careful electron-diffraction study.

Four of the hydrogen atoms have ligancy 1. Their H—B distance is 1.187 ± 0.030 Å. This value agreeš moderately well with the single-bond value 1.13 Å; it corresponds to bond number 0.80 ± 0.08, which shows that the bonds are not pure single bonds. The bridging hydrogen atoms, with ligancy 2, have B—H bond length 1.334 ± 0.027 Å, corresponding to bond number 0.46 ± 0.05, and the B—B distance is 1.770 ± 0.013 Å, corresponding to bond number 0.56 ± 0.03. (The bond numbers are calculated with radius 0.81 Å for boron and 0.32 for hydrogen.)

The sum of the bond numbers of the nine bonds is 5.60 ± 0.55. It should be six, because there are twelve valence electrons in the molecule.

A simple theoretical treatment that can be applied to electron-deficient substances in general can be given for the diborane molecule. Let us consider the various valence-bond structures that can be written for the molecule (with its known configuration) with use of the six electron pairs and the stable valence orbitals (one for hydrogen, four for boron). Twenty structures may be written: they are of type A (2 structures), B (2), C (4), D (8), and E (4).

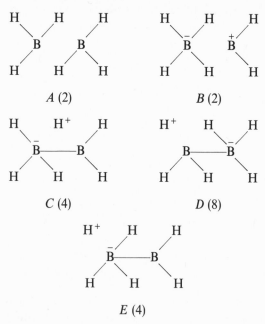

We may, as a first approximation, assume that these structures contribute equally to the normal state of the molecule. The bond numbers calculated in this way are 0.85 for nonbridging B—H, 0.45 for bridging B—H, and 0.80 for B—B. The two B—H values agree well with those obtained from the interatomic distances, but the B—B value does not. Possibly the structures with neutral atoms should be given greater weight than those with separated charges. If the structures of type A are given triple weight the calculated bond numbers become 0.875 for nonbridging B—H, 0.459 for bridging B—H, and 0.667 for B—B.

The most stable borane is $B_{10}H_{14}$. It is made by heating the simpler boranes, and it decomposes only very slowly at 200°C. In the decaborane molecule every boron atom has one nonbridging H attached and also forms five half-bonds (Fig. 10-4).   The conclusion may be drawn that the structural feature leading to greatest stability is ligancy 6 with one nonbridging B—H bond (or B—B bond, as in elementary boron).

We may ask if there are any possible boranes other than $B_{10}H_{14}$ that are based entirely on this structural feature.   One is $B_{12}H_{12}$, with a B_{12} icosahedron.   It is possible that this molecule is stable, but the substance

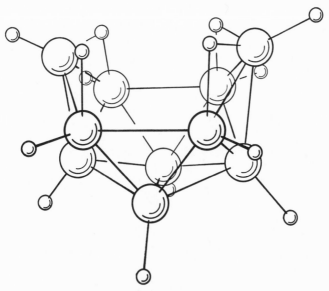

FIG. 10-4.—The atomic arrangement in the molecule of deca-borane, $B_{10}H_{14}$.   Note that 10 boron atoms are approximately at corners of a regular icosahedron.   Each of the two remaining corners of the icosahedron may be considered to have been replaced by two bridging hydrogen atoms.   The other 12 hydrogen atoms are bonded to boron atoms in such a way that the B—H bonds extend out from the center of the icosahedron.

has not yet been reported.   The ion $B_{12}H_{12}^{--}$ has been found to exist, in the crystal $K_2B_{12}H_{12}$; it has the icosahedral structure, with boron-boron bond length 1.78 Å.

10-8. SUBSTANCES CONTAINING BRIDGING METHYL GROUPS

Several electron-deficient compounds in which there are bridging methyl groups, with ligancy 5 or 6 for carbon, are known.   The first one to be recognized was the tetramer of platinum tetramethyl, $Pt_4(CH_3)_{16}$.   This substance was found by x-ray examination to have the structure shown in Figure 10-5.   Each carbon atom has ligancy 6; it is bonded to its three hydrogen atoms and also to the three neighboring platinum atoms.   The bond lengths were not accurately determined (the platinum-platinum distance was found to be 3.44 Å); however, it is likely that the Pt—C bridging bonds are approximately half-bonds.

The increase in ligancy of the carbon atom illustrates the principle, mentioned in Section 10-6, that an electron-deficient atom causes adjacent atoms to increase their ligancy.   The platinum atom in the monomer,

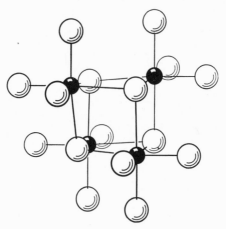

FIG. 10-5.—The molecular structure of the tetramer of platinum tetramethyl, $Pt_4(CH_3)_{16}$. The small circles represent platinum atoms and the large circles carbon atoms of the methyl groups.

$Pt(CH_3)_4$, would make use of only seven of its nine valence orbitals: four for bonds to the four carbon atoms and three for the three unshared pairs of $5d$ electrons. The electron deficiency of this atom then permits the increase in ligancy of carbon.

10-9. FERROCENE AND RELATED SUBSTANCES

A few years ago the synthesis of a substance of a new type, dicyclopentadienyl iron, $Fe(C_5H_5)_2$ (commonly called ferrocene), was reported almost simultaneously by two groups of investigators.   Ferrocene forms orange crystals, which vaporize without decomposition.   It can be oxidized to the blue ferricinium cation $[Fe(C_5H_5)_2]^+$.   Many similar substances have been reported: ruthenocene, $Ru(C_5H_5)_2$; ruthenicinium ion, $[Ru(C_5H_5)_2]^+$; corresponding compounds of titanium, vanadium, chromium, manganese, and cobalt and of their congeners; corresponding compounds with indenyl replacing dicyclopentadienyl; and corresponding benzene compounds, such as dibenzenechromium, $Cr(C_6H_6)_2$, and its cation, $[Cr(C_6H_6)_2]^+$. The ferrocene molecule was found by the x-ray determination of its crystal structure to have the configuration shown in Figure 10-6. Ruthenocene forms crystals that are not isomorphous with those of ferrocene; the molecules have a related structure,

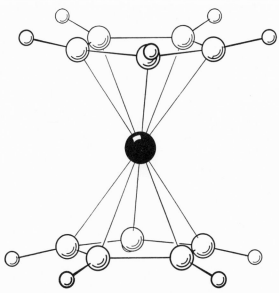

FIG. 10-6.—The structure of ferrocene, $Fe(C_5H_5)_2$.

differing from that of ferrocene only in that the two cyclopentadienyl rings are in the eclipsed rather than the staggered relative orientation.

The C—C bond length found for ferrocene (by electron diffraction of gas molecules) is 1.435 ± 0.015 Å. The C—C distance in ruthenocene is 1.43 ± 0.02 Å. The experimental values of the Fe—C and Ru—C bond lengths are 2.05 ± 0.01 Å and 2.21 ± 0.02 Å, respectively.

EXERCISES

10-1.—Discuss the electronic structure of ClO. Would you expect the odd electron to be involved in a three-electron bond? What value would you expect for the chlorine-oxygen distance (the single-bond value, in Cl_2O, is 1.72 ± 0.02 Å)? The observed bond length is 1.546 Å.

10-2.—(a) Using the arguments of Appendix IX and the value 99 kcal/mole for the enthalpy of dissociation of Cl_2O into atoms, estimate the first and second bond-dissociation energies of Cl_2O.   (b) The total bond energy of ClO is 61 kcal/mole.   Compare this value with the second bond-dissociation energy of Cl_2O to obtain a value for the energy of the three-electron bond.   (c) What is its ratio to the Cl—O single-bond energy? Is this a reasonable value, in light of the nature of the three-electron bond? (Ans. (a) 59, 40 kcal/mole; (b) 24 kcal/mole; (c) 49 percent.)

10-3.—Assign a reasonable electronic structure to nitryl chloride, NO_2Cl.   To what values of the interatomic distances and bond angles does it correspond?   (Ans. N—O about 1.24 Å, N—Cl about 1.73 Å, angle ONO about 125°, ONCl about 117°.)

10-4.—The parameters found by microwave study of nitryl chloride are N—O = 1.21 Å, N—Cl = 1.83 Å, angle ONO = 129.5°, ONCl 115.3°. What electronic structure in resonance with the principal one would account for these values?

10-5.—Bartlett and Lohmann have prepared the crystal O_2PtF_6 by reaction of oxygen and platinum hexafluoride.   It contains the O_2^+ ion. What electronic structure would you assign to this ion?   What bond length (see Table 7-3)?   What magnetic moment?   (Ans. About 1.16 Å, observed 1.12 Å; about 2 Bohr magnetons, observed 2.4.)

10-6.—Three substances have been prepared with molecular formula $B_{10}C_2H_{12}$.   What structures would you assign them?   Would you expect more than three isomers with this formula?

10-7.—The molecule B_4Cl_4 contains a B_4 tetrahedron with edge 1.70 Å, and the molecule B_8Cl_8 contains a B_8 octahedron with edge 1.80 Å.   Each boron atom has an attached chlorine atom at distance 1.70 Å.   Discuss the electronic structures of these molecules.

10-8.—(a) The carbon-carbon bond length in the cyclopentadienyl rings of ferrocene has been found by electron diffraction to have the value 1.435 ± 0.015 Å.   By reference to Figure 7-3 estimate the amount of double-bond character.   (b) What fraction of the carbon atoms are free to form bonds with the iron atom?   What is the corresponding bond number for the Fe—C bonds?   (The observed Fe—C bond length is approximately that for a half-bond.)   (Ans. (a) 26 ± 6 percent; (b) 0.48 ± 0.12.)

CHAPTER 11

The Metallic Bond

11-1. THE PROPERTIES OF METALS

THE elements that are classed as metals display to a larger or smaller extent certain characteristic properties, including high thermal conductivity and electric conductivity, metallic luster, ductility and malleability, power to replace hydrogen in acids, etc. These properties are shown most strikingly by the elements in the lower left region of the periodic table; in fact, metallic character is closely associated with electropositive character, and in general a small value of the electronegativity of an element, as given by the bond-energy method, the electromotive-force series, or any similar treatment, corresponds to pronounced metallic properties of the elementary substance.

Lorentz advanced a theory of metals that accounts in a qualitative way for some of their characteristic properties and that has been extensively developed in recent years by the application of quantum mechanics. He thought of a metal as a crystalline arrangement of hard spheres (the metal cations), with free electrons moving in the interstices. This free-electron theory provides a simple explanation of metallic luster and other optical properties, of high thermal and electric conductivity, of high values of heat capacity and entropy, and of certain other properties.

One of the most interesting of these properties is the small temperature-independent paramagnetism shown by many metals, including the alkali metals. It was the discussion of this phenomenon by Pauli in 1927 that initiated the development of the modern electronic theory of metals. The fundamental concept is that there exists in a metal a continuous or partially continuous set of energy levels for the "free" electrons. At the absolute zero the electrons (N in number) would occupy the $N/2$ most stable levels in pairs, and, as required by the Pauli exclusion principle, the spins of the electrons of each pair would be opposed, so that the spin magnetic moments of the electrons would

203

not be available for orientation in an applied magnetic field. At higher temperatures some of these pairs are broken, as one of the electrons of a pair is raised to a higher energy level, and the spin moments of these unpaired electrons then make a contribution to the paramagnetic susceptibility of the metal. The number of unpaired electrons increases with increasing temperature; the contribution of one unpaired electron spin to the paramagnetic susceptibility decreases with increasing temperature, however (App. VIII), and the two effects are found on quantitative discussion to lead to an approximately temperature-independent paramagnetic susceptibility of the observed order of magnitude.

The quantum-mechanical theory of metals has been extensively developed. Discussion of it is beyond the scope of this book, however, and instead we shall consider the problem of the structure of metals from a more chemical point of view. The treatment given in the following sections is not to be interpreted as being a rival of the quantum-mechanical theory, but rather as offering an alternative avenue of approach toward the same goal as that of the theoretical physicists.

11-2. METALLIC VALENCE

The great field of chemistry comprising the compounds of metals with one another has been largely neglected by chemists in the past. Approximately three-quarters of the elements are metals. This means that the binary systems of pairs of metals constitute about $\frac{9}{16}$—well over one-half—of the binary systems, and one might conclude that the chemistry of the metals should be the major part of chemistry, more extensive than the chemistry of metals in combination with nonmetals, or of nonmetals and nonmetals. In fact, textbooks of general chemistry may devote only one or two pages out of several hundred to a discussion of the compounds of metals with one another. Perhaps part of the reason for the neglect by chemists of this branch of chemistry is that many compounds of metals with one another show a range of composition, so that the chemist, who likes the precision of compounds with definite composition, daltonides, rather than the imprecision of the berthollides, turns away from them. Moreover, there is the non-existence of good solvents for metallic systems; both the inorganic chemist and the organic chemist are accustomed to beginning their work on a solid substance by purifying it by recrystallization from a suitable solvent. This process can only occasionally be used with intermetallic compounds—one can, for example, obtain beautiful big crystals of KHg_{13} by cooling a solution of potassium in mercury, but purification by recrystallization is in general not a feasible process for intermetallic compounds. I think, however, that the most important reason for the neglect of this branch of chemistry during the past century is that a theory of valence and structure for intermetallic compounds was not developed at the same time as for other compounds.

In the assignment of valences to metals in intermetallic compounds the chemist would have faced a problem similar to that faced by Frankland, Cowper, Kekulé, and other chemists in their attack on the valence theory of organic chemistry. The compound KHg_{13} might be compared with naphthalene, $C_{10}H_8$. In KHg_{13} the valence of potassium might well be taken as 1, corresponding to its position in the periodic table—presumably the valences of the first-group elements and the second-group elements can be taken as 1 and 2, respectively. But the formula KHg_{13} should not then be taken to require that the valence of mercury be $\frac{1}{13}$. The organic chemist did not conclude from the formula $C_{10}H_8$ for naphthalene that the valence of carbon should be taken as $\frac{4}{5}$, because as soon as the idea of the carbon-carbon bond was developed he accepted for naphthalene a structure in which carbon atoms are bonded to one another, as well as to hydrogen atoms, so as to permit carbon to retain its valence of 4. In the same way we might assume that in KHg_{13} mercury atoms are bonded to one another, as well as to potassium atoms; but the formula does not tell us what the metallic valence of mercury is.

The organic chemist was successful in developing valence theory and discovering the quadrivalence of carbon because he could make many simple compounds, such as CH_4 and CH_3Cl, in which the carbon atom was indicated to be attached to four other (univalent) atoms. If a similar attack on intermetallic compounds could have been made valence theory would probably have been extended to cover this field of chemistry. In fact, however, we see that it fails. In addition to KHg_{13}, potassium forms with mercury the compounds KHg_5, KHg_3, KHg_2, and KHg. If we were to assume that the last of these, with the highest potassium content, involves only bonds between mercury and potassium, we would assign to mercury the metallic valence 1. The compound of sodium with mercury with the highest sodium content is Na_3Hg, which we should similarly interpret as indicating metallic valence 3 for mercury; and the compound Li_3Hg indicates the same valence. The compound of magnesium with mercury with highest magnesium content is Mg_3Hg; this indicates metallic valence 6 for mercury, if the same assumption, that this compound contains only mercury-magnesium bonds, is made. It is evident that this procedure, analogous to that used by the organic chemist in discovering the quadrivalence of carbon, fails to disclose the metallic valence of mercury.

The properties of the metals themselves can be used to indicate, at least approximately, the values of the metallic valence. If, in the sequence of elements beginning with potassium, we assume that the metallic valence of potassium is 1 and that of calcium is 2, we recognize the expected correlation between valence and properties: the metal calcium is harder, stronger, and denser than potassium, it has a higher melting point, boiling point, enthalpy of fusion, and enthalpy of vaporization than calcium, and in general its properties correlate well with the assumption that the bonds holding the atoms together are twice as strong in calcium as in potassium, corresponding to the respective valences 2 and 1. Similarly, there is a further increase in hardness, density, melting point, and some other properties from calcium to scandium, permitting us to conclude reasonably that scandium has the valence 3 that corresponds to its position in the periodic table. The change in these properties continues from scandium to titanium, titanium to vanadium, and vanadium to chromium, and we may well feel justified in concluding that the metallic valences of titanium, vanadium, and chromium are 4, 5, and 6, respectively. These are just the maximum valences shown by these elements in inorganic compounds—the maximum oxidation numbers for titanium, vanadium, and chromium are $+4$, $+5$, and $+6$, respectively, as in the oxides TiO_2, V_2O_5, and CrO_3.

The properties of the following transition metals do not suggest a further increase in metallic valence, to 7 for manganese, 8 for iron, and 9 for cobalt. Instead, the properties mentioned above, hardness, density, melting point, and so on, indicate that the metallic valence remains roughly constant from chromium to nickel, then decreases somewhat from nickel to copper, and shows a further decrease from copper to zinc. I think that it is reasonable to assign the metallic valence 6 as the normal metallic valence for the elements manganese, iron, cobalt, and nickel, and about $5\frac{1}{2}$ for copper, $4\frac{1}{2}$ for zinc, $3\frac{1}{2}$ for gallium, $2\frac{1}{2}$ for germanium (when functioning as a metal), and $1\frac{1}{2}$ for arsenic.

11-3. THE METALLIC ORBITAL

The atoms of the first long period have nine orbitals in the valence shell, five $3d$, one $4s$, and three $4p$ orbitals. These orbitals can be expected to serve as bond orbitals or for occupancy by unshared pairs. The observed magnetic properties of the iron-group metals and their alloys indicate, however, that in metallic substances only 8.28 of the nine orbitals are used in these ways. (A detailed discussion can be found in *The Nature of the Chemical Bond*.) The remaining 0.72 orbital per atom, called the metallic orbital, serves a special purpose. It permits the unsynchronized resonance of electron-pair bonds from one interatomic position to another by the jump of one electron from one atom to an adjacent atom, leading to great stabilization of the metal by resonance energy, and to the characteristic properties of metals.

It is known that lithium, for example, forms some diatomic molecules in the gas phase; these molecules are described as consisting of two atoms held together by a single covalent bond. In lithium metal each atom has eight nearest neighbors and one valence electron, which permits the formation of an electron-pair bond for each pair of atoms. The bonds may be considered to resonate among alternative positions, the eight positions between each atom and its nearest neighbors. If each atom were to remain electrically neutral, by retaining its valence electron, the stabilization through the permitted synchronized bond resonance,

$$\begin{array}{cccc} \text{Li—Li} & \qquad & \text{Li} & \text{Li} \\ & & | & | \\ \text{Li—Li} & \qquad & \text{Li} & \text{Li} \end{array}$$

analogous to that in the benzene molecule, would be relatively small. Much greater stabilization could result from unsynchronized resonance,

$$\begin{array}{cccc} \text{Li—Li} & \qquad & \text{Li—Li}^- & \\ & & | & \text{etc.} \\ \text{Li—Li} & \qquad & \text{Li}^+\ \text{Li} & \end{array}$$

This unsynchronized resonance would require the use of an additional orbital on the atom receiving an extra bond. It is assumed that this additional orbital is the metallic orbital.

A discussion of the nonintegral value, 0.72, of metallic orbitals per atom will be given in the following section, in connection with the discussion of interatomic distances in the allotropic forms of tin.

11-4. INTERATOMIC DISTANCES AND BOND NUMBERS IN METALS

The following empirical equation for the relation between the corresponding bond distance $D(n)$ for bonds with bond number n less than 1 and the bond distance for $n = 1$, $D(1)$, has been formulated:

$$D(n) = D(1) - 0.600 \log n \qquad (11\text{-}1)$$

Experience has shown that Equation 11-1 can usually be applied in the interpretation of observed interatomic distances with considerable confidence. Some intermetallic compounds, however, have structures such as to make it possible that some of the interatomic distances represent bonds in tension and others represent bonds in compression. The application of Equation 11-1 in the interpretation of these interatomic distances would lead to error, and it is necessary in using the equation to keep this possibility in mind.

Let us consider the element tin as the first example of the application of the equation. From the argument given above about the necessity of having 0.72 metallic orbital per atom in order for a substance to be a metal we predict the metallic valence 2.56 for tin. The calculation is made in the following way: The tin atom has 14 electrons outside its krypton shell. There are 9 stable orbitals outside this shell, $4d^5 5s 5p^3$. Of these 9 orbitals, 0.72 is allocated as metallic orbital, leaving 8.28 for occupancy by bonding electrons and unshared electron pairs. This requires that there be $14 - 8.28 = 5.72$ unshared electron pairs, leaving 2.56 orbitals for occupancy by bonding electrons; hence the metallic value of tin is predicted to be 2.56.

Now let us consider the interatomic distances in the two allotropic forms of tin, gray tin and white tin. Gray tin has the diamond structure: each tin atom is surrounded by four other tin atoms, at the distance 2.80 Å. It is known that in the molecule tin tetramethyl, $Sn(CH_3)_4$, in which tin is surely quadrivalent, forming single bonds with each of the carbon atoms, the tin-carbon distance is 2.17 Å; and, inasmuch as the single-bond radius of carbon is 0.77 Å, the single-bond radius of tin can be taken as 1.40 Å. The observed distance 2.80 Å in gray tin is, then, just that expected for a single covalent bond, and we are led to the conclusion that tin in this form has valence 4. The tin atom can achieve valence 4 by using all of its nine outer orbitals, either for occupancy by unshared pairs (5 orbitals holding 10 electrons) or by bonding electrons (4 orbitals, holding the remaining 4 of the 14 outer electrons of the tin atom). Accordingly there is no metallic orbital in gray tin; all nine outer orbitals are used either in bond formation or for occupancy by unshared pairs (the electron configuration is $4d^{10} 5s 5p^3$); but gray tin is not a metal—it is a metalloid, and it does not have the characteristic properties of a metal: high electric conductivity, negative temperature coefficient of electric conductivity, malleability, etc.

White tin, on the other hand, has the characteristic properties of a metal. In white tin each tin atom has four nearest neighbors at 3.016 Å and two others at 3.175 Å, its structure being that shown in Figure 11-1. We may apply Equation 11-1 to calculate the valence of tin in white tin, assuming the single-bond distance to be 2.80 Å.   The bond numbers for the bonds with length 3.016 Å and 3.175 Å are respectively, 0.44 and 0.24; these values correspond to the valence 2.24.   It will be pointed out later that it is likely that the single-bond radius for tin, as for many other metals, depends somewhat on the nature of the bond orbitals and has the value 1.424 Å, rather than 1.40 Å, for valence 2.56.   With this value the bond numbers corresponding to the distances 3.016 Å and 3.175 Å are calculated to be 0.52 and 0.28, respectively, leading to the valence 2.64 for tin in the metallic form of the element, in good agreement with the predicted value 2.56 Å.

We may now ask why the valence of tin in the metallic form of the

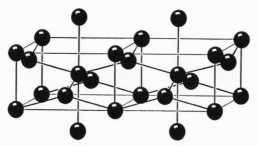

Fig. 11-1.—The arrangement of atoms in the tetragonal crystal white tin (metallic).   The tetragonal axis is vertical.

element is not 2, corresponding to one metallic orbital per atom and the electron configuration $4d^{10}5s^25p^2$, but is 2.56.   The answer is, I think, given by the quantum-mechanical principle that the actual structure for the normal state of a system is that structure, from among all conceivable ones, that minimizes the energy of the system.   Let us consider a hypothetical form of tin, resembling white tin, but with valence 2 and one metallic orbital per atom.   This structure would be stabilized by the essentially completely unsynchronized resonance of the two valence bonds per atom among the alternative positions, six around each atom.   Now let us introduce a single quadrivalent tin atom.   The number of bonds would be increased, which would further stabilize the crystal.   There would be, it is true, a small interference with resonance of the bonds, because this one atom would not have a metallic orbital; but the amount of interference would be so small as not to diminish the resonance energy comparable to the increase in stabilization caused by the extra bond.   A second quadrivalent tin atom would stabilize the metal still further, but finally, as the number

TABLE 11-1.—METALLIC VALENCES AND RADII OF THE ELEMENTS

	Li	Be	B		Si	P	S
v	1	2	3		2.56	(3)	(2)
$R(L\,12)$	1.549	1.123	0.98		1.375	1.28	1.27
R_1	1.225	0.889	.80		1.173	1.10	1.04

	Na	Mg	Al		Ge	As	Se
v	1	2	3		2.56	1.56	(2)
$R(L\,12)$	1.896	1.598	1.429		1.444	1.476	1.40
R_1	1.572	1.364	1.248		1.242	1.210	1.17

	K	Ca	Sc	Ti	V	Cr	Mn	Fe	Co	Ni	Cu	Zn	Ga	Sn	Sb	Te
v	1	2	3	4	5	6	6	6	6	6	5.56	4.56	3.56	2.56	1.56	(2)
$R(L\,12)$	2.349	1.970	1.620	1.467	1.338	1.276	1.268	1.260	1.252	1.244	1.276	1.339	1.404	1.623	1.657	1.60
R_1	2.025	1.736	1.439	1.324	1.224	1.186	1.178	1.170	1.162	1.154	1.176	1.213	1.246	1.421	1.391	1.37

	Rb	Sr	Y	Zr	Nb	Mo	Tc	Ru	Rh	Pd	Ag	Cd	In	Pb	Bi
v	1	2	3	4	5	6	6	6	6	6	5.56	4.56	3.56	2.56	1.56
$R(L\,12)$	2.48	2.148	1.797	1.597	1.456	1.386	1.361	1.336	1.342	1.373	1.442	1.508	1.579	1.704	1.776
R_1	2.16	1.914	1.616	1.454	1.342	1.296	1.271	1.246	1.252	1.283	1.342	1.382	1.421	1.502	1.510

	Cs	Ba	La	Hf	Ta	W	Re	Os	Ir	Pt	Au	Hg	Tl
v	1	2	3	4	5	6	6	6	6	6	5.56	4.56	3.56
$R(L\,12)$	2.67	2.215	1.871	1.585	1.457	1.394	1.373	1.350	1.355	1.385	1.439	1.512	1.595
R_1	2.35	1.981	1.690	1.442	1.343	1.304	1.283	1.260	1.265	1.295	1.339	1.386	1.437

	Th	U
v	4	6
$R(L\,12)$	1.795	1.516
R_1	1.652	1.426

	Ce	Pr	Nd	Pm	Sm	Eu	Gd	Tb	Dy	Ho	Er	Tm	Yb	Lu
v	3.2	3	3	3	3	3	3	3.5	3	3	3	3	2	3
$R(L\,12)$	1.818	1.824	1.818	1.814	1.804	2.084	1.804	1.773	1.781	1.762	1.761	1.759	1.933	1.738
R_1	1.646	1.643	1.637	1.633	1.623	1.850	1.623	1.613	1.600	1.581	1.580	1.578	1.699	1.557

of quadrivalent tin atoms became significant, the interference with resonance of the bonds would become so great as to cause a decrease in resonance energy equal to the increase in bond energy accompanying the increase in the number of quadrivalent atoms. At this point the minimum in energy (the maximum stability) of the system would be reached, and this would represent the actual structure of the crystal of white tin.

With use of the observed values of interatomic distances in metals, discussed in the following sections, and Equation 11-1, values of R_1,

Fig. 11-2.—The arrangement of spheres in a closest-packed layer.

the metallic radius, have been derived. These values are given in Table 11-1, together with the assumed values of the metallic valence v and the values of the metallic radius for ligancy 12, $R(L12)$.

11-5. THE CLOSEST PACKING OF SPHERES

It is not surprising that often a crystalline substance is a rather closely packed aggregate of atoms or ions, since the van der Waals interactions, Coulomb interactions, and interactions involving metallic valence tend to stabilize structures in which the atoms have large ligancies. It has been found that the structures of many crystals can be profitably discussed in terms of the packing of spheres, to which we now direct our attention.

There is only one way of arranging spheres in a single closest-packed layer. This is the familiar arrangement in which each sphere is in contact with six others, as in Figure 11-2. A second similar layer can be superimposed on this layer in such a way that each sphere is in contact with three spheres of the adjacent layer, as shown in Figure 11-3. A third layer can then be added in either one of two possible positions, with its spheres either directly above those of the first layer, as in Figure 11-3, or over the holes in the first layer not occupied by the second layer. Once either choice is made, the structure is determined, if all of the spheres are to be equivalent. The first structure, with hexagonal symmetry, is shown in Figure 11-3 and at the left in Figure 11-4; it is called *hexagonal*

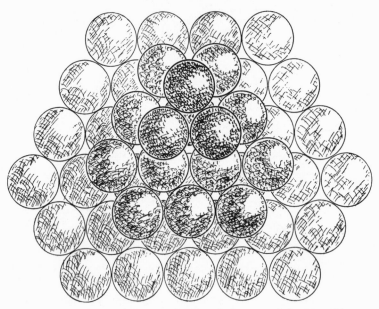

Fig. 11-3.—The arrangement of spheres in hexagonal closest packing.

closest packing. The second structure, called *cubic closest packing*, is shown at the right in Figure 11-4.

A convenient description of these structures utilizes the symbols *A*, *B*, and *C* for the three layers of close-packed spheres differing from one another in position. Hexagonal closest packing corresponds to the sequence of layers *ABABAB*···(or *BCBC*··· or *ACAC*···), and cubic closest packing to *ABCABCABC*···. The structure repeats itself after two layers in hexagonal closest packing and after three layers in cubic closest packing.

In each of the closest-packed structures each sphere is in contact with twelve others, a hexagon of six in the same plane and two triangles of three above and below. In hexagonal closest packing the upper triangle has the same orientation as the lower triangle and in cubic closest packing it is rotated through 60°.

For crystals involving spherical or nearly spherical molecules that are attracted to one another by van der Waals forces, closest-packed structures, giving the maximum number of intermolecular contacts, can be

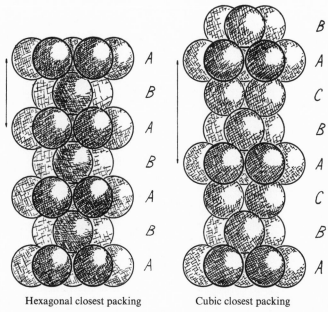

Hexagonal closest packing   Cubic closest packing

FIG. 11-4.—The modes of superposition of closest-packed layers of spheres in hexagonal closest packing (left) and cubic closest packing (right).

expected to be stable. It has been shown that all the noble gases (He, Ne, Ar, Kr, and Xe) crystallize in cubic or hexagonal closest packing. Moreover, it has been found that in many molecular crystals of simple gases the molecules are rotating with considerable freedom, permitting them to simulate spheres in their interactions with neighboring molecules; these crystals are usually closest-packed. The crystals of molecular hydrogen consist of rotating H_2 molecules in hexagonal closest packing, and in crystalline HCl, HBr, HI, H_2S, H_2Se, CH_4, and SiH_4 the molecules are arranged in cubic closest packing, and show evidence of molecular rotation in the observed values of the heat capacity and entropy.

11-6. THE ATOMIC ARRANGEMENTS IN CRYSTALS
OF METALLIC ELEMENTS

About three-quarters of the metallic elements crystallize with the cubic or hexagonal closest-packed structure or both.   The observed interatomic distances for these crystals are equal to twice the radii $R(L12)$ given in Table 11-1.

The Cubic Body-centered Arrangement.—In the cubic body-centered arrangement each atom has eight neighbors at the distance $a_0 \sqrt{3/2}$ and six neighbors at the 15 percent larger distance a_0.   If the valence of the atom were used only for bonds to the eight nearest neighbors, the effective radius would be that for ligancy 8.   But Equation 11-1 indicates that each of the six long bonds has bond number about one-fifth that of the short bonds, and in consequence the effective radius is that for ligancy 9.2, and is 0.035 Å less than for ligancy 12.   The observed differences for all those elements that have both a body-centered and a closest-packed modification are between 0.03 and 0.04 Å, which supports the description of these metals as involving the formation of eight strong bonds and six weaker bonds between each atom and its neighbors.

The body-centered structure is found for the alkali metals, barium, the fifth-group metals, the sixth-group metals, and as one allotropic form for titanium, zirconium, iron, and thallium.   The factors determining the choice of this structure by certain elements are not known.

Several metals have more complex structures; an example is tin (Fig. 11-1).

Many intermetallic compounds have structures that involve the disordered or ordered distribution of metal atoms of two or more kinds among the atomic positions for cubic or hexagonal closest packing. Among the substances with structures of this type based on cubic closest packing are the following: $AuCu$, $PtCu$, $AuCu_3$, $PdCu_3$, $PtCu_3$, $CaPb_3$, $CaTl_3$, $CaSn_3$, $CePb_3$, $CeSn_3$, $LaPb_3$, $LaSn_3$, $PrPb_3$, and $PrSn_3$.   In general there is rather small difference in radius of the atoms in a compound of this type.

Among the intermetallic compounds that crystallize with structures based on the cubic body-centered structure are the binary compounds $CuPd$, $CuBe$, $CuZn$, $AgMg$, $FeAl$, $AgZn$, $AgCd$, $AuZn$, $AuCd$, $NiAl$, $NdAl$, $SrCd$, $SrHg$, $BaCd$, $BaHg$, and $LaCd$, with the cesium chloride structure.   In these crystals each atom has as nearest neighbors, at the corners of a cube about it, eight unlike atoms, whereas in $NaTl$, $LiZn$, $LiCd$, $LiGa$, $LiIn$, $NaIn$, and $LiAl$, which represent another type of structure based on the body-centered arrangement, each atom has as nearest neighbors four like atoms and four unlike atoms.

11-7. ICOSAHEDRAL STRUCTURES

The maximum number of rigid spheres that can be brought into contact with another sphere with the same radius is twelve. The corresponding coordination polyhedra, seen in the cubic and hexagonal closest-packed structures, have eight triangular faces and six square faces.

It is possible to retain ligancy 12 with a central sphere as much as 10 percent smaller than the surrounding spheres. These spheres are then arranged at the corners of a regular icosahedron, which has 20 triangular faces (Figure 10-1).

There are many known structures of intermetallic compounds that involve icosahedral coordination about the smaller atoms. Usually these structures are complex, with 20, 52, 58, 162, 184, or more atoms in a cubic unit of structure. Many of the crystals are cubic. The icosahedron has 6 fivefold axes of symmetry, 10 threefold axes, and 15 twofold axes; the fivefold axes cannot be retained in the crystal, but some of the others can be (a maximum of four threefold axes in a cubic crystal).

A simple icosahedral structure is that of $MoAl_{12}$, WAl_{12}, and $(Mn,-Cr)Al_{12}$. In this structure, based on a body-centered cubic lattice, there is at each lattice point a nearly regular icosahedron of twelve aluminum atoms about the smaller central atom (Fig. 11-5).

One of the most complex structures known is that of the compound $Mg_{32}(Zn, Al)_{49}$. The unit of structure is a cube containing 162 atoms. The structure is based on icosahedral coordination of larger atoms about somewhat smaller ones. It is characteristic of the icosahedron that groups of four contiguous atoms occur only at corners of a tetrahedron; every triangle formed by three contiguous atoms in the icosahedron has a fourth atom lying approximately above its center. Accordingly a structure involving icosahedral packing may be built up by placing atoms out from the centers of the triangular faces of an inner polyhedron. The metrical nature of the icosahedron is such that the distances from the atom at the center to its twelve ligands is 5 percent smaller than the distances between these ligands; hence the retention of icosahedral packing through successive ligation spheres requires a continued steady increase in average size of the atoms in these spheres. This increase in size can be achieved by placing the smaller atoms, zinc and aluminum, alone in the inner spheres, and introducing the larger atoms, magnesium, as part of the outer spheres.

The structure is based on a body-centered lattice. At each lattice point there is a small atom (Zn, Al). It is surrounded by an icosahedron of twelve atoms (Fig. 11-6). This group is then surrounded

by 20 atoms, at the corners of a pentagonal dodecahedron, each atom
lying directly out from the center of one of the 20 faces of the icosahedron.   The next 12 atoms lie out from the centers of the pentagonal faces of the dodecahedron; this gives a complex of 45 atoms, the
outer 32 of which lie at the corners of a rhombic triacontahedron.   The
next shell consists of 60 atoms, each directly above the center of a triangle
that forms one-half of one of the 30 rhombs bounding the rhombic

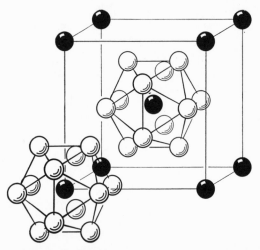

Fig. 11-5.—The atomic arrangement in the cubic
crystal $MoAl_{12}$.   There is a molybdenum atom at
the corner and the center of each cube.   It is surrounded by 12 aluminum atoms, at icosahedral
corners.

triacontahedron; these 60 atoms lie at the corners of a truncated icosahedron, which has 20 hexagonal faces and 12 pentagonal faces.   Twelve
additional atoms are then located out from the centers of 12 of the 20
hexagonal faces.   The very large complexes, shown in Figure 11-6, are
then condensed together in such a way that each of the 72 outer atoms
is shared between two complexes; each outer atom then contributes 36
atoms per lattice point, which with inner complexes of 45 atoms gives 81
atoms per lattice point, 162 in the unit cube.   All of the smaller atoms
(Al, Zn) have icosahedral coordination; the larger ones (Mg) have
ligancy 14, 15, or 16.

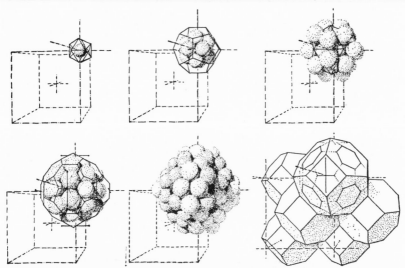

Fig. 11-6.—The atomic arrangement in the cubic crystal $Mg_{32}(Zn, Al)_{49}$. The six drawings, from left to right in the top row and then left to right in the bottom row, have the following significance: A central atom surrounded by 12 atoms at the points of a nearly regular icosahedron; the icosahedral group of 13 atoms surrounded by 20 atoms at the points of a pentagonal dodecahedron; the complex of 33 atoms surrounded by 12 atoms at the corners of an icosahedron; the outermost shell of 60 atoms at the corners of a truncated icosahedron, plus 12 atoms out from the centers of 12 of the hexagons of this polyhedron; packing drawing showing the outer shell of 72 atoms surrounding the central complex of 45 atoms; the structure of the crystal, in which these complexes located about the points of a body-centered cubic lattice share all of the 72 atoms of the outermost shell with neighboring complexes.

11-8. MOLECULES AND CRYSTALS CONTAINING METAL-METAL BONDS

The existence of the mercury-mercury bond in the mercurous ion, Hg_2^{++}, and in molecules such as mercurous chloride, Cl—Hg—Hg—Cl, has been recognized for decades, but until recently other examples of molecules containing metal-metal bonds had not been reported. Now a great many are known.

The complex ion $[W_2Cl_9]^{---}$ was discovered to have such a structure through the determination of the structure of $K_3W_2Cl_9$. The complex ion consists of two WCl_6 octahedra sharing a face. The W—Cl bond lengths are 2.40 Å (unshared Cl) and 2.48 Å (shared Cl). The tungsten atoms are closer to the plane of the shared face than to the plane of the peripheral chlorine. The W—W distance, 2.409 Å, is less than in metallic tungsten, and about equal to the value 2.40 Å ex-

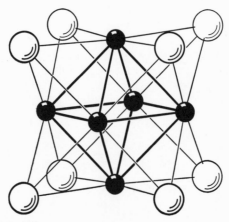

FIG. 11-7.—The structure of the complex ion $[Mo_6Cl_8]^{++++}$.

pected for a double bond between the tungsten atoms. Each tungsten atom has three valence electrons in addition to those involved in the bonds to the chlorine atoms. The tungsten-tungsten bond can be described as involving resonance among the structures $\ddot{W}\text{—}\ddot{W}$, $\dot{W}\text{=}\dot{W}$, $W\text{=}\ddot{W}$, and $W\text{≡}W$.

Whereas $K_3W_2Cl_9$ is diamagnetic, the closely similar substance $K_3Cr_2Cl_9$ is paramagnetic, with three unpaired electrons per chromium atom. In the $[Cr_2Cl_9]^{---}$ ion the chromium atoms are 3.12 Å apart, corresponding to bond number 0.05 (that is, there is no Cr—Cr bond).

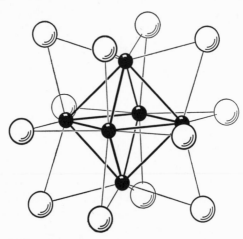

FIG. 11-8.—The structure of the complex ion $[Ta_6Cl_{12}]^{++}$.

The ion $[Mo_6Cl_8]^{++++}$ is found in solutions of molybdenum dichloride, Mo_6Cl_{12}, and in the crystals $[Mo_6Cl_8](OH)_4 \cdot 14H_2O$, $[Mo_6Cl_8]Cl_4 \cdot 8H_2O$, and $(NH_4)_2[Mo_6Cl_8]Cl_6 \cdot 2H_2O$. Its structure is shown in Figure 11-7. Each molybdenum atom uses two of its six valence electrons in the bonds to the chlorine atoms and the other four to form single Mo—Mo bonds along the edges of the Mo_6 octahedron. The Mo—Mo bond length, 2.63 Å, is close to the single-bond value 2.592 Å derived from the metal (Table 11-1).

The ions $[Nb_6Cl_{12}]^{++}$, $[Ta_6Cl_{12}]^{++}$, and $[Ta_6Br_{12}]^{++}$ have a related structure, shown in Figure 11-8. The number of valence electrons is such that the bonds along the edges of the Nb_6 and Ta_6 octahedra have bond number $\frac{2}{3}$. The observed Nb—Nb and Ta—Ta bond lengths, 2.85 Å and 2.90 Å, respectively, agree moderately well with the expected value 2.79 Å.

EXERCISES

11-1.—Evaluate the factor A in the equation $D(n) = D(1) - A \log n$ by use of the observed C=C bond length 1.334 Å and the value 1.504 Å for $n = 1$ (obtained from the single-bond value as described in Section 7-4). (Ans. 0.57 Å.)

11-2.—An alloy of tin with about 5 percent of mercury is known to have a simple hexagonal structure, such that hexagonal layers (Fig. 11-2) are directly above and below one another. Each tin atom forms six bonds (within its layer) with length 3.198 Å and two bonds with length 2.980 Å. Using a value for the single-bond radius (with a small correction for the mercury present; Table 11-1), evaluate the bond numbers by Equation 11-1, and the valence. (Ans. 0.25, 0.54, 2.58.)

11-3.—Cementite, Fe_3C, is a hard white crystalline substance that occurs in white cast iron and some forms of steel. In the cementite crystal each carbon atom is surrounded by six iron atoms, at the distance 2.01 Å, and each iron atom is bonded to two carbon atoms as well as to several iron atoms. The strong iron-carbon bonds are responsible for the great hardness of cementite, as compared with pure iron. (a) What is the bond number of the iron-carbon bonds? (b) With use of the iron radius from Table 11-1 and the electronegativity correction, calculate a value for the length of the iron-carbon single bond. (c) Calculate the bond length appropriate to cementite. (Ans. (b) 1.886 Å; (c) 1.992 Å.)

11-4.—The unit cube of iron nitride, Fe_4N, with edge 3.79 Å, has iron atoms at the corners and at the center of each face, and the nitrogen atom at the center of the cube. (a) How many bonds does each nitrogen atom form? (b) What is the nitrogen-iron bond length? (c) Calculate the expected single-bond length. (d) What is the state of the nitrogen atom in this crystal? (Ans. (c) 1.81 Å; (d) Quadricovalent N^+.)

11-5.—Verify the statements in the last paragraph of Section 11-8 that the expected M—M bond number is $\frac{2}{3}$ and the expected bond length is 2.79 Å.

11-6.—The molecule diphenylacetylenedicobalt hexacarbonyl, $(C_6H_5)_2C_2Co_2(CO)_6$, has been found by X-ray crystallographic examination to have a structure in which each cobalt atom is bonded to the carbon atoms of three of the six carbonyl groups, to the two acetylenic carbon atoms, and to the other cobalt atom (thus forming a C_2Co_2 tetrahedron). The bond lengths of the tetrahedron edges (C—C = 1.47 Å, Co—C = 1.96 Å, Co—Co = 2.47 Å) have approximately the single-bond values. The observed Co—C (carbonyl) distance is 1.75 Å. (a) How would you describe this bond? (b) Discuss the use by the cobalt atom of its orbitals and valence electrons.

CHAPTER 12

The Hydrogen Bond

12-1. THE NATURE OF THE HYDROGEN BOND

It was recognized some decades ago that under certain conditions an atom of hydrogen is attracted by rather strong forces to two atoms, instead of only one, so that it may be considered to be acting as a bond between them. This is called the *hydrogen bond*. The bond was for some time thought to result from the formation of two covalent bonds by the hydrogen atom, the hydrogen fluoride ion $[HF_2]^-$ being assigned the structure $[:\ddot{F}:H:\ddot{F}:]^-$. It is now recognized that the hydrogen atom, with only one stable orbital (the $1s$ orbital), can form only one covalent bond, that the hydrogen bond is largely ionic in character, and that it is formed only between the most electronegative atoms. A detailed discussion of its nature is given in the following sections.

Although the hydrogen bond is not a strong bond (its bond energy, that is, the energy of the reaction $XH + Y \rightarrow XHY$, lying in most cases in the range 2 to 10 kcal/mole), it has great significance in determining the properties of substances. Because of its small bond energy and the small activation energy involved in its formation and rupture, the hydrogen bond is especially suited to play a part in reactions occurring at normal temperatures. It has been recognized that hydrogen bonds restrain protein molecules to their native configurations, and I believe that as the methods of structural chemistry are further applied to physiological problems it will be found that the significance of the hydrogen bond for physiology is greater than that of any other single structural feature. Recognition of the importance of the hydrogen bond and of its extensive occurrence was made in 1920 by the American chemists W. M. Latimer and W. H. Rodebush, who used this concept in the discussion of highly associated liquids, such as water and hydrogen fluoride, with their abnormally high dielectric constant values, of the small ionization of ammonium hydroxide, and of the formation of double molecules by acetic acid.   The number of molecules recognized as containing hydrogen bonds has been greatly increased by spectroscopic and crystal-structure studies and by analysis of physicochemical information.

With the development of the quantum-mechanical theory of valence it was recognized that a hydrogen atom, with only one stable orbital, cannot form more than one pure covalent bond and that the attraction of two atoms observed in hydrogen-bond formation must be due largely to ionic forces.   This conception of the hydrogen bond leads at once to the explanation of its important properties.

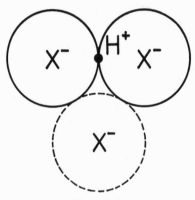

Fig. 12-1.

First, the hydrogen bond is a bond by hydrogen between *two* atoms; the coordination number of hydrogen does not exceed two.   The positive hydrogen ion is a bare proton, with no electron shell about it.   This vanishingly small cation would attract one anion (which we idealize here as a rigid sphere of finite radius—Section 7-9) to the equilibrium internuclear distance equal to the anion radius, and could then similarly attract a second anion, as shown in Figure 12-1, to form a stable complex.   A third anion, however, would be stopped by anion-anion contacts, which prevent its close approach to the proton.   From the ionic point of view the coordination number of hydrogen is thus restricted to the value two, as is observed in general.

Second, only the most electronegative atoms should form hydrogen bonds, and the strength of the bond should increase with increase in the electronegativity of the two bonded atoms.   Referring to the electronegativity scale, we might expect that fluorine, oxygen, nitrogen, and chlorine would possess this ability, to an extent decreasing in this order. It is found empirically that fluorine forms very strong hydrogen bonds, oxygen weaker ones, and nitrogen still weaker ones.   Although it has the same electronegativity as nitrogen, chlorine has only a very small hydro-gen-bond-forming power; this may be attributed to its large size (relative to nitrogen), which causes its electrostatic interactions to be weaker than those of nitrogen.

Increasing the electronegativity of an atom increases its power of form-ing hydrogen bonds. The ammonium ion and its derivatives, such as $[RNH_3]^+$, form stronger hydrogen bonds than ammonia or normal amines. The phenols form stronger hydrogen bonds than aliphatic al-cohols because of the increase in electronegativity of the oxygen atom resulting from resonance with structures such as

$$: \overset{-}{\underset{}{\bigcirc}} = \overset{+}{\underset{\cdot\cdot}{O}}H$$

In almost all hydrogen bonds the hydrogen atom is nearer to one of the two adjacent electronegative atoms than to the other. In ice, for example, the distance between two hydrogen-bonded oxygen atoms is 2.76 Å, and the proton has been shown by neutron diffraction to be 1.01 Å from one oxygen atom and 1.75 Å from the other (Sec. 12.4).

The amount of partial ionic character expected for the O—H bond from the electronegativity difference of the atoms is 39 percent. Hence the $1s$ orbital of the hydrogen atom is liberated from use in covalent-bond forma-tion with the adjacent oxygen atom to the extent of 39 percent, and hence available for formation of a fractional covalent bond with the more distant oxygen atom of the hydrogen-bonded group O—H$\cdots$O; the hydrogen bond in ice can be described as involving resonance among the three structures A, B, and C:

A	O—H	:O	
B	O:	H$^+$	:O
C	O:	H——O	

(Here the dashes represent pure covalent bonds.) A rough idea of the amount of covalent bonding to the more distant oxygen atom can be ob-tained by use of the equation relating interatomic distance to bond number for fractional bonds, Equation 11-1. The long H$\cdots$O distance in ice is 0.80 Å greater than the single-bond distance, corresponding to bond number 0.05. Hence we conclude that for the hydrogen bonds in ice the three structures A, B, and C contribute about 61 percent, 34 percent, and 5 percent, respectively. The shortest reported O—H$\cdots$O bonds have oxygen-oxygen distance 2.40 Å. This is only 0.06 Å greater than the distance expected for two half-bonds, 2.34 Å, and it is likely that symmetrical hydrogen bonds between oxygen atoms are present in a few substances.

12-2. THE EFFECT OF THE HYDROGEN BOND ON THE
PHYSICAL PROPERTIES OF SUBSTANCES

It is the hydrogen bond that determines in the main the magnitude and nature of the mutual interactions of water molecules and that is conse-

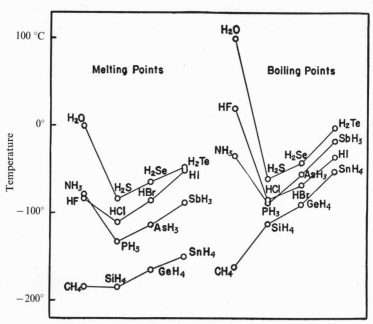

FIG. 12-2.—The melting points and boiling points of
isoelectronic sequences of hydride molecules.

quently responsible for the striking physical properties of this uniquely important substance. In this section we shall discuss the melting point, boiling point, and dielectric constant of water and related substances; other properties of water are treated later (Sec. 12-4).

For the sequence of related substances H_2Te, H_2Se, and H_2S the melting points and boiling points show the decreasing courses expected in view of the decreasing molecular weights and van der Waals forces (Fig. 12-2). The continuation of the sequence in the way indicated by the values for the noble gases would lead to the expectation of values of about $-100°C$ and $-80°C$, respectively, for the melting point and boiling point of water.

The observed values of these quantities are very much higher; this is the result of the formation of hydrogen bonds, which have the extraordinary effect of doubling the boiling point of the substance on the Kelvin scale.

The melting points and boiling points of ammonia and hydrogen fluoride are also considerably higher than the values extrapolated from the sequences of analogous compounds, the effects being, however, somewhat smaller than for water. This decrease for ammonia is due in part to the smaller electronegativity of nitrogen than of oxygen and in part to the presence in the ammonia molecule of only one unshared electron pair, which must serve as the source of attraction for the protons involved in all the hydrogen bonds formed with the N—H groups of other molecules. Hydrogen fluoride can form only one-half as many hydrogen bonds as water, and, although its F—H$\cdots$F bonds are stronger than the O—H$\cdots$O bonds in water and ice, the resultant effects are smaller for this substance than for water.

It is worthy of note that from the existence of both the melting point effect and the boiling point effect the deduction can be made that some of the hydrogen bonds existing in crystals of hydrogen fluoride, water, and ammonia are ruptured on fusion and that others (more than one-half of the total) are retained in the liquid, even at the boiling point, and are then ruptured on vaporization. Indeed, the very strong hydrogen bonds of hydrogen fluoride tend to hold the molecules together even in the vapor, which is partially polymerized.

The abnormally high dielectric-constant values observed for certain liquid substances, such as water and ammonia, were attributed by Latimer and Rodebush to continued polymerization through hydrogen-bond formation. In Figure 12-3 the comparison is made of the values of the dielectric constant of liquid substances, measured at 20°C, and the values of the electric dipole moments of the molecules of the substances in the gaseous state or in solution in nonpolar solvents. It is seen that most of the points lie close to a simple curve, represented in the figure. The points for methylamine, ammonia, the alcohols, water, hydrogen peroxide, hydrogen fluoride, and hydrogen cyanide, however, lie above the curve. For all of these substances except the last hydrogen-bond formation is expected, to an extent, indeed, which is roughly related to the magnitude of the deviation from the curve, which is small for methylamine and ammonia and larger for the substances containing oxygen and fluorine.

The very high value observed for the dielectric constant of liquid hydrogen cyanide is surprising in that it shows that in this substance the carbon atom is able to use its attached hydrogen atom in hydrogen-bond formation. The observed density of hydrogen cyanide gas shows the presence

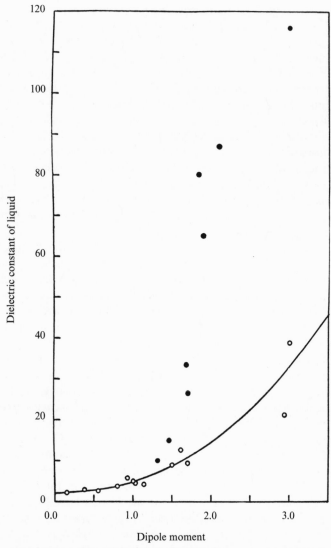

FIG. 12-3.—The dielectric constants of polar liquids plotted against the dipole moments of the gas molecules. From left to right the substances shown by open circles are AsH_3, HI, PH_3, HBr, H_2S, $CHCl_3$, HCl, $(C_2H_5)_2O$, $SOCl_2$, SO_2, SO_2Cl_2, $(CH_3)_2CO$, CH_3NO_3; by solid circles, CH_3NH_2, NH_3, CH_3OH, C_2H_5OH, H_2O, HF, H_2O_2, HCN.

of polymers $(HCN)_n$. The enthalpy of the hydrogen bond in the dimer, $H—C≡N···H—C≡N$, is 3.28 kcal/mole, and the sum of the enthalpies of the two bonds in the trimer, $H—C≡N···H—C≡N···H—C≡N$, is 8.72 kcal/mole. The increase in hydrogen-bond strength with increasing degree of polymerization is interesting, and can be given a simple interpretation in terms of resonance.

Evidence of intermolecular association through weak hydrogen-bond formation with use of a hydrogen atom attached to a carbon atom of a halogenated hydrocarbon molecule (chloroform and similar substances with ethers and glycols) has been reported. The technique of proton magnetic resonance applied to solutions of chloroform in acetone and in triethylamine has shown that $1:1$ complexes between solute and solvent are formed, and the energy of the hydrogen bond has been shown to be 2.5 kcal/mole for $Cl_3C—H···OC(CH_3)_2$ and 4.0 kcal/mole for $Cl_3C—H···N(C_2H_5)_3$.

12-3. ICE AND WATER

Ordinary ice (ice I, hexagonal) has the crystal structure shown in Figure 12-4. Each water molecule is tetrahedrally surrounded by four water molecules, to which it is attached by hydrogen bonds. The $O—H···O$ bond length is 2.76 Å; neutron-diffraction studies of D_2O have shown the deuterium atom to be 1.01 Å from one oxygen atom and 1.75 Å from the other.

An interesting verification of the existence of discrete water molecules in ice is provided by the discussion of its residual entropy. It is found experimentally that ice I (H_2O) and heavy ice I (D_2O) retain appreciable amounts of entropy at very low temperatures. If each water molecule in the ice crystal were oriented in a definite way, permitting the assignment of a unique configuration to the crystal, the residual entropy would vanish. We accordingly conclude that the water molecules are disordered in their orientation. The number of orientations allowed by the requirement that two protons are close to each oxygen atom and two are farther away corresponds to the value $R \ln 3/2 = 0.806$ cal mole^{-1} deg^{-1} for the residual entropy, in excellent agreement with the experimental values 0.82 for H_2O and 0.77 for D_2O.

The crystal structures of several high-pressure forms of ice are known (ice II, ice III, ice V, ice VI, ice VII). In each form there are hydrogen bonds, usually distorted from the regular tetrahedral arrangement. The protons are ordered in ice II and disordered in all the others. The effect of order (disorder) is observed in the residual entropy (zero for ice II, about 0.8 cal mole^{-1} deg^{-1} for the others) and the dielectric constant (about 4 for ice II, 100 for the others).

Of the enthalpy of sublimation of ice, 12.20 kcal/mole, about one-fifth can be attributed to ordinary van der Waals forces (as estimated from

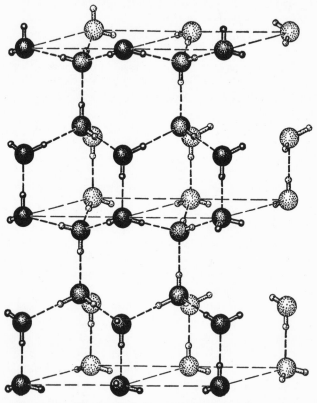

FIG. 12-4.—The arrangement of molecules in the ice crystal. The orientation of the water molecules, as represented in the drawing, is arbitrary; there is one proton along each oxygen-oxygen axis, closer to one or the other of the two oxygen atoms.

values for other substances); the remainder, 10 kcal/mole, represents the rupture of hydrogen bonds and leads to the value 5 kcal/mole for the energy of the O—H⋯O hydrogen bond in ice. The small value 1.44 kcal/mole of the enthalpy of fusion of ice shows that on melting only about 15 percent of the hydrogen bonds are broken. There is no doubt that water, like other liquids, has a structure that involves a great deal of randomness, and yet it is likely that there are certain configurations of groups of water molecules that occur with high frequency in the liquid. One possibility is that these groups resemble both ice I (density 0.92) and ice II (density 1.17) in structure. The increase in density of water that occurs on warming from 0°C to 4°C may be attributed to a decrease in the number of aggregates with the ice-I structure and increase in the number with ice-II structure.

12-4. HYDROGEN BONDS IN PROTEINS

The polypeptide chains of protein molecules are coiled in a precise way. Hydrogen bonds play an important part in determining the configurations of these molecules. A great deal has been learned in recent years about

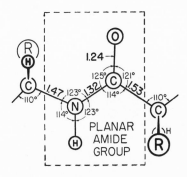

FIG. 12-5.—Fundamental dimensions of polypeptide chains as derived from x-ray crystal-structure determinations of amino acids and simple peptides.

the N—H···O hydrogen bonds formed by the peptide groups of the polypeptide chains; little is as yet known about the hydrogen bonds formed by the side chains of the amino-acid residues.

From the determination of the structure of crystals of amides and simple peptides the structure shown in Figure 12-5 has been assigned to the amide group in polypeptide chains. The N—C bond has about 40 percent double-bond character (bond length 1.32 Å). The group is planar, and it has been found to have the trans configuration in all substances studied except the cyclic dipeptides (diketopiperazine).

There is essential freedom of rotation about the single bonds between the amide groups and the α carbon atoms, permitting the polypeptide chain to assume many configurations. Certain configurations are stabilized by the formation of N—H···O hydrogen bonds.

Structure determinations of crystals of amino acids and simple peptides have shown that in general the N—H···O bond is linear (to within about 10°), and that the nitrogen-oxygen distance is equal to 2.79 ± 0.12 Å. The oxygen atom lies on the extension of the N—H bond axis. The energy of the hydrogen bond seems not to depend greatly on the angle at

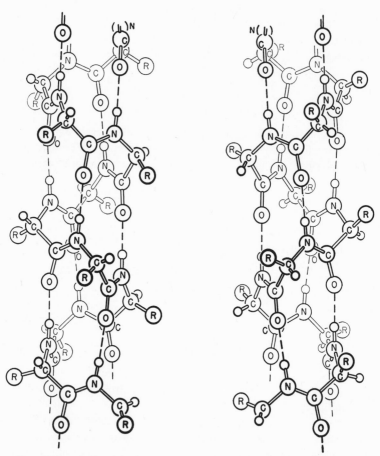

FIG. 12-6.—A drawing showing two possible forms of the alpha helix; the one on the left is a left-handed helix, and the one on the right is a right-handed helix. The amino acid residues have the L-configuration in each case.

the oxygen atom, but there is some evidence that maximum stability results from having all four atoms N—H···O=C′ on the same axis.

Two helical configurations of polypeptide chains have been found that satisfy the structural requirements for maximum stability of the amide groups and the N—H···O bonds. One of these is a rather large helix, with a hole along its axis. It is probably made unstable, relative to other structures, by its small van der Waals attraction energy, and it has not been recognized in nature. The other structure, the α helix, is a compact arrangement of the polypeptide chain about the helical axis. It has been verified by x-ray diffraction and infrared birefringence as the configuration of many synthetic polypeptides and proteins, especially the fibrous proteins of the α-keratin class (hair, horn, fingernail, muscle). There is evidence also that the α helix is a principal structural feature of many globular proteins, such as hemoglobin.

The α helix is represented in Figure 12-6. Each amide group is attached by a hydrogen bond to the third one from it in either direction along the polypeptide chain. There are 3.60 amino-acid residues per turn of the helix. The total rise of the helix per turn—the pitch of the helix—is about 5.38 Å, which corresponds to 1.49 Å per residue. The amino-acid side chains extend away from the helix axis, as shown in Figure 12-6.

EXERCISES

12-1.—Formic acid vapor contains dimers $(HCOOH)_2$ in equilibrium with HCOOH, the enthalpy of dimerization being 14.12 kcal/mole. (a) Assign an electronic structure to the dimer. (b) To what value of the energy of the O—H⋯O hydrogen bond does it lead?

12-2.—The vapor of methanol, CH_3OH, contains small polymers in equilibrium with the monomer. The enthalpy of formation of the tetramer is 24.2 kcal/mole. What structure would you assign to the tetramer? To what value of the O—H⋯O hydrogen-bond energy does it correspond? (Ans. 6.0 kcal/mole.)

12-3.—The standard boiling points of dimethyl ether and ethanol are −24°C and 78.5°C, and their heats of vaporization are 5.0 and 9.4 kcal/mole, respectively. Discuss the structural explanation of the difference in properties of these two substances. About how many hydrogen bonds remain unbroken in liquid ethanol at the boiling point? (Ans. About 73 percent.)

12-4.—The molecular weight of formic acid is the same as that of dimethyl ether and ethanol. Its boiling point at 1 atm pressure is 101°C and its heat of vaporization (per HCOOH) is 5.5 kcal/mole. (a) Discuss these values in relation to those of the preceding Exercise. (b) What value would you estimate for the heat of vaporization at very low pressure? (Ans. (b) About 12 kcal/mole.)

12-5.—In phloroglucinol (1,3,5-trihydroxybenzene) and other phenols the hydroxyl hydrogen atoms lie in the plane of the benzene ring. What feature of the electronic structure of these molecules causes them to be planar rather than nonplanar?

12-6.—Boric acid, $B(OH)_3$, forms hexagonal crystals that cleave easily into thin plates. On the basis of your knowledge of structural chemistry, formulate a structure for a layer in this crystal.

12-7.—Oxalic acid, HOOCCOOH, forms crystals that can easily be cleaved into thin sheets and also crystals that can easily be cleaved into fibers. Discuss possible structures for these crystals.

12-8.—Spectroscopic study of the vapor of *o*-chlorophenol has shown the presence of molecules of two kinds, with enthalpy difference 1.4 kcal/mole. Assign structures to the more stable and less stable isomer.

12-9.—The pyrocatechol molecule, o-$C_6H_4(OH)_2$, shows two somewhat different infrared absorption bands in the infrared corresponding to the O—H stretching vibration, whereas hydroquinone, p-$C_6H_4(OH)_2$, shows only one, with frequency nearly the same as that of the less intense band for pyrocatechol. The boiling points are 240°C for pyrocatechol and 286°C for hydroquinone. Discuss the structural interpretation of these facts.

12-10.—Some liquid mixtures that are not well fractionated by distillation can be fractionated by steam distillation (bubbling steam through the liquid). Can you suggest a structural explanation?

APPENDICES AND INDEX

APPENDIX I

Values of Physical Constants

(Carbon-12 Scale)

Velocity of light c	$= 2.99793 \times 10^{10}$ cm/sec
Electronic charge e	$= 4.8029 \times 10^{-10}$ statcoulomb
Mass of electron m	$= 9.1083 \times 10^{-28}$g
Mass of proton M_p	$= 1.67239 \times 10^{-24}$g
Mass of neutron M_n	$= 1.67470 \times 10^{-24}$g
Planck's constant h	$= 6.6252 \times 10^{-27}$ erg sec
Avogadro's number N	$= 0.60229 \times 10^{24}$ mole^{-1}
Faraday F	$= 96,490$ coulomb/mole
Boltzmann's constant k	$= 1.3805 \times 10^{-16}$ erg/deg
Gas constant R	$= 1.9872$ cal deg^{-1} mole^{-1}
Bohr magneton μ_B	$= 0.9273 \times 10^{-20}$ erg/gauss
Energy of 1 ev	$= 1.60206 \times 10^{-12}$ erg
Energy of 1 ev	$= 23.053$ kcal/mole
Wave length of 1-ev quantum	$= 12,397.67$ Å
Wave number of 1-ev quantum	$= 8,066.03$ cm^{-1}
Energy of 1 g of mass	$= 5.6100 \times 10^{32}$ ev

235

APPENDIX II

The Bohr Atom

IN his first paper on atomic structure Niels Bohr discussed quantized circular orbits of the electron (mass m, charge $-e$) about the nucleus in the hydrogen atom and hydrogenlike ions (mass M, charge $+Ze$). A possible state of motion of the electron is in a circular orbit. According to classical mechanics, the orbit might have any radius. Bohr derived a set of quantized orbits by making the assumption that the angular momentum of the atom should be an integral multiple of $h/2\pi$, where h is Planck's constant.

The relation between the speed v of the electron in a circular orbit about the nucleus and the radius r of the orbit can be derived by use of Newton's laws of motion. A geometrical construction shows that the acceleration of the electron toward the center of the orbit is v^2/r, and hence the force required to produce this acceleration is mv^2/r. This force is the force of attraction Ze^2/r^2 of the electron and the nucleus; hence we write the equation

$$mv^2/r = Ze^2/r^2$$

or, multiplying by r,

$$mv^2 = Ze^2/r \tag{II-1}$$

The angular momentum for the electron in its orbit is mrv. Bohr's postulate for quantizing the circular orbits is represented by the equation

$$mrv = nh/2\pi \tag{II-2}$$

In this equation n is the quantum number for the hydrogen atom, assumed to have the values 1 (for the normal state of the atom), 2 (for the first excited state), 3, 4, 5, and so on.

These two equations are easily solved. It is found that the radius of the circular Bohr orbit for quantum number n is equal to $n^2h^2/4\pi^2Zme^2$. This can be written as n^2a_0/Z, in which a_0 has the value 0.530 Å. The speed of the electron in its orbit is found to be $v = 2\pi Ze^2/nh$. For

236

the normal hydrogen atom, with $Z = 1$ and $n = 1$, this speed is 2.18×10^8 cm/sec, about 0.7 percent that of the speed of light.

The energy of the atom, the sum of the kinetic energy and the potential energy, is

$$E_n = -2\pi^2 Z^2 e^4 m / n^2 h^2 \qquad \text{(II-3)}$$

In the above calculation the system has been treated as though the nucleus were stationary and the electron moved in a circular orbit about the nucleus. The correct application of Newton's laws of motion to the problem of two particles with inverse-square force of attraction leads to the result that both particles move about their center of mass. The center of mass is the point on the line between the centers of the two particles such that the two radii are inversely proportional to the masses of the two particles. The equations for the Bohr orbits with consideration of motion of the nucleus are the same as those given above, except that the mass of the electron, m, is to be replaced by the reduced mass of the two particles, μ, defined by the expression $1/\mu = 1/m + 1/M$, where M is the mass of the nucleus.

Hydrogenlike Orbitals

THE wave functions for a state of a hydrogenlike atom described by the quantum numbers n (total quantum number), l (azimuthal quantum number), and m (magnetic quantum number) are usually expressed in terms of the polar coordinates r, θ, and ϕ. The orbital wave function is a product of three functions, each depending on one of the coordinates:

$$\psi_{nlm}(r, \theta, \phi) = R_{nl}(r)\Theta_{lm}(\theta)\Phi_m(\phi) \tag{III-1}$$

In this equation the functions Φ, Θ, and R have the forms

$$\phi_m(\phi) = \frac{1}{\sqrt{2\pi}} e^{im\phi} \tag{III-2}$$

$$\Theta_{lm}(\theta) = \left\{ \frac{(2l + 1)(l - |m|)!}{2(l + |m|)!} \right\}^{1/2} P^{|m|}(\cos \theta) \tag{III-3}$$

and

$$R_{nl}(r) = -\left[\left(\frac{2Z}{na_0} \right)^3 \frac{(n - l - 1)!}{2n\{(n + l)!\}^3} \right]^{1/2} e^{-\rho/2}\rho^l L_{n+l}^{2l+1}(\rho) \tag{III-4}$$

in which

$$\rho = \frac{2Z}{na_0} r \tag{III-5}$$

and

$$a_0 = \frac{h^2}{4\pi^2 \mu e^2} \tag{III-6}$$

The quantity a_0 is interpreted in the Bohr theory as the radius of the smallest orbit in the hydrogen atom; its value is 0.530 Å.

The functions $P^{|m|}(\cos \theta)$ are the associated Legendre functions, and the functions $L_{n+l}^{2l+1}(\rho)^l$ are the associated Laguerre polynomials.

TABLE III-1.—THE FUNCTIONS $\Phi_m(\phi)$

$\Phi_0(\phi) = \dfrac{1}{\sqrt{2\pi}}$	or	$\Phi_0(\phi) = \dfrac{1}{\sqrt{2\pi}}$
$\Phi_1(\phi) = \dfrac{1}{\sqrt{2\pi}} e^{i\phi}$	or	$\Phi_{1\ \cos}(\phi) = \dfrac{1}{\sqrt{\pi}} \cos\phi$
$\Phi_{-1}(\phi) = \dfrac{2}{\sqrt{2\pi}} e^{-i\phi}$	or	$\Phi_{1\ \sin}(\phi) = \dfrac{1}{\sqrt{\pi}} \sin\phi$
$\Phi_2(\phi) = \dfrac{1}{\sqrt{2\pi}} e^{i2\phi}$	or	$\Phi_{2\ \cos}(\phi) = \dfrac{1}{\sqrt{\pi}} \cos 2\phi$
$\Phi_{-2}(\phi) = \dfrac{1}{\sqrt{2\pi}} e^{-i2\phi}$	or	$\Phi_{2\ \sin}(\phi) = \dfrac{1}{\sqrt{\pi}} \sin 2\phi$

TABLE III-2.—THE WAVE FUNCTIONS $\theta_{lm}(\theta)$

$l = 0$, s orbitals:

$$\Theta_{00}(\theta) = \frac{\sqrt{2}}{2}$$

$= 1$ p orbitals:

$$\Theta_{10}(\theta) = \frac{\sqrt{6}}{2} \cos\theta$$

$$\Theta_{1\pm 1}(\theta) = \frac{\sqrt{3}}{2} \sin\theta$$

$= 2$, d orbitals:

$$\Theta_{20}(\theta) = \frac{\sqrt{10}}{4} (3\cos^2\theta - 1)$$

$$\Theta_{2\pm 1}(\theta) = \frac{\sqrt{15}}{2} \sin\theta \cos\theta$$

$$\Theta_{2\pm 2}(\theta) = \frac{\sqrt{15}}{4} \sin^2\theta$$

TABLE III-3.—THE HYDROGEN RADIAL WAVE FUNCTIONS

$n = 1$, K shell:

$\quad l = 0$, $1s \quad R_{10}(r) = (Z/a_0)^{3/2} \cdot 2e^{-\rho/2}$

$n = 2$, L shell:

$\quad l = 0$, $2s \quad R_{20}(r) = \dfrac{(Z/a_0)^{3/2}}{2\sqrt{2}}(2 - \rho)e^{-\rho/2}$

$\quad l = 1$, $2p \quad R_{21}(r) = \dfrac{(Z/a_0)^{3/2}}{2\sqrt{6}}\rho e^{-\rho/2}$

$n = 3$, M shell:

$\quad l = 0$, $3s \quad R_{30}(r) = \dfrac{(Z/a_0)^{3/2}}{9\sqrt{3}}(6 - 6\rho + \rho^2)e^{-\rho/2}$

$\quad l = 1$, $3p \quad R_{31}(r) = \dfrac{(Z/a_0)^{3/2}}{9\sqrt{6}}(4 - \rho)\rho e^{-\rho/2}$

$\quad l = 2$, $3d \quad R_{32}(r) = \dfrac{(Z/a_0)^{3/2}}{9\sqrt{30}}\rho^2 e^{-\rho/2}$

The wave functions are normalized, so that

$$\int_0^\infty \int_0^\pi \int_0^{2\pi} \psi_{nlm}^*(r, \theta, \phi)\psi_{nlm}(r, \theta, \phi)r^2 \sin\theta\, d\phi\, d\theta\, dr = 1 \qquad \text{(III-7)}$$

ψ^* is the complex conjugate of ψ. The functions in r, θ, and ϕ are separately normalized to unity:

$$\int_0^{2\pi} \Phi_m^*(\phi)\Phi_m(\phi)d\phi = 1 \qquad \text{(III-8)}$$

$$\int_0^\pi \{\Theta_{lm}(\theta)\}^2 \sin\theta\, d\theta = 1 \qquad \text{(III-9)}$$

$$\int_0^\infty \{R_{nl}(r)\}^2 r^2 dr = 1 \qquad \text{(III-10)}$$

APPENDIX IV

Russell-Saunders States of Atoms
Allowed by the Pauli
Exclusion Principle

IN Section 2-6 it was pointed out that the allowed Russell-Saunders states of an atom with two electrons with different total quantum numbers can be found by combining the electron spins to produce a resultant spin, corresponding to the total spin quantum number S (in this case 0 and 1), combining the orbital angular momenta of the electrons to produce the values of the total orbital angular momentum quantum number L permitted by the magnitudes of the individual orbital angular momenta of the electrons, and then combining the total spin angular momentum vector and the total orbital angular momentum vector in all of the ways permitted by the magnitudes of the vectors that correspond to the total angular momentum quantum number J, with J having integral values when S is integral (an even number of electron spins) and half-integral values ($\frac{1}{2}, \frac{3}{2}, \cdots$) when S has half-integral values (corresponding to an odd number of electrons). Then, in Section 2-7, it was mentioned that the Pauli exclusion principle introduces a restriction in case that the two electrons have the same value of the total quantum number. In particular, the normal state of the helium atom corresponds to the electron configuration $1s^2$, with each electron having $n = 1$, $l = 0$, $m_l = 0$, and, of course, $s = \frac{1}{2}$; the Pauli exclusion principle requires that one of the electrons have $m_s = +\frac{1}{2}$ and the other have $m_s = -\frac{1}{2}$, so that the resultant spin angular momentum is zero, and the state must be a singlet state, $^1S_0$. The corresponding triplet state, $^3S_1$, is excluded by the exclusion principle, and in fact does not exist.

The application of the Pauli exclusion principle is necessary for the understanding of the normal states of atoms. There is a simple way of determining the allowed Russell-Saunders states for an atom with two or more electrons in the same subgroup (same values of n and l). It is discussed in Appendix IV of *The Nature of the Chemical Bond*. The allowed states for equivalent s, p, and d electrons are given in Table IV-1.

The Landé g-Factor.—The magnetic moment of an atom can be expressed in a simple way in terms of its angular momentum. The Bohr unit of angular momentum is $h/2\pi$, and the Bohr unit of magnetic mo-

TABLE IV-1

Equivalent s Electrons

$$s - {}^2S$$
$$s^2 - {}^1S$$

Equivalent p Electrons

$p^1 -$	${}^2P$			
$p^2 - {}^1S$		${}^1D$		${}^3P$
$p^3 -$	${}^2P$		${}^2D$	${}^4S$
$p^4 - {}^1S$		${}^1D$		${}^3P$
$p^5 -$	${}^2P$			
$p^6 - {}^1S$				

Equivalent d Electrons

d^1	${}^2D$						
$d^2 - {}^1(SDG)$		${}^3(PF)$					
$d^3 -$	${}^2D$		${}^2(PDFGH)$	${}^4(PF)$			
$d^4 - {}^1(SDG)$		${}^3(PF)$	${}^1(SDFGI)$	${}^3(PDFGH)$	${}^5D$		
$d^5 -$	${}^2D$		${}^2(PDFGH)$	${}^4(PF)$	${}^4(SDFGI)$	${}^4(DG)$	${}^6S$
$d^6 - {}^1(SDG)$		${}^3(PF)$	${}^1(SDFGI)$	${}^3(PDFGH)$	${}^5D$		
$d^7 -$	${}^2D$		${}^2(PDFGH)$	${}^4(PF)$			
$d^8 - {}^1(SDG)$		${}^3(PF)$					
$d^9 -$	${}^2D$						
$d^{10} - {}^1S$							

ment (the Bohr magneton) is $he/4\pi mc$. An electron moving in an orbit with x units of angular momentum has orbital magnetic moment equal to x Bohr magnetons.

However, the magnetic moment of electron spin bears a different relation to the spin angular momentum; it is approximately twice as great. This can be expressed by saying that the Landé g-factor for orbital motion of the electron is 1 and that for spin of the electron is 2. The Landé g-factor for an atom is the ratio of the magnetic moment of the atom in Bohr magnetons and the angular momentum of the atom in Bohr units $h/2\pi$.

It is possible to calculate the g-factor for an atom in a Russell-Saunders state by considering the angles between the vectors S and L and the vector J. The total angular momentum, in units $h/2\pi$, is $\sqrt{J(J+1)}$. The magnetic moment in the direction of the angular momentum vector (the component perpendicular to the angular momentum vector cancels out) is equal to the components of the magnetic moment along S and that along L in the direction of J. The value can be calculated by trigonometry, the magnitudes of the vectors S and L being taken to be proportionally equal to $\sqrt{S(S+1)}$ and $\sqrt{L(L+1)}$, respectively. The equation obtained in this way is

$$g(J) = \frac{3J(J+1) + S(S+1) - L(L+1)}{2J(J+1)}$$

Values of the Landé g-factor calculated with this equation are given in Table IV-2.

TABLE IV-2.—THE LANDÉ g-FACTOR FOR RUSSELL-SAUNDERS COUPLING

Singlets, $S = 0$					
$J =$		0	1	2	3
^{1}S	$L = 0$	0/0			
^{1}P	1		1		
^{1}D	2			1	
^{1}F	3				1

Doublets, $S = 1/2$					
$J =$		1/2	3/2	5/2	7/2
^{2}S	$L = 0$	2			
^{2}P	1	2/3	4/3		
^{2}D	2		4/5	6/5	
^{2}F	3			6/7	8/7

Triplets, $S = 1$					
$J =$	0	1	2	3	4
^{3}S	$L = 0$		2			
^{3}P	1	0/0	3/2	3/2		
^{3}D	2		1/2	7/6	4/3	
^{3}F	3			2/3	13/12	5/4

(continued)

Quartets, $S = 3/2$

$J =$		1/2	3/2	5/2	7/2	9/2
^4S	$L = 0$	..	2			
^4P	1	8/3	26/15	8/5		
^4D	2	0	6/5	48/35	10/7	
^4F	3	..	2/5	36/35	26/21	4/3

Quintets, $S = 2$

$J =$	0	1	2	3	4	5
^5S	$L = 0$ ..	..	2			
^5P	1 ..	5/2	11/6	5/3		
^5D	2 0/0	3/2	3/2	3/2	3/2	
^5F	3 ..	0	1	5/4	27/20	7/5

Sextets, $S = 5/2$

$J =$	1/2	3/2	5/2	7/2	9/2	11/2
^6S	$L = 0$ ..	..	2			
^6P	1 ..	12/5	66/35	12/7		
^6D	2 10/3	28/15	58/35	100/63	14/9	
^6F	3 −2/3	16/15	46/35	88/63	142/99	16/11

EXERCISES

IV-1.—Consider an atom containing two $2p$ electrons with parallel spin ($m_s = +\frac{1}{2}$, say). (a) What are their values for the four quantum numbers s, m_s, n, and l? (b) What statement can you make about the fifth quantum number, m_l? (c) What maximum values of m_l can the two electrons have? (d) Their sum is the maximum value of M_L. To what value of L does it correspond? (e) From these considerations, what is the allowed Russell-Saunders triplet state for two equivalent p electrons? (Ans. (b) They must be different; (c) 1, 0; (d) 1; (e) ^3P.)

IV-2.—By the method of the preceding Exercise, determine the allowed states of maximum multiplicity and maximum L for two equivalent d, f, and g electrons, and also for three equivalent p, d, f, and g electrons. (Ans. ^3F, ^3H, ^3J; ^4S, ^4F, ^4I, ^4L.)

IV-3.—Without using the equation for the g-factor, but instead by considering the vectors, obtain the value of g for (a) $^3P_1$; (b) $^7F_6$. (Ans. (a) 3/2.)

IV-4.—What is the most stable allowed Russell-Saunders state for seven equivalent f electrons?

Resonance Energy

A DETAILED discussion of responance energy can be found in books on quantum mechanics. A simple problem, the dependence of the energy of resonance between two structures on the difference in energy of the structures, is discussed in the following paragraphs.

The value of the energy of a system corresponding to a wave function ψ (normalized to unity) is

$$E = \int \psi^* H \psi \, d\tau \tag{V-1}$$

Here τ represents the coordinates for the system (x, y, z for each electron and each nucleus) and H is the Hamiltonian operator corresponding to the total energy of the system. The integral is taken over the whole of configuration space for the system. ψ^* is the complex conjugate of ψ.

Let us now consider a normalized function ψ_I corresponding to a reasonable structure for the system. The corresponding value of the energy, as given by Equation V-1, is H_{II}, defined by the equation

$$H_{ij} = \int \psi_i^* H \psi_j \, d\tau \tag{V-2}$$

Similarly, the energy for another function ψ_{II}, corresponding to another structure for the system, is $H_{II\,II}$.

Now let us consider resonance between the two structures. We may write for the resonance structure the wave function

$$\psi = a\psi_I + b\psi_{II} \tag{V-3}$$

In order for this function to be normalized ($\int \psi^* \psi \, d\tau = 1$) the coefficients must satisfy the condition

$$a^2 + 2ab\Delta_{I\,II} + b^2 = 1 \tag{V-4}$$

(Note that $\Delta_{II\,I} = \Delta_{I\,II}$ if the functions are real, as we shall assume.) Here Δ is the overlap integral

$$\Delta_{ij} = \int \psi_i^* \psi_j d\tau \qquad (V\text{-}5)$$

The variation principle of quantum mechanics states that the true wave function for the normal state of a system is the one that minimizes the energy. We may accordingly find the best function ψ by finding the ratio a/b that minimizes E (Equation V-1).

A simple way of achieving this end is by application of Lagrange's method of undetermined multipliers. Let us consider the function F, such that

$$F = \int \psi^* H \psi d\tau - \lambda \int \psi^* \psi d\tau \qquad (V\text{-}6)$$

The second integral is constant, and hence for any value of λ the function F has its minimum at the same place as E.

The expression for F is

$$F = a^2 H_I + 2ab H_{I\,II} + b^2 H_{II} - \lambda(a^2 + 2ab\Delta_{I\,II} + b^2) \qquad (V\text{-}7)$$

Here and in the following equations H_I is written for $H_{I\,I}$ and H_{II} for $H_{II\,II}$. To find the minimum we differentiate F with respect to a and to b and equate to zero:

$$\left. \begin{aligned} \frac{\partial F}{\partial a} &= 2a(H_I - \lambda) + 2b(H_{I\,II} - \lambda\Delta_{I\,II}) = 0 \\[2mm] \frac{\partial F}{\partial b} &= 2a(H_{I\,II} - \lambda\Delta_{I\,II}) + 2b H_{II} = 0 \end{aligned} \right\} \qquad (V\text{-}8)$$

These are two homogeneous linear equations in the two unknowns a and b; they have a solution if the determinant formed by their coefficients vanishes:

$$\begin{vmatrix} H_I - \lambda & H_{I\,II} - \lambda\Delta_{I\,II} \\ H_{I\,II} - \lambda\Delta_{I\,II} & H_{II} - \lambda \end{vmatrix} = 0 \qquad (V\text{-}9)$$

This equation can be solved for the two values of λ that satisfy it. Each of them may then be substituted in Equations V-8 and V-4 to evaluate a and b. When this is done it is found that the quantity λ is equal to the energy E.

Often the approximation of neglecting the overlap integral $\Delta_{I\ II}$ is made. Equation V-9, which is called the secular equation, then becomes

$$\begin{vmatrix} H_I - E & H_{I\ II} \\ H_{I\ II} & H_{II} - E \end{vmatrix} = 0 \qquad \text{(V-10)}$$

The roots of this equation are

$$E = (H_I + H_{II})/2 \pm \{H^2_{I\ II} + (H_{II} - H_I)^2/4\}^{1/2}$$

The lower of these roots (with the negative sign) lies below $H_{I\ II}$, the energy of the more stable structure, by the amount

Effective resonance energy =

$$- (H_{II} - H_I)/2 + \{H^2_{I\ II} + (H_{II} - H_I)^2/4\}^{1/2} \qquad \text{(V-11)}$$

The effective resonance energy, given in this equation, is the amount of stabilization of the normal state of the system relative to the more stable of the two structures, structure I. It is shown in Figure 1-6, as a function of the difference in energy of the two structures, $H_{II} - H_I$.

The secular equation minimizing the energy for a more general wave function can easily be set up in the same way. Let the assumed wave functions be

$$\psi = c_1\psi_1 + c_2\psi_2 + \cdots + c_m\psi_m \qquad \text{(V-12)}$$

Application of the Lagrange method, used above, leads to the following set of homogeneous simultaneous linear equations as the condition for minimum energy:

$$\sum_{k=1}^{m} c_k(H_{nk} - \Delta_{nk}E) = 0, \qquad n = 1, 2, \cdots m \qquad \text{(V-13)}$$

The condition that the set have a have solution is

$$\begin{vmatrix} H_{11} - \Delta_{11}E & H_{12} - \Delta_{12}E & \cdots & H_{1m} - \Delta_{1m}E \\ H_{21} - \Delta_{21}E & H_{22} - \Delta_{22}E & \cdots & H_{2m} - \Delta_{2m}E \\ \cdots & \cdots & \cdots & \cdots \\ H_{m1} - \Delta_{m1}E & H_{m2} - \Delta_{m2}E & \cdots & H_{mm} - \Delta_{mm}E \end{vmatrix} = 0 \qquad \text{(V-14)}$$

The lowest root of this equation gives the best approximation to the value of the energy E provided by the wave functions of the assumed form V-12. The values of the coefficients c_k can then be found by use of Equations V-13 with this value of E inserted.

Wave Functions for Valence-
Bond Structures

IN his valuable paper "Molecular Energy Levels and Valence Bonds" Slater developed a method of formulating approximate wave functions for molecules and constructing the corresponding secular equations. Let a, b, $\cdots$ represent atomic orbitals, each occupied by one valence electron, and α and β represent the electron spin functions for spin orientation $+\frac{1}{2}$ and $-\frac{1}{2}$, respectively. Slater showed that the following function corresponds to a valence-bond structure with bonds a——b, c——d, and so forth:

$$\frac{1}{2^{n/2}} \sum_R (-1)^R R \left\{ \frac{1}{((2n)!)^{1/2}} \right.$$
$$\left. \cdot \sum_P (-1)^P a(1)\beta(1)b(2)\alpha(2)c(3)\beta(3)d(4)\alpha(4) \cdots \right\} \quad \text{(VI-1)}$$

Here 1, 2, $\cdots$ represent the electrons. P is the operation of permuting the electrons among the spin-orbit functions, for example, interchanging 1 and 2 between $a\beta$ and $b\alpha$. There are $(2n)!$ of these operations in the permutation group; $2n$ is the number of electrons for n bonds. The symbol $(-1)^P$ is 1 if P involves an even number of interchanges of pairs of electrons and -1 if it involves an odd number. The function in the brackets satisfies the Pauli exclusion principle. R represents the 2^n operations of interchanging the spin functions α and β for orbitals (such as a and b) that are bonded together.

The Slater valence-bond function leads to an energy expression that contains the single exchange integrals between bonded orbitals, such as a and b, with the coefficient $+1$. These integrals are usually negative, and hence, with coefficient $+1$, stabilize the system, corresponding to attraction and bond formation. The single exchange integrals between orbitals not bonded to one another, such as a and c, occur with the coefficient $-\frac{1}{2}$, which corresponds to repulsion.

Electric Polarizabilities and Electric Dipole Moments of Atoms, Ions, and Molecules

A GREAT deal of information has been obtained about the structure of molecules by the study of the electric properties of substances. A sample of a substance placed in an electric field undergoes a change in structure that is described as *electric polarization*. In general this change in structure involves motion of the electrons relative to the adjacent atomic nuclei, and also motion of the atomic nuclei relative to one another. Theoretical treatments have been developed that permit the observed polarization to be related to the properties of the atoms, ions, or molecules that compose the substance.

Electric Polarization and Dielectric Constant.—Under the influence of an electric field E acting upon a gas, liquid, or cubic crystal (the restriction to cubic crystals is made because of the complication introduced for other crystals by the dependence of their properties upon direction relative to the crystal axes), the positively and negatively charged particles that make up the substance undergo some relative motion, producing an induced average electric moment. Let P be the induced average electric moment per unit volume. The electric moment is defined as the product of the charge, positive and negative, by the distance of separation; for example, the electric moment of a pair of ions, with charge $+e$ and $-e$, the distance d apart being de. In electromagnetic theory the *electric induction D* is defined as

$$D = E + 4\pi P \qquad \text{(VII-1)}$$

and the dielectric constant ε is defined as

$$\varepsilon = D/E = 1 + 4\pi P/E \qquad \text{(VII-2)}$$

The dielectric constant of a substance may be measured by determining the ratio of the capacity of a condenser filled with the substance and the capacity of the empty condenser. The electrical apparatus involves the condenser whose capacity is to be determined in parallel with a calibrated variable condenser, in a tuned resonant circuit; the determination is made by adjusting the variable condenser to keep the resonance frequency constant, and this requires that the sum of the capacities of the two condensers be constant.

Let us first consider the dielectric constant of a gas. We assume that the molecules are far enough apart for them to contribute independently to the polarization and that the electric field E induces an electric dipole moment αE in each molecule. The quantity α is called the electric polarizability of the molecule. The number of moles per unit volume of gas is the density ρ divided by the molecular weight M, and the number of molecules in unit volume is this ratio multiplied by Avogadro's number N. Hence the polarization of the gas (the induced dipole moment per unit volume) is given by the following equation:

$$P = N \frac{\rho}{M} \alpha E \qquad \text{(VII-3)}$$

Combining this equation with Equation VII-2, we obtain

$$(\varepsilon - 1) \frac{M}{\rho} = 4\pi N\alpha \qquad \text{(VII-4)}$$

This equation is not valid for liquids or crystals, but only for substances for which the dielectric constant is very close to unity, as for gases. For other substances an equation derived by consideration of the effect of the induced moments of neighboring molecules upon the molecule undergoing polarization must be used. In a polarized medium each molecule is affected by the electric field in the region occupied by the molecule, called the local field. For many substances the local field is satisfactorily represented by the Clausius-Mossotti expression, derived in 1850. Each molecule is considered to occupy a spherical cavity. The part of the substance outside the spherical cavity undergoes polarization in the applied field. A simple calculation shows that the shift of positive charges and negative charges corresponding to the polarization P produces inside the cavity the field $(4\pi/3)P$, in addition to the applied field E; hence the local field is given by the equation

$$E_{\text{local}} = E + \frac{4\pi}{3} P \qquad \text{(VII-5)}$$

The polarization in unit volume is accordingly given by the expression

$$P = N \frac{\rho}{M} \alpha E_{local} = N\rho \frac{\alpha}{M} \left(E + \frac{4\pi}{3} P \right) \qquad \text{(VII-6)}$$

This equation, together with the definition of the dielectric constant (Equation VII-2), leads at once to the equation

$$\frac{\varepsilon - 1}{\varepsilon + 2} \frac{M}{\rho} = \frac{4\pi}{3} N\alpha \qquad \text{(VII-7)}$$

This equation, called the Lorenz-Lorentz equation, was derived in 1880 by combining the Clausius-Mossotti expression for the local field with the idea of molecular polarizability.

The principal interaction of an electromagnetic wave, such as visible light, with a substance is that of the electric field of the wave and the electric charges of the substance. The dielectric constant of the substance determines the magnitude of this interaction; in fact, it is equal to the square of the dielectric constant:

$$\varepsilon = n^2 \qquad \text{(VII-8)}$$

The amount of polarization of the medium by the electric field of the electromagnetic wave is a function of the frequency; for example, the dielectric constant of water is 81 when the frequency is very low or zero (static field) and falls to 1.78 for visible light. The reason for the difference is that in a static electric field or the field of an electromagnetic wave with very low frequency the molecules of water, which have a permanent electric dipole moment, are able to orient themselves in the field, and thus to produce a great increase in polarization of the liquid; whereas in the electric field of high frequency of visible light the molecular orientation cannot occur, and the only polarization that contributes to the dielectric constant is electronic polarization. A detailed discussion of the contribution of orientation of permanent molecular electric dipoles to the dielectric constant is given in a following section.

The Lorenz-Lorentz equation for the index of refraction is

$$R = \frac{n^2 - 1}{n^2 + 2} \frac{MW}{\rho} = \frac{4\pi}{3} N\alpha \qquad \text{(VII-9)}$$

The quantity R is called the mole refraction.

Electronic Polarizability.—When an atom is placed in an electric field the charge distribution is changed to some extent as the electrostatic forces caused by the field operate in one direction on the nucleus and in the opposite direction on the electrons. A dipole moment is induced in the atom, with magnitude

$$\mu = \alpha E \tag{VII-10}$$

The dimensions of the polarizability α are those of volume.

The Debye Equation for Dielectric Constant.—The Debye equation for the dielectric constant of a gas whose molecules have a permanent electric moment μ_0 is

$$P = \frac{\varepsilon - 1}{\varepsilon + 2} \frac{M}{\rho} = \frac{4\pi N}{3}\left(\frac{\mu_0^2}{3k_T} + \alpha\right) \tag{VII-11}$$

This equation can be derived from Equation VII-4 by including in the expression for the polarization the contribution due to preferential orientation of the permanent dipole moments μ_0 in the field direction. The component of the dipole moment of a molecule in the field direction is $\mu_0 \cos \theta$, where θ is the polar angle between the dipole-moment vector and the field direction, and the energy of interaction is $-\mu_0 E \cos \theta$. The relative probability of orientation in volume element $\sin \theta d\theta d\phi$ (in polar coordinates) is given by the Boltzmann principle[*] as $e^{\mu_0 E \cos \theta / kT} \sin \theta d\theta d\phi$. The average value of the component is hence given by the expression

$$\bar{\mu} = \frac{\displaystyle\int_0^{2\pi}\int_0^{\pi} \mu_0 \cos \theta e^{\mu_0 E \cos \theta / kT} \sin \theta d\theta d\phi}{\displaystyle\int_0^{2\pi}\int_0^{\pi} e^{\mu_0 E \cos \theta / kT} \sin \theta d\theta d\phi} \tag{VII-12}$$

(The integral in the denominator normalizes the probability.) The integrals are easily evaluated by expanding the exponential functions and retaining the first nonvanishing term:

$$\bar{\mu} = \frac{\mu_0^2 E}{k_T} \frac{\displaystyle\int_0\int_0^{\pi} \cos^2 \theta \sin \theta d\theta d\phi}{4\pi} \tag{VII-13}$$

The integral (with the divisor 4π) is just the mean value of $\cos^2 \theta$ over the surface of a sphere. Its value is $\frac{1}{3}$. (The same value is found in quantum mechanics, as the average of $M_J^2/J(J + 1)$, with $M_J = J$,

---

[*] See *The Nature of the Chemical Bond*, App. VIII.

$J - 1, \cdots -J$, for J either integral or half-integral.) Hence we obtain $\bar{\mu} = \mu_0^2 E/3k_T$. This expression for the contribution of the permanent dipole moments of the molecule leads to the first term on the right in Equation VII-11. The second term, α, includes the electronic polarizability of the molecule and also the so-called atom polarization, the

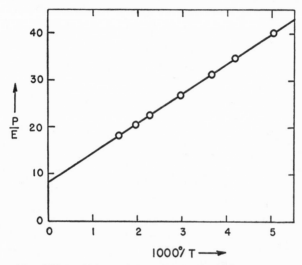

FIG. VII-1.—Values of the ratio of polarization P to field strength E for hydrogen chloride gas, as a function of the reciprocal of the absolute temperature. The slope of the line is a measure of the permanent electric dipole moment of the molecules, and the intercept of the line is a measure of the temperature-independent polarizability of the molecules.

small change in relative positions of the nuclei caused by the field. This term is independent of the temperature.

Hydrogen chloride, for example, has dielectric constant that decreases from 1.0055 at 200°K to 1.0028 at 500°K, for constant density, corresponding to 1 atm at 0°C. Values of the polarization P (proportional to $\varepsilon - 1$) are shown plotted against $1/T$ in Figure VII-1. The slope leads to the value 1.03 D for μ_0, as given in Chapter 3. (The unit 1 D, 1 debye, is equal to 1×10^{-18} statcoulomb centimeter.) The intercept of the extrapolated straight line on the P axis gives the value of the temperature-independent polarizability.

An extensive table of values of dipole moments for gases and solute molecules has been published.* During recent years some very accurate values have been determined by microwave spectroscopy and molecular-beam techniques.

EXERCISES

VII-1.—Using Equations VII-7 and VII-8, evaluate the molecular polarizabilities of Cl_2 and CCl_4. The values of the density of the liquids are 1.330 and 1.595 g/cm^3 and those of the index of refraction (at the same temperature) are 1.367 and 1.471, respectively.

VII-2.—Observed values of n^2 for the gases at standard conditions are 1.000447 for CH_4, 1.000753 for C_2H_6, 1.000723 for C_2H_4, and 1.000510 for C_2H_2. From these obtain values of the molecular polarizability α and mole refraction R. Derive a set of values of R for H, C, double-bond correction, triple-bond correction.

VII-3.—The dielectric constant of liquid benzene at 20°C is 2.283, and its density is 0.874 g/cm^3. Evaluate R, and compare with the value expected for a Kekulé structure (Ex. VII-2).

VII-4.—The observed dielectric constant of HCl(g) at 1 atm is 1.0076 at −75°C, 1.00460 at 0°C, 1.00250 at 100°C, and 1.00162 at 200°C. From a graph of the values determine R and the electric dipole moment.

VII-5.—The observed value of the molar polarization P of $B_{10}H_{14}$ dissolved in benzene (corrected for polarization of the solvent) is 297.0 cm^3/mole at 25°C. Assuming 2.1 for the value of R for B and 1.1 for H, calculate the value of the electric dipole moment of the molecule.

---

* A. L. McClellan, *Tables of Experimental Dipole Moments*, W. H. Freeman and Company, San Francisco, Calif., **1963**.

The Magnetic Properties of Substances

THE principal types of interaction of a substance with a magnetic field are called diamagnetism, paramagnetism, ferromagnetism, anti-ferromagnetism, and ferrimagnetism. They are useful in providing information about the electronic structures of the substances, especially as discussed in Chapters 5 and 11.

Diamagnetism.—It was discovered by Faraday that most substances when placed in a magnetic field develop a magnetic moment opposed to the field. Such a substance is said to be diamagnetic. (Substances that develop a moment parallel to the field are called paramagnetic substances.)*

A sample of a diamagnetic substance placed in an inhomogeneous magnetic field is acted on by a force that tends to push it away from the strong-field region. This force is proportional to the diamagnetic susceptibility of the substance, which is defined as the ratio of the induced moment, μ, to the field strength, H:

$$\mu = \chi H \qquad \text{(VIII-1)}$$

The common methods of determining the magnetic susceptibility involve measuring this force.

Let us consider a metal wire in the form of a circle. If a magnetic field is applied perpendicularly to the plane of the circle a current is induced in the wire. Corresponding to this current there is a magnetic field, resembling that of a magnetic dipole with orientation opposed to the field (Lenz's law).

The effect of the application of a magnetic field to an atom or mon-

---

* There is a common misapprehension that a bar of a paramagnetic substance in a uniform magnetic field sets itself parallel to the lines of force of the field and that a bar of a diamagnetic substance sets itself perpendicular to the lines of force; in fact, a bar of a substance either paramagnetic or diamagnetic sets itself parallel to the lines of force in a uniform field.

atomic ion is to cause the electrons to assume an added rotation about
an axis parallel to the field direction and passing through the nucleus.
This rotation, called the Larmor precession, has the angular velocity
$eH/2mc$. The angular momentum of an electron with cylindrical radius
ρ about the field axis and the angular velocity $eH/2mc$ is $eH\rho^2/2c$, and its
magnetic moment is related to its angular momentum by the factor
$-e/2mc$ and therefore has the value $-e^2\rho^2H/4mc^2$. Hence the molar
diamagnetic susceptibility is

$$\chi_{\text{molar}} = -\frac{Ne^2}{4mc^2} \sum_i \overline{\rho_i^2} \qquad \text{(VIII-2)}$$

Here ρ^2 is the average value of ρ^2 for the ith electron, and the sum is to
be taken over all the electrons in the atom. For spherically symmetrical atoms, with $\rho^2 = x^2 + y^2$ and $r^2 = x^2 + y^2 + z^2$, where r is the
distance of the electron from the nucleus, $\overline{\rho^2} = \frac{2}{3}\overline{r^2}$, and hence we may
write

$$\chi_{\text{molar}} = -\frac{Ne^2}{6mc^2} \sum_i \overline{r_i^2} \qquad \text{(VIII-3)}$$

Measured values of the diamagnetic susceptibility of the noble gases
correspond to reasonable values of $\Sigma \overline{r^2}$. For polyatomic molecules the
interpretation of the diamagnetic susceptibility in terms of structural
features is in general uncertain, and this property has not been found to
be valuable in structural chemistry.

Some diamagnetic crystals (graphite, bismuth, naphthalene and other
aromatic substances) show pronounced diamagnetic anisotropy. The
observed anisotropy of crystals of benzene derivatives correspond to the
molar diamagnetic susceptibility -91×10^{-6} with the field direction
perpendicular to the plane of the benzene ring and -37×10^{-6} with it
in the plane. This molecular anisotropy has been found to be of some
use in determining the orientation of the planes of aromatic molecules in
crystals.

Diamagnetic susceptibility (per mole or per gram) is in general independent of the temperature.

Paramagnetism.—It is customary to restrict the use of the word
paramagnetism to substances that in a magnetic field of ordinary
strength develop a magnetic moment in the field direction that is proportional to the strength of the field. (This usage excludes ferromagnetic substances.) Most paramagnetic substances have susceptibilities a hundred or a thousand times as great as the customary diamag-

netic susceptibilities, and with opposite sign (mass susceptibility [per *g*] $+10^{-4}$ or 10^{-3}, as compared with about -1×10^{-6} for diamagnetic substances). They also have, of course, a diamagnetic contribution to the total susceptibility.

It was shown by Pierre Curie in 1895 that paramagnetic susceptibility is strongly dependent on temperature, and for many substances is inversely proportional to the absolute temperature. The equation

$$\chi_{\text{molar}} = \frac{C_{\text{molar}}}{T} + D \tag{VIII-4}$$

is called Curie's law, and the constant C_{molar} is called the molar Curie constant. D represents the diagmagnetic contribution (it is negative).

Weber in 1854 had attributed paramagnetism to the orientation of little permanent magnets in the substance (and diamagnetism to induced currents, as discussed above). A quantitative treatment was developed by Paul Langevin in 1895, by application of the Boltzmann principle. The theory is the same as for the orientation of electric dipoles (see App. VII). It leads to the equation

$$C_{\text{molar}} = \frac{N\mu^2}{3k} \tag{VIII-5}$$

in which μ is the value of the magnetic dipole moment per atom or molecule.

The value of the Bohr magneton is 0.927×10^{-20} erg gauss^{-1}. The magnetic moment μ is hence related to the molar Curie constant by the equation

$$\mu \text{ (in Bohr magnetons)} = 2.824 C_{\text{molar}}^{1/2} \tag{VIII-6}$$

Curie's equation applies to gases, solutions, and some crystals. For other crystals a more general equation, the Weiss equation, may be used (derived by P. Weiss in 1907). Weiss assumed that the local magnetic field orienting the dipoles is equal to the applied field plus an added field proportional to the magnetic volume polarization M:

$$H_{\text{local}} = H + aM \tag{VIII-7}$$

Application of the Boltzmann distribution law leads to the equation

$$M = \frac{N\rho\mu^2}{3kTW}(H + aM) \tag{VIII-8}$$

in which ρ is the density and W the molecular weight. The molar susceptibility is defined as

$$\chi_{molar} = WM/\rho H \qquad \text{(VIII-9)}$$

These equations lead to the Weiss equation:

$$\chi_{molal} = C_{molal}/(T - \Theta) \qquad \text{(VIII-10)}$$

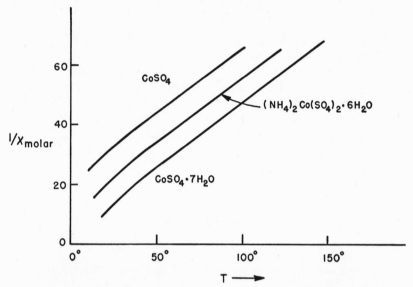

Fig. VIII-1.—Curves showing the reciprocal of molar magnetic susceptibility of compounds of cobalt(II) as a function of the absolute temperature.

with Θ, the Curie temperature, given by the expression

$$\Theta = N\rho\mu^2 a/3kW \qquad \text{(VIII-11)}$$

and C_{molar} by Equation VIII-5.

In a graph of $1/\chi_{molar}$ against T, the points lie on a straight line if the Weiss equation is valid. Measurements for three salts of cobalt(II) are shown in Figure VIII-1. It is seen that the curves are straight lines except at very low temperatures. Their slopes are the same; the slope is the reciprocal of the Curie constant, and accordingly the cobalt(II) atom has the same magnetic moment in the three substances.

Ferromagnetism, antiferromagnetism, and ferrimagnetism are discussed in Appendix X of *The Nature of the Chemical Bond.*

EXERCISES

VIII-1.—The volume magnetic susceptibility (per cm^3) of $H_2(g)$ at 20°C is -0.000167×10^{-6}, and that of $H_2O(l)$ is -0.80×10^{-6}. Evaluate the molar magnetic susceptibilities, and from these obtain values for H and O. From these calculate the root-mean-square values of the radius r for the valence electrons (ignore the contribution of the K electrons of oxygen).

VIII-2.—The observed volume magnetic susceptibility of $O_2(g)$ at 20°C is 0.140×10^{-6}. From this quantity and the diamagnetic correction (Ex. VIII-1), evaluate the magnetic dipole moment of the O_2 molecule.

VIII-3.—Measure the slope of the straight-line portions of the curves in Figure VIII-1, and evaluate the magnetic dipole moment of the cobaltous ion in these salts.

Bond Energy and Bond-Dissociation Energy

IN Chapter 3 and other chapters of this book much use is made of bond-energy values. These values are chosen in such a way that their sum over all of the bonds of a molecule which can be satisfactorily represented by a single valence-bond structure is equal to the enthalpy of formation of the molecule from its constituent atoms in their normal states. For example, the value of the O—H bond energy, 110 kcal/mole, is one-half the enthalpy of formation of $H_2O(g)$ from $2H(g)$ and $O(g)$.

Another quantity of much interest is the bond-dissociation energy. The bond-dissociation energy of a bond in a molecule is the energy required to break that bond alone, that is, to split the molecule into the two parts that were previously connected by the bond under consideration.

The bond energy and bond-dissociation energy are the same for the bond in a diatomic molecule but are different for a bond in a polyatomic molecule. For example, the bond-dissociation energy for the O—H bond in the water molecule (splitting H_2O into H + OH) is 119.9 kcal/mole and that for the O—H bond in the OH radical is 101.2 kcal/mole. Their average, 110.6 kcal/mole, is the O—H bond energy.

The difference between the O—H bond-dissociation energies for H_2O and OH can be ascribed to the stabilization energy of the normal state, ^3P, of the oxygen atom. When one O—H bond is broken in the water molecule there is produced, in addition to a hydrogen atom, an OH radical, with structure $:\overset{\cdot}{O}$—H. The radical has an unpaired electron on the oxygen atom, which interacts only with electron pairs. When the second O—H bond is broken, however, an oxygen atom, $:\overset{\cdot}{O}\cdot$, with two unpaired electrons, configuration $1s^2 2s^2 2p^4$, is produced. There are three Russell-Saunders states corresponding to this configuration: ^1S, ^1D, and ^3P. The normal state, ^3P, involves a considerable amount of stabilization, resulting from the resonance energy of the two odd electrons (Hund's first rule); the stabilization energy has been estimated to be 17.1 kcal/mole. Hence the bond-dissociation energy of OH to an oxygen atom in its valence state, rather than the more stable ^3P state, would be 118.3 kcal/mole, essentially equal to the O—H bond-dissociation energy of the first O—H bond in H_2O.

Many of the differences between values of bond-dissociation energy and bond energy are to be attributed to this effect, the resonance stabilization of Russell-Saunders atomic states with high multiplicity. In addition, the energy of resonance among two or more valence-bond structures makes an important contribution in many cases. For example, the C—H bond-dissociation energy is about 101 kcal/mole for methane, ethane, and other alkanes, but is only 77 kcal/mole for toluene, as determined from its rate of pyrolysis and by electron impact. The difference, 24 kcal/mole, can be attributed to the resonance stabilization of the benzyl radical that is produced by removing one hydrogen atom from the methyl group of toluene; this radical resonates among the several structures

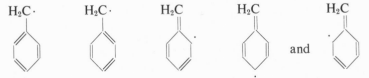

About the same value, 25 kcal/mole, is found for the resonance energy of the allyl radical; the resonance energy stabilizing the product is that for the structures $H_2C=CH—\dot{C}H_2$ and $H_2\dot{C}—CH=CH_2$.

Index

Acetone, 227
Acetylene, 139
Acid strength, 161f
Adjacent-charge rule, 158ff
Alkali aluminates:
  atoms, 29
  metals, 70
Alkaline-earth compounds metals, 70
Allene, 140
Allyl radical, 261
Aluminum fluoride, 52
Amides, 162ff
Amino acids, 163, 229
Ammonia-borane, 84
Ammonium ion, 8
Anthracene, 125
Antiferromagnetism, 259
Aromatic molecules, 124ff
  resonance in, 128
Atomic arrangement, 52ff
Atomic orbitals, 74ff
Azide ion, 158
Azimuthal quantum number, 26

Balmer series of spectral lines, 25
Bent single bonds, 88
Benzene, 113, 117f, 121f, 130ff, 140, 166
Benzyl radical, 261
Beryllium atom, 34
Bicovalent complexes, 85
Biphenyl, 165
Bismuth, 256
Bohr atom, 27, 236f
Bohr frequency principle, 22, 23f
Bohr magneton, 45, 257
Bohr orbit, 27, 28f
Bohr theory, 11
Bond, electron-pair, 17ff

Bond angles, 74ff, 77, 80, 87ff
Bond-dissociation energy, 59ff, 260f
Bond energy, 57ff, 260f
Bond involving d orbitals, 92f
Bond orbitals, 74
  complex, 92ff
  concentration of, 85f
Bond strengths, 74ff
Bond type, 52ff
  change in, 49ff
  magnetic criterion for, 99f
Boranes, 197ff
Borazole, 166
Boric acid, 164
Boron, 194ff
  hydrides, 197ff
  trimethyl, 84
Bromine pentafluoride, 110
  trifluoride, 111
1,3-Butadiene, 141, 165
Butatriene, 141

Calcium hexaboride, 196
Carbon atom, 42, 77f
  tetrahedral, 77ff, 80
Carbon dioxide, 157
  disulfide, 157
  monoxide, 156f
  oxysulfide, 157
Carbon tetrachloride, 153
Carbonate ion, 164
Carbonic acid, 164
Carboxyl group, 160f
Carboxylate ion, 161
Chemical bond, 5ff
Chemical structure, 3f
Chemical thermodynamic properties,
  61f

Chlorine, 151f
    dioxide, 194
Chloroacetylene, 140
Chloroform, 153, 227
Circular orbit, 27
Clausius-Mossotti local field, 251
Closest packing, of large ions of spheres, 211ff
Cobalt complexes, 182f
Cobalt(II), magnetic susceptibility of compounds of, 258
Cobalt(III) hexammoniate ion, 107
Complex bond orbitals, 92ff
Complex ions, 218f
Conjugated systems, 165f
Covalent bond, 6ff
    directed, 74ff
    formal rules for formation of, 45ff
    normal, 57
    with partial ionic character, 51
Covalent octahedral complexes, 94
Covalent radii, 135ff
Cubic body-centered arrangement, 214
Cubic closest packing, 212, 213
Curie constant, 257
Curie's equation, 257
Cyanide complexes, 181f
Cyanuric triazide, 159
Cyclopentadiene, 165

Decaborane, 199
Deuterium atom, 227
Diamagnetic anisotropy, 256
Diamagnetism, 255f
Diamond, 145, 146
Diaspore, 223
Dibenzenechromium, 201
Diborane, 197f
Dicyclopentadienyl iron, 200f
Dielectric constants, 225, 226, 249ff
    Debye equation for, 252f
Diketopiperazine, 229
p-Dinitrobenzene, 160
Dinitrogen dioxide, 190
Diphosphate ion, 175
Double-bond character, 171ff
Double-bond radii, 139f

Electric dipole moments, 56f, 69, 249ff
Electric polarizabilities, 249ff, 252
Electron affinity, 68

Electron configuration of atoms, 40f
Electron-deficient substances, 194ff
Electron distribution, 27
Electron shell, 27f, 37
Electronegativity, 63f
    and bond length, 138f
    scale, 63ff, 66ff
    values, 65
Electroneutrality principle, 107f
Electroneutrality rule, 158ff
Electronic structure of atoms, 21ff, 33ff
Electrostatic bond, 5f
Energy curves, 55
Energy levels, diagrams of, 42, 43
Enthalpy of hydrogenation of monatomic gases, 61
Ethane, 87, 114
Ethylene, 87, 89, 114, 132, 139
Exclusion principle, 36

Ferrimagnetism, 259
Ferrocene, 200f
Ferrocyanide ion, 100, 178, 180f
Ferromagnetism, 259
Formal charges, 7
Formaldehyde, 89
Formamide, 163
Formic acid, 161
Fractional bonds, 149f
Furan, 166, 167

Glycine, 140f
Graphite, 141, 142, 256

Halogen halogenides, 58
Halogenide molecules, diatomic, 54ff
Heats of combustion, 61
Heats of formation of compounds, 64ff
Heisenberg uncertainty principle, 27
Heitler-London treatment of the hydrogen molecule, 18
Helium atom, 10, 37
Helium molecule-ion, 189
α-Helix, 230f
Hemoglobin, 231
Heterocyclic molecules, 166f
Hexachloropalladate ion, 46f
Hexagonal closest packing, 211ff
Hexamminocobaltic ion, 93
Hund's rules, 39
Hybrid bond orbitals, 77ff

Hybridization, 82ff
Hydrazoic acid, 159
Hydrogen atom, 11, 24ff
Hydrogen bond, 221ff, 227, 228
  effect on physical properties of sub-
    stances, 224f
  in proteins, 229ff
Hydrogen chloride, 50, 54, 253
  cyanide, 225, 227
  fluoride, 55f
  halogenide molecules, 55, 56
  halogenides, 58, 69
  sulfide, 77
Hydrogen molecule, 17ff
  Condon's treatment of, 17
Hydrogen molecule-ion, 11ff, 15f
Hydrogenlike orbitals, 238ff
Hyperconjugation, 167f
Hyperligated complexes, 102
Hypoligated complexes, 102

Ice, 227ff
Icosahedral structures, 215f, 217
Interatomic distances, 135ff
  for fractional bonds, 149f
Ionic bond, 5f
Ionic character, 49ff, 69
Ionic crystals, 151
Ionic radii, 150f
Ionization energy, 68
Iron, 206
  atom, 180f
  pentacarbonyl, 179

α-Keratin, 231

Landé g-factor, 102, 242ff
  equation for, 45
Larmor precession, 256
Lewis electronic formulas, 7f
Ligancy, 46f, 194, 200
Ligand field theory, 108f
Light quantum, 23
Lithium, 207
  atom, 29f
Lorenz-Lorentz equation, 251
Lyman series, 25

Magnesium, 215f, 217
Magnetic moments, 101ff, 105ff
  of iron-group ions, 103

of octahedral complexes, 105
Magnetic quantum number, 26
Magneton, 45
Mercurous chloride, 217
Mercurous ion, 217
Mercury dimethyl, 85
Mercury-mercury bond, 217
Metal-metal bonds, 217ff
Metallic bond, 8, 203ff
Metallic elements, 203ff
Metallic orbital, 206f
Metallic radii, 150
Metallic valence, 204ff
Metals, 203ff, 206ff, 210
Methyl chloride, 153
Methyl cyanide, 167
Methylacetylene, 139
Methylchloroacetylene, 140
Methylene chloride, 153
Molecular-orbital method, 17, 130ff
Molybdenum complex ion, 218f
Molybdenum dichloride, 219
Multiple bonds, 87ff
  bond energies for, 119
  partial ionic character of, 90
Multiplets, normal, 39f
  inverted, 40
Multiplicity, of energy level, 33

Naphthalene, 124f, 256
Nickel, 206
  acetylacetone, 106
  cyanide ion, 98f
  tetracarbonyl, 178f
Nitrate ion, 164
Nitric oxide, 189f
Nitro complexes, 180ff
Nitro group, 160f
Nitrogen, 66
  dioxide, 191f
  oxides of, 189ff
Nitrosyl halogenides, 190f
Nitrous oxide, 114ff, 158
Nitryl chloride, 160
Nonpenetrating orbit, 31

Octahedral bond orbitals, 94ff, 97f
Octahedral complexes, 101ff, 107f
  magnetic moments of, 105
Octahedral radii, 147ff
Octet, Lewis, 46

One-electron bond, 11ff, 186f
  conditions for formation of, 16f
Orbital, 26f, 28
  angular momentum, 26
  for incomplete shells, 84f
  wave function, 238ff
Overlapping of atomic orbitals, 74
Oxides of the heavier elements, 175ff
Oxygen atom, 41f, 227
Oxygen fluoride, 114
Oxygen molecule, 192f
Ozone, 62f

p bonds, 76
Packing radius, 152
Palladium dimethylglyoxime, 106
Palladous nitrate, 106
Paramagnetism, 203f, 256ff
Paschen series, 25
Pauli exclusion principle, 36ff, 241
Penetrating orbit, 31
Peptides, 162f, 229ff
Perchlorate ion, 174
Phenanthrene, 125
Phenol, 162
Phosphate ion, 174
Phosphine, 77
Phosphorus pentachloride, 46, 62
Photon, 23
Physical constants, 235
Pi (π) bond, 88
Platinum tetramethyl, 199f
Polypeptide chains, 229ff
Probability distribution function, 11
Proteins, 229ff
Prussian blue, 104, 106
Pyrazine, 166
Pyridine, 166
Pyrite, 147, 148
Pyrrole, 166f

Quantum number, 26
Quinoline, 166

Resonance, 8ff
  among several valance-bond struc-
    tures, 114ff
  and interatomic distances, 140ff
  energy, 10, 118, 119ff, 121ff, 132, 245ff
  hybrid, 10
  phenomenon, 35

single-bond:double-bond, 143
Restricted rotation about single bonds,
  86f
Russell-Saunders coupling, 34
Russell-Saunders states, 241ff
Russell-Saunders symbols, 32f
Russell-Saunders vector model, 35
Ruthenicinium ion, 200
Ruthenocene, 200, 201
Rutile, 53
Rydberg constant, 25

s bonds, 76
Sigma (σ) bond, 88
Silicate ion, 174
Silicon fluoride, 52
  tetrachloride, 171ff
Single-bond energies, 59ff
  energy values, 60
Single-bond metallic radii, 150
Sodium, 151
  chloride, 150
  chloride crystal, 6, 151
Spectral lines, 31
Spectral terms, 24
Spectrum:
  absorption, 21
  band, 21f
  emission, 21
  line, 21
Sphalerite, 145, 146
Spin quantum number, 33
Spinning electron, 32f
Square bond orbitals, 98f
Stationary state, 22, 23
  of hydrogen atom, 24ff
Substances, magnetic properties of
  255ff
Sulfate ion, 8, 173, 174
Sulfur dioxide, 175
  trioxide, 175f
Superoxide ion, 192f

Term values, 24
Tetrahedral orbitals, 78ff, 81
Tetrahedral radii, 145, 147
Tetramethyl orthosilicate, 174
s-Tetrazine, 90
Thiophen, 166f
Three-electron bond, 187ff
Tin, 208f, 211, 214

Toluene, 168, 261
Transition from one bond type to another, 49ff
s-Triazine, 90
Triethylamine, 227
Trihalogenomethanes, 79
Trimethylamine, 114
  oxide, 7, 8
Triphosphate ion, 175
Triple-bond radii, 139f
Tungsten, 217f

Unshared electron pairs, 83f, 110f

Valence, 3f
Valence-bond method, 17
Valence-bond structures, wave function for, 248
van der Waals radii, 79, 151ff
Vector model, 33ff

Water, 59f, 227ff
Weiss equation, 258
Wurtzite, 145, 147

Zinc, 215